THE
SOLVENT EXTRACTION OF
METAL CHELATES

The
Solvent Extraction of
Metal Chelates

BY

JIŘÍ STARÝ, D.Sc.

Department of Nuclear Chemistry,
Faculty of Technical and Nuclear Physics,
College of Technology, Prague

EDITED, WITH A FOREWORD BY

H. IRVING

Professor of Inorganic and Structural Chemistry,
University of Leeds

A Pergamon Press Book

THE MACMILLAN COMPANY
NEW YORK

THE MACMILLAN COMPANY
60 Fifth Avenue
New York 11, N.Y.

This book is distributed by
THE MACMILLAN COMPANY
pursuant to a special arrangement with
PERGAMON PRESS LIMITED
Oxford, England

First published 1964

Library of Congress Catalog Card No. 64–22291

Set in Monotype Times 10 on 12 pt.
and printed in Great Britain at
the Pitman Press, Bath

CONTENTS

FOREWORD

Although the applications of liquid–liquid extraction to inorganic problems were foreshadowed by Péligot's discovery in 1842 that ether could extract uranium (VI) from nitric acid, and by Skey's proposals (1867) for the separation of cobalt from nickel, gold from platinum, and iron from many other metals by exploiting the different solubilities of their thiocyanates in ether, up to forty years ago only the solvent extraction of ferric chloride (Rothe, 1892) and gallium trichloride (Swift, 1924) had found their way into general analytical practice.

A new era was opened up with the introduction of the very versatile organic reagent "dithizone" by Hellmuth Fischer in 1925. Unlike the phenomena of liquid–liquid extraction of ion-association complexes, which is frequently so selective and for which the physical-chemical interpretations are so intrinsically complicated, the interaction of cations with suitable organic chelating agents to give formally neutral and less hydrophilic entities provides an immediate clue to their role in promoting the solvent extraction of inorganic species. But what is more significant is that the systems are more ideal in the thermodynamic sense so that the partition equilibria can be expressed by relatively simple equations that relate the percentage of metal extracted to those important experimental variables, *viz.* the pH of the aqueous phase, the excess concentration of reagent, and the nature and concentration of auxiliary "masking" agents. Such equations were developed some time ago (Kolthoff and Sandell, 1941; Irving and Williams, 1949) and have since been rigorously tested and found to be very generally applicable.

Provided he has access to a compilation of data on extraction constants or values of $pH_{1/2}$ under specified experimental conditions, any analyst now has the opportunity and the simple means for devising separation procedures on a sound theoretical basis. This is where Prof. Starý has performed a really great service to analytical chemistry, for in this book he has collected the great wealth of material that has accumulated in the last few decades and which hitherto has been scattered throughout the literature, much of it in papers not readily accessible to the Western world. While the uses of dithizone, oxine, cupferron, thenoyltrifluoroacetone and dialkylammonium-carbamates will be familiar to many workers, few will not be surprised at the wide range of reagents that have been applied to the field of liquid–liquid extraction and many will be unaware of the many elegant separation procedures that are now possible and indeed of the various extensions of extraction techniques to the determination of sub-microgram quantities.

xiii

While paying tribute to Prof. Starý's pioneering efforts on behalf of analytical chemists it may not be inappropriate to raise a note of warning. No author would feel justified in omitting literature data from a comprehensive monograph unless he had certain and personal knowledge of its incorrectness: in such a book as this it may well be that some unreliable observations may be reported side by side with data of impeccable quality. But this is a problem that confronts all scientific workers in a rapidly developing field and would in no way detract from the value of this unique book on the solvent extraction of inner complexes which will surely prove indispensable to all engaged in analysis and interested in the problems of inorganic chemistry.

HARRY IRVING

The University of Leeds,
1964.

CHAPTER 1

INTRODUCTION

ALTHOUGH solvent extraction (liquid–liquid extraction) of metal chelate complexes has been recognized as an excellent separation method for a long time, it has gained prominence only during the last decade. This method enjoys a favoured position among separation techniques because of its simplicity, speed, and wide scope. By utilizing apparatus no more complicated than a separatory funnel and requiring several minutes at most to perform, extraction procedures offer much to the analytical chemist. As solvent extraction does not involve co-precipitation, which is such an undesirable feature of separations based on precipitation, it frequently appears to be the ideal method of separating trace constituents from large amounts of other substances. The process is often very selective and the isolation of the metal in question can usually be made as complete as desired by several repetitions of the extraction procedure. When the metal chelate is coloured, and this is often the case, the isolation and concentration of minute amounts of the metal in question into a small volume of an organic phase can substantially increase the sensitivity of its absorptiometric determination.

In chemical technology, the liquid–liquid extraction of metal chelates plays an important role in the purification of chemical reagents and semi-conductor materials. This method is also frequently used in nuclear chemistry and technology for the separation of various radioisotopes and for the reprocessing of nuclear fuels.

Last but not least, by using solvent extraction, important theoretical problems concerning the composition and stability of soluble as well as insoluble metal complexes can be solved. This quality is very useful especially for the case when it is not possible to obtain reliable results by other methods.

1.1. DISTRIBUTION LAW

Solvent extraction is based on the distribution of a solute between two immiscible phases. For this case the classical phase rule of Gibbs can be applied, viz.:

$$P + F = C + 2 \tag{1}$$

where P is the number of phases, F the number of degrees of freedom, and C the number of components. According to eq. (1) a system consisting of two immiscible solvents and one solute distributed between them has one degree of freedom at constant temperature and pressure. Thus if the concentration of the solute in one phase is constant, the concentration of the solute in the other phase is also fixed. The relationship between the concentration of solute in each of the solvent phases led to Nernst's formulation of the distribution law (N 9) on the basis of experiments by Berthelot and Jungfleisch (B 55).

The constant giving the concentration ratio of the solute between both phases at equilibrium is called the (stoicheiometric) partition coefficient p and it can be expressed by the following equation:

$$p = c_{org}/c \qquad (2)$$

where c_{org} and c denote the concentration of the distributed compound in the organic and aqueous phases respectively.

It follows from eq. (2) that the partition coefficient p does not depend on the total solute concentration or on the actual phase volumes.

The distribution law is only valid if the solute is in both phases in the identical chemical form.

Equation (2) can be also derived thermodynamically from the equality of the chemical potentials of the solute in organic and aqueous phases at equilibrium:

$$\mu_{org} = \mu \qquad (3)$$

Substituting suitable expressions for μ_{org} and μ the following relation can be obtained:

$$\mu_{org}^0 + RT \log c_{org} + RT \log \gamma_{org} = \mu^0 + RT \log c + RT \log \gamma \qquad (4)$$

where μ_{org}^0 and μ^0 represent the standard chemical potentials of the solute in the organic and aqueous phases and γ_{org} and γ represent the activity coefficients in the organic and aqueous phases respectively.

From the above relation we may obtain the expression for the partition coefficient p:

$$p = \frac{c_{org}}{c} = \frac{\gamma}{\gamma_{org}} \exp\left(-[\mu_{org}^0 - \mu^0]/RT\right) \qquad (5)$$

When the solute concentration is low, the activity coefficients γ_{org}, γ approach unity and the stoicheiometric partition coefficient p becomes constant because μ_{org}^0 and μ^0 are also constant.

1.2. SOLUBILITY—EXTRACTABILITY

The partition coefficient p of a compound is approximately equal to the ratio of its solubilities in the organic and aqueous phases. Thus only such compounds can be usefully extracted as are only slightly soluble in water but readily soluble in organic solvents.

Solubility in organic solvents is not a characteristic usually attributed to simple metal salts. As can be expected from their highly ionic nature, most metal salts are strong electrolytes with a large solubility in aqueous media, in which the ions are solvated by molecules of water.

In essentially all metal extraction systems some or all of the solvated water molecules must be removed to obtain a species extractable by organic solvents. This species must, however, be uncharged because of the low dielectric constants of the organic solvents that are generally used in extraction procedures.

Organic reagents having one anionic group (e.g. —OH, —SH, etc.) and one uncharged basic group (e.g. =N—, =O, etc.) can easily replace co-ordinated water molecules from many metal ions forming neutral, essentially covalent chelate compounds. Chelate compounds, in which the metal has become part of the organic structure and is more or less buried inside the molecule, are only slightly soluble in water but dissolve readily in organic solvents.

A typical organic reagent which can form extractable chelates with many metal ions is 8-hydroxyquinoline (oxine).

CHAPTER 2

COMPOSITION AND STABILITY
OF METAL CHELATES

2.1. GENERAL EQUATIONS

WHEN a metal M with a charge N^+ is equilibrated with an organic and an aqueous phase (containing solvent molecules S and H_2O), then in the presence of an organic reagent, HA, complexes of the general composition $M_mA_n(OH)_p(HA)_rS_s(H_2O)_t$ may be formed.

During the years 1955–6 Rydberg (R 46, R 48) considered the formation of such a hypothetical complex and showed that its composition and stability could be determined from measurements of the distribution ratio of the total metal between the organic and aqueous phases as a function of the different variables.

The stability constant of the composite complex $M_mA_n(OH)_p(HA)_rS_s(H_2O)_t$ is defined by eq. (6):†

$$\beta_{m,n,p,r,s,t} = \frac{[M_mA_n(OH)_p(HA)_rS_s(H_2O)_t]}{[M]^m[A]^n[OH]^p[HA]^rS^s[H_2O]^t} \tag{6}$$

All the variables in this equation are not independent of each other as may be seen from the relationships:

$$K_{HA} = [H][A]/[HA] \tag{7}$$

and
$$K'_w = [H][OH]/[H_2O] \tag{8}$$

From eqs. (7) and (8) it follows that

$$[M]^m[A]^n[OH]^p[HA]^rS^s[H_2O]^t$$
$$= [M]^m[HA]^{n+r}[H]^{-n-p}S^s[H_2O]^{p+t}(K_{HA})^n(K'_w)^p \tag{9}$$

If, following Rydberg (R 46, R 48), we now introduce the quantities x, y, and z defined by

$$n + r = x \tag{10}$$

$$n + p = y \tag{11}$$

and
$$p + t = z \tag{12}$$

into the above equations the formula of the composite complex becomes:

$$M_m(HA)_x(H)_{-y}S_s(H_2O)_z$$

† For the sake of simplicity the charges on ions are omitted.

It follows from eq. (10) that it will not be possible to distinguish between certain complexes, e.g. the complexes $MA_2(HA)S(H_2O)$ and $MA(OH)(HA)_2S$ are both included in the complex of the general formula $M(HA)_3(H)_{-2}S(H_2O)$.

It is very difficult to determine the number of H_2O molecules attached to a complex in aqueous solution. If the coordination number of the metal M with respect to all ligands is known, the number z of H_2O molecules may be calculated from the difference between this coordination number and the number of coordinative positions around the metal in the complex occupied by ligands other than H_2O.

However, if the experiments are carried out at constant ionic strength, which ensures that the concentration of H_2O molecules is practically constant, the effect of hydration may be included in the stability constant without need for special attention.

Further discussion can therefore be limited to the complex $M_m(HA)_x(H)_{-y}S_s$ whose stability constant is defined by eq. (13):

$$\beta_{m,x,y,s} = \frac{[M_m(HA)_x(H)_{-y}S_s]}{[M]^m[HA]^x[H]^{-y}[S]^s} \tag{13}$$

According to eqs. (10) and (11), x means the total number of HA and A molecules and y the total number of A and OH molecules in the complex per metal atom. The charge of the metal complex is $mN - y$ and therefore for an uncharged complex we must have $mN = y$, where N is the charge on the metal cation M^{N+}.

In the following section we shall assume that only uncharged complexes are dissolved and extracted by the organic solvents. This will be true for most organic solvents and especially for those of low dielectric constant.

The general formula of the complex in the organic phase will then be $M_m(HA)_x(H)_{-mN}S_s$.

The following equation will be valid for the distribution ratio of the metal M between the organic and aqueous phases:

$$q = \frac{\text{total concentration of metal in the organic phase}}{\text{total concentration of metal in the aqueous phase}}$$

$$= \frac{\sum\limits_{m=1}\sum\limits_{x=0}\sum\limits_{s=0} m\beta_{m,x,mN,s}P_{m,x,mN,s}[M]^m[HA]^x[H]^{-mN}[S]^s}{\sum\limits_{m=1}\sum\limits_{x=0}\sum\limits_{s=0} m\beta_{m,x,mN,s}[M]^m[HA]^x[H]^{-mN}[S]^s} \tag{14}$$

where $p_{m,x,mN,s}$ is the partition coefficient of the complex $M_m(HA)_x(H)_{-mN}S_s$ as defined by the following eq. (15):

$$p_{m,x,mN,s} = \frac{[M_m(HA)_x(H)_{-mN}S_s]org}{[M_m(HA)_x(H)_{-mN}S_s]} \tag{15}$$

where the subscript 'org' designates the organic phase.

2.2. POLYMERIZATION OF METAL CHELATES

Let us assume according to Irving (I 20) that the mixture of complexes in the aqueous phase can be represented by that of a single complex $M_{\bar{m}}(HA)_{\bar{x}}(H)_{-\bar{m}N}S_{\bar{s}}$ where the values $\bar{m}$, $\bar{x}$, and $\bar{s}$ denote the mean values of the corresponding subscripts in the aqueous phase. Similarly we postulate that the formula $M_{\bar{m}_{org}}(HA)_{\bar{x}_{org}}(H)_{\bar{m}_{org}}S_{\bar{s}_{org}}$ represents the average composition of the complexes in the organic phase, where the values of $\bar{m}_{org}$, $\bar{x}_{org}$, and $\bar{s}_{org}$ denote the mean values of the corresponding subscripts for the organic phase. Equation (14) can now be simplified into the form:

$$q = \frac{\bar{m}_{org}\beta_{\bar{m}_{org},\,\bar{x}_{org},\,\bar{m}_{org}N,\,\bar{s}_{org}}P_{\bar{m}_{org},\,\bar{x}_{org},\,\bar{m}_{org}N,\,\bar{s}}[M]^{\bar{m}_{org}}[HA]^{\bar{x}_{org}}[H]^{-\bar{m}_{org}N}[S]^{\bar{s}_{org}}}{\bar{m}\,K_{\bar{m},\,\bar{x},\,-\bar{m}N,\,\bar{s}}[M]^{\bar{m}}[HA]^{\bar{x}}[H]^{-\bar{m}N}[S]^{\bar{s}}} \tag{16}$$

By partial differentiation of eq. (16) with respect to the concentration of free metal ions we have:

$$\left(\frac{\log q}{\log [M]}\right)_{[HA],\,[H],\,[org]} = \bar{m}_{org} - \bar{m} \tag{17}$$

Thus when the extent of polymerization of metal chelates is the same in each phase the value of this derivative is zero. In the limiting case, if the concentration of free metal ion M^{N+} tends to zero, $\bar{m}$ tends to unity, so that a zero value of the derivative at low metal concentration signifies that all the species are monomolecular. Positive values of the derivative indicate that the degree of polymerization (or polymerization number) is greater in the organic phase ($\bar{m}_{org} > \bar{m}$), while negative values indicate that it is higher in the aqueous phase ($\bar{m} > \bar{m}_{org}$) (I 21, C 43, R 20).

In general the distribution coefficient q remains constant for metal concentration of the order of 10^{-3} M and less, except when this metal is considerably hydrolysed; e.g. the distribution ratio of indium between benzene containing acetylacetone or benzoylacetone and an aqueous phase is practically the same for an indium concentration of 10^{-3} M as for "carrier-free" concentrations ($<10^{-10}$ M). (R 24, R 25).

This fact is of very great importance, especially for radiochemical separations, since it will be possible to predict the extraction behaviour and best conditions for separation of "carrier-free" radioisotopes from extraction experiments carried out with macroamounts of the element in question.

2.3. ADDITIVE COMPLEXES WITH ORGANIC SOLVENTS

For the determination of the number of the organic solvent molecules bounded in the metal complex one may vary the value of [S] by the addition of a suitable third solvent. However, though this solvent may not react chemically with any part of the general composite complex, the activity coefficients in the system often vary to such an extent that relatively little useful new information about the system will be obtained (R 46, R 48).

According to Rydberg (R 46, R 48) the formation of the additive complex with organic solvents can be confirmed from the distribution ratios obtained for a certain metal M using two different organic solvents. The distribution ratio of metal between the organic solvent S′ and water is q' and that between S″ and water is q''. The stability constants and partition coefficients for monomolecular complexes will be $\beta'_{x,y,s}$, $\beta''_{x,y,s}$, $p'_{x,sN}$, and $p''_{x,sN}$ respectively.

If the two distribution curves are compared at the same [H] and [HA] in the aqueous phase, the ratio between the two distribution ratios q' and q'' will become:

$$\frac{q'}{q''} = \frac{\sum\limits_{x=0}\sum\limits_{s=0}\beta'_{x,sN}p'_{x,sN}[HA]^x[H]^{-N}[S']^s}{\sum\limits_{x=0}\sum\limits_{s=0}\beta''_{x,sN}p''_{x,sN}[HA]^x[H]^{-N}[S'']^s} \times \frac{\sum\limits_{x=0}\sum\limits_{y=0}\sum\limits_{s=0}\beta''_{x,y,s}[HA]^x[H]^{-y}[S'']^s}{\sum\limits_{x=0}\sum\limits_{y=0}\sum\limits_{s=0}\beta'_{x,y,s}[HA]^x[H]^{-y}[S']^s}$$
(18)

In equilibrium the aqueous phase will be saturated with the organic solvent and vice versa. The solubility of the organic solvent in water is practically constant at constant ionic strength and therefore the constant values of [S′] and [S″] can be included in the values of $\beta'_{x,y}$, which are defined thus:

$$\beta'_{x,y} = \sum\limits_{s=0}\beta'_{x,y,s}[S']^s$$
(19)

Using similar equations for $\beta''_{x,y}$, $\beta'_{x,N}p'_{x,N}$, and $\beta''_{x,N}p''_{x,N}$ eq. (18) can be reduced to:

$$\frac{q'}{q''} = \frac{\sum\limits_{x=0}\beta'_{x,N}p'_{x,N}[HA]^x[H]^{-N}\sum\limits_{x=0}\sum\limits_{y=0}\beta''_{x,y}[HA]^x[H]^{-y}}{\sum\limits_{x=0}\beta''_{x,N}p''_{x,N}[HA]^x[H]^{-N}\sum\limits_{x=0}\sum\limits_{y=0}\beta'_{x,y}[HA]^x[H]^{-y}}$$
(20)

If complexes are formed between the metal complex and the organic solvents S′ and S″, $\beta'_{x,y}$ and $p'_{x,N}$ must be different from $\beta''_{x,y}$ and $p''_{x,N}$ except for a rare coincidence. The ratio q'/q'' will also depend on pH at constant [HA], or on [HA] at constant pH.

Rydberg (R 46) confirmed by the above method the formation of an additive complex of thorium acetylacetonate with methyl isobutyl ketone (hexone).

The formation of additive complexes is observed especially if hydrophobic reagents such as tri n-butylphosphate or tri n-butylphosphineoxide are used as organic solvents. In such cases the organic reagent can often replace the water molecules attached to the metal chelate to form an additive complex which is less hydrophilic and can be readily extracted by nonpolar solvents

(A 31).   Irving and Edgington (I 26, I 28–32) found that this synergic en-
hancement of the distribution ratio may appear in a number of metal chelate
systems if the following conditions are fulfilled:

1. The organic reagent is capable of displacing any residual coordinated
water molecules from the neutral chelate and rendering it less hydrophilic.

2. The organic reagent is not itself hydrophilic and is coordinated less
strongly than the organic chelating agent.

3. The maximum coordinated number of the metal and the geometry of
the ligands is favourable.

Most organic reagents are bidentate and when the coordination number
equals $2N$ the metal chelate will be coordinatively saturated and not hydrated;
it should be unable to form an additive complex. When the coordination
number is higher than $2N$ a synergic effect should be possible provided the
geometry of the metal chelate can be adapted to accommodate the additional
molecules. In the actinide or lanthanide series when the value of the coordination number is probably eight synergic effect could be predicted with
tri, penta and hexavalent ions. This effect cannot be expected for tetravalent
ions since N equals to a half of the coordination number (I 28–32, T 21).

If no complex is formed between the metal chelate and the organic solvent
the value s is equal to zero. For this case the stability constants of metal
chelates in both systems must be the same, i.e.

$$\beta'_{x,y} = \beta''_{x,y} \tag{21}$$

Introducing this condition in eq. (20) we obtain:

$$\frac{q'}{q''} = \frac{\sum\limits_{x=0} \beta'_{x,N} p'_{x,N}[HA]^x}{\sum\limits_{x=0} \beta''_{x,N} p''_{x,N}[HA]^x} \tag{22}$$

In this case the ratio q'/q'' depends only on the concentration of the organic
reagent HA. Experimentally this may be tested by plotting $\log q'$ and $\log q''$
against pH at the same and constant [HA]. If $\log(q'/q'')$ is found to be
constant no complexes are formed between the metal chelate and molecules
of the organic solvents used.

When one uncharged metal chelate dominates over all in the organic
solvent, x has a single value and eq. (17) reduces to

$$\frac{q'}{q''} = \frac{p'_{x,N}}{p''_{x,N}} \tag{23}$$

The ratio q'/q'' is then independent of both [H] and [HA] and the curves
for $\log q'$ and $\log q''$ run parallel when plotted either as a function of pH
(or pA $= -\log[A]$) at constant [HA], or as a function of [HA] at constant
pH (R 46, R 48).

Figure 1 shows the distribution ratio of indium between three organic solvents (chloroform, benzene, and carbon tetrachloride) and an aqueous phase containing acetylacetone (R 24) as a function of pA (pA = $-\log$ [A]). As is seen from Fig. 1, $\log(q'/q'')$ does not depend on the pA-values and

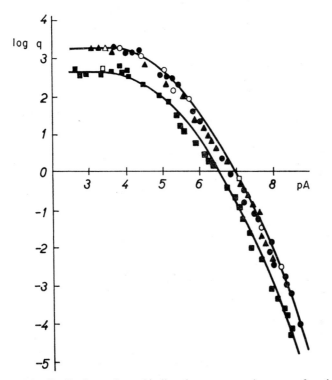

FIG. 1. The distribution ratio q of indium between two phases as a function of pA in the presence of acetylacetone (HAA). ● 0·10 M HAA in chloroform, ○ 0·05 M HAA in chloroform, ▲ 0·10 M HAA in benzene, △ 0·05 M HAA in benzene, ■ 0·10 M HAA in carbon tetrachloride, □ 0·05 M HAA in carbon tetrachloride.

therefore no complexes are formed between indium acetylacetonate and molecules of the organic solvents used.

This fact was also established for all other metal chelate systems investigated when organic solvents of low dielectric constant were used.

2.4. COMPLEXES OF THE TYPE $MA_n(OH)_p(HA)_r$

When only monomolecular complexes are formed which do not contain organic solvent molecules, the general formula of these complexes is $MA_n(OH)_p(HA)_r$. Since it is not possible to distinguish by the distribution method between these complexes and $MA_{n+k}(OH)_{p-k}(HA)_{r-k}(H_2O)_k$, we shall only discuss the complex $M(HA)_x(H)_y$, which includes all these isomers (R 46).

For this case eq. (14) can be reduced to:

$$q = \frac{\sum\limits_{x=0} \beta_{x,N} p_{x,N} [HA]^x [H]^{-N}}{\sum\limits_{x=0} \sum\limits_{y=0} \beta_{x,y} [HA]^x [H]^{-y}} \tag{24}$$

Rydberg (R 46) was the first to show that the distribution of metal between two phases may vary with pH and the concentration of HA in several ways, depending on the types of complexes which are formed (see Figs. 2–4).

If complexes of general type $MA_n(OH)_p(HA)_r$ are formed, the q-values are in no region a function of pA alone (Fig. 2). Stability constants of these

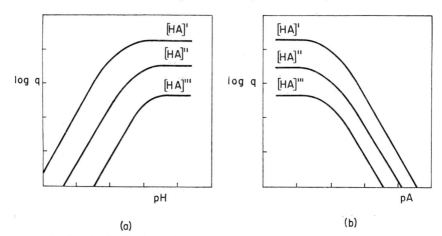

FIG. 2. The distribution ratio q of metal M between two phases as a function (a) of pH, (b) of pA at different concentrations of HA ($[HA]' > [HA]'' > [HA]'''$), when complexes of type $MA_n(OH)_p(HA)_r$ are formed.

complexes can be calculated from eq. (24) by the "limiting value method" of Leden (L 11) or by the "least squares method" (R 52, R 53).

For the calculations we introduce (R 46, R 48) a series of functions of $[HA]$, f_p and f_y, defined by

$$f_p = \sum\limits_{x=0} \beta_{x,N} p_{x,N} [HA]^x \tag{25}$$

and

$$f_y = \sum\limits_{x=0} \beta_{x,y} [HA]^x \tag{26}$$

Equation (24) can now be rewritten in the form:

$$q = \frac{f_p [H]^{-N}}{\sum\limits_{y=0} f_y [H]^{-N}} = \frac{f_p [H]^{-N}}{f_0 + f_1 [H]^{-1} + f_2 [H]^{-2} + \dots} \tag{27}$$

To obtain values of f_p and f_y we shall transform eq. (27) to

$$q^{-1}[H]^{-N} = F_0 = f_0 f_p^{-1} + f_1 f_p^{-1}[H]^{-1} + f_2 f_p^{-1}[H]^{-2} + \ldots \quad (28)$$

which is then solved for $f_0 f_p^{-1}$, $f_1 f_p^{-1}$, etc. For each concentration of HA (see Fig. 2) a plot of F_0 against $[H]^{-1}$ will yield a curve with a limiting value of $f_0 f_p^{-1}$ and a limiting slope of $f_1 f_p^{-1}$ when $[H]^{-1}$ approaches to zero:

$$\lim_{[H] \to \infty} F_0 = f_0 f_p^{-1} \quad (29)$$

With the value of $f_0 f_p^{-1}$ thus obtained, F_1 can be calculated according to eqs. (30) and (31):

$$F_1 = \frac{F_0 - f_0 f_p^{-1}}{[H]^{-1}} = f_1 f_p^{-1} + f_2 f_p^{-1}[H]^{-1} + \ldots \quad (30)$$

whence
$$\lim_{H \to \infty} F_1 = f_1 f_p^{-1} \quad (31)$$

By successive formation of F_y-functions, all values of $f_y f_p^{-1}$ for different [HA] can be obtained.

In practically all cases it can be shown that $f_0 = 1$ (i.e. that complexes of the type $M(HA)_x$ can be neglected), thus $f_0 f_p^{-1} = f_p^{-1}$. For each concentration of HA a certain value is obtained for f_p^{-1}. From a previously determined value of $f_y f_p$ at the same concentration of HA the corresponding value of f_y can be obtained.

The f_p and the different f_y-functions are then solved for $\beta_{x,N} p_{x,N}$ and $\beta_{x,y}$. With these values the partition coefficients $p_{x,N}$ for different uncharged complexes can be found.

With the above method the composition and stability constants of complexes of uranium (VI) with acetylacetone (R 46, R 47), benzoylacetone (S 100), dibenzoylmethane (M 122) and salicylic acid (H 32) were investigated.

In this type of metal complex additive complexes with the organic reagent of type $MA_N(HA)_r$ can also be included. Such complexes were found to be formed at higher reagent concentrations so it is possible that molecules of the organic reagent can displace water molecules in the metal chelate. In this manner the strongly hydrated chelates (e.g. oxinates of calcium, strontium, barium, zinc, cadmium, etc.) become hydrophobic and can be readily extracted with organic solvents (D 32, S 106).

2.5. COMPLEXES OF THE TYPE $MA_n(OH)_p$

If a complex of the type $MA_n(OH)_p$ is formed, the distribution ratio q is a function of pA only in the pH region where hydrolysis of the metal is negligible (R 46, R 48) (see Fig. 3). In this region only complexes MA_n should be formed. No additive complexes between MA_n and HA should then exist here even at the highest reagent concentration used. From eq. (24) it can be seen that pH has no influence on the formation of additive complexes with HA and therefore such complexes can be neglected in the whole pH region indicated in Fig. 3. However, at high pH-values the hydrolysis of the

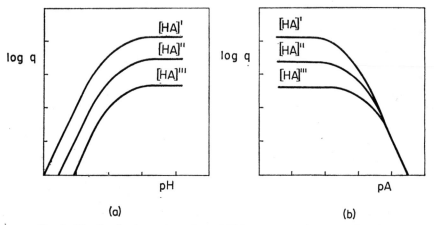

FIG. 3. The distribution ratio q of metal M between two phases as a function (a) of pH, (b) of pA at different concentrations of HA ([HA]$'$ > [HA]$''$ > [HA]$'''$), when complexes of type $MA_n(OH)_p$ are formed.

metal takes place and complexes of the type $MA_n(OH)_p$ are formed. For this case the distribution ratio becomes:

$$q = \frac{\sum\limits_{n=0} \beta_{n,N-n} p_{n,N-n}[A]^n[OH]^{N-n}}{\sum\limits_{n=0}\sum\limits_{p=0} \beta_{n,p}[A]^n[OH]^p} \tag{32}$$

As the partition coefficient of hydroxycomplexes between the organic solvent (especially those with low dielectric constant) and the aqueous phase will in practically all cases be low in comparison with the partition co-efficient of the neutral metal chelate MA_N, eq. (32) can be reduced to:

$$q = \frac{\beta_N p_N[A]^N}{\sum\limits_{n=0}\sum\limits_{p=0} \beta_{n,p}[A]^n[OH]^p} \tag{33}$$

Stability constants of hydroxycomplexes $\beta_{n,p}$ can be determined by using the "limiting value method" (L 11) or some other method from q-values at various pH and concentrations of HA.

To calculate the stability constants (R 46, R 48) we introduce functions f_p and f_y defined by:

$$f_p = \beta_N p_N \tag{34}$$

$$f_p = \sum\limits_{p=0} \beta_{n,p}[OH]^p \tag{35}$$

so that eq. (33) becomes:

$$q = \frac{f_p[A]^N}{\sum\limits_{n=0} f_p[A]^n} \tag{36}$$

The stability constants $\beta_{n,p}$ can be calculated from eq. (36) in the manner shown above.

The concentration of the anion A can easily be calculated from the total concentration of organic reagent c_{HA}. Assuming that the total metal

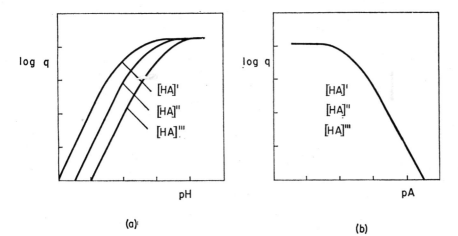

FIG. 4. The distribution ratio q of metal M between two phases as a function (a) of pH, (b) of pA at different concentrations of HA ($[HA]' > [HA]'' > [HA]'''$), when complexes of type MA_n are formed.

concentration c_M is negligible in comparison with that of the reagent, c_{HA} equals the sum of concentrations of all forms of the reagent in both phases. Thus for a dibasic acid:

$$c_{HA} = [HA]_{org} + [HA] + [A] + [H_2A] \tag{37}$$

From eq. (37) it follows that

$$[A] = c_{HA}/(p_{HA}K_{HA}^{-1}[H] + K_{HA}^{-1}[H] + 1 + K_{HA}^{-1}K_{H_2A}^{-1}[H]^2) \tag{38}$$

where

$$p_{HA} = [HA]_{org}/[HA] \tag{39}$$

$$K_{HA} = [H][A]/[HA] \tag{40}$$

$$K_{H_2A} = [HA][H]/[H_2A] \tag{41}$$

Since the values of the partition coefficient p_{HA} and the acid dissociation constants K_{HA} and K_{H_2A} of many organic reagents are known (see Appendix) the concentration [A] can easily be calculated from eq. (38) for any pH and total organic reagent used. In Fig. 5 log [A] values of cupferron (curve 1), dithizone (curve 2), oxine (curve 3), and dibenzoylmethane (curve 4) are plotted versus pH values for $c_{HA} = 1 \cdot 00$ M.

Complexes of the type $MA_n(OH)_p$ are formed in the aqueous phase especially when the metal begins to extract in a pH-region where it is partially hydrolysed (P 47, S 100, S 101). By using higher concentrations of organic

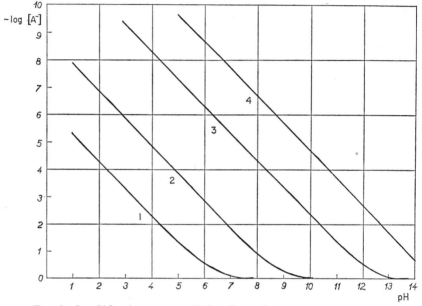

FIG. 5. Log [A] values versus pH for (1) cupferron–chloroform system; (2) dithizone–carbon tetrachloride system; (3) 8-hydroxyquinoline–chloroform system; (4) dibenzoylmethane–benzene system.

reagent the extraction curves are shifted to the acid side and the formation of hydroxycomplexes may thus be hindered.

2.6. COMPLEXES OF THE TYPE MA_n

The complexes of the type MA_n are formed if the value of q varies both with pH and [HA] in such a way that it is constant for constant pA value over the whole [H] and [HA] region investigated (R 46). This behaviour is illustrated in Fig. 4.

The left part of the curves illustrated in Fig. 4a have a constant slope which is equal to N, the charge of the uncomplexed metal ion. This is the maximum slope of the curve. In this region the metal cation M^{N+} predominates in the aqueous phase. By forming the complex cation $M_n^{(N-n)+}$ the slope of the curve diminishes and in the region where the slope is equal to zero the uncharged complex MA_N predominates in both phases and q becomes equal to p_N.

For the distribution ratio q the following equation is valid:

$$q = \frac{\beta_N p_N [A]^N}{\sum\limits_{n=0} \beta_n [A]^n} \tag{42}$$

It has been shown experimentally (D 38, R 50, S 98, etc.) that in most cases the distribution of the metal between the organic and aqueous phases can be explained by the above equation.

Stability constants β_n of metal chelates MA_n can be calculated from eq. (42) using the "limiting value method" (Leden L 11), the "two-parameter method" (Dyrssen and Sillén D 29), the "average number method" (Bjerrum B 61) or the "least squares method" (R 52, R 53). A review of these methods is given by Starý (S 98), Zozulya and Peshkova (Z 21), and Šůcha (S 131).

2.6.1. *The limiting value method*

For the determination of stability constants β_n using the limiting value method eq. (42) must be transformed into the form:

$$q^{-1}[A]^N = f_p^{-1} + f_p^{-1}\beta_1[A] + f_p^{-1}\beta_2[A]^2 + \ldots = F_0 \tag{43}$$

where $f_p = \beta_N \cdot p_N$ as in eq. (34).

The value of f_p^{-1} can easily be determined as $\lim\limits_{[A]\to 0} F_0$. By the successive formation of functions

$$F_1 = \frac{F_0 - f_p^{-1}}{[A]} = \beta_1 f_p^{-1} + \beta_2 f_p^{-1}[A] + \ldots \tag{44}$$

$$F_2 = \frac{F_1 - \beta_1 f_p^{-1}}{[A]} = \beta_2 f_p^{-1} + \beta_3 f_p^{-1}[A] + \ldots \tag{45}$$

the stability constants β_1, β_2, etc., can be found from $\lim\limits_{[A]\to 0} F_1$, $\lim\limits_{[A]\to 0} F_2$, etc., and from the known value of f_p^{-1}.

Rydberg (R 42) was the first to use the limiting value method for determining the stability of thorium acetylacetonate from distribution data. Till the present time this method was proved to be very successful for the investigations of many metal chelates using extraction methods (D 9, P 17, P 19, R 24–26, R 43–51, S 99, etc.).

2.6.2. *The two-parameter method*

Dyrssen and Sillén (D 29) suggest a two-parameter approximation for the formation of the consecutive complexes MA_1, $MA_2 \ldots MA_N$. As one parameter they use the quantity a defined by:

$$\beta_N = 10^{Na} \qquad \text{or} \qquad \log \beta_N = Na \tag{46}$$

On the assumption that the ratio of the consecutive (stepwise) constants K_n/K_{n+1} is equal for each step, the following equation is valid:

$$K_n/K_{n+1} = 10^{2b} \quad \text{or} \quad \log K_n - \log K_{n+1} = 2b = 2 \log \alpha \quad (47)$$

where

$$K_n = [MA_n]/[MA_{n-1}][A] \quad (48)$$

With the use of eqs. (46), (47), and (48) the stability constants β_n and K_n can be expressed as follows:

$$\log K_n = a + b(N + 1 - 2n) \quad (49)$$

$$\log \beta_n = an + bn(N - n) \quad (50)$$

For convenience a variable y is introduced defined by:

$$y = [A]10^a \quad \text{or} \quad \log y = \log [A] + a \quad (51)$$

Introducing the new parameters a, b and y into eq. (42) we obtain:

$$\log q = \log p_N + N \log y - \log \sum_{n=0} y^n \alpha^{n(N-n)} \quad (52)$$

To determine a, b and thus also the stability constants β_n (see eq. (50)) one can prepare a templet giving ($\log q - \log p$) versus $\log y$ according to eq. (52) for a fixed value of N and various values of b (see Fig. 6). The templet

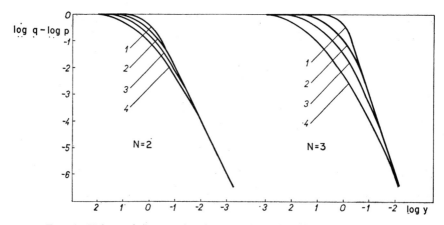

FIG. 6. Values of ($\log q - \log p$) versus $\log y$ for bivalent ($N = 2$) and for tervalent ($N = 3$) metal ions for: (1) $b = 0.0$; (2) $b = 0.3$; (3) $b = 0.6$; and (4) $b = 1.0$.

should have a mark at $\log y = 0$. This templet is moved parallel with the experimental plot of $\log q$ versus pA ($= -\log [A]$), and b can be determined from the curve of the templet which gives the best fit with the experimental curve. Then a can be read as pA at the mark for $\log y = 0$ of the templet.

The experimental curves given in Fig. 1 completely fulfil eq. (52) with $a = 6\cdot18$ and $b = 0\cdot94$.

The two-parameter method can be especially useful when the value of p is so high that it is not possible to determine its value experimentally.

Dyrssen (D 29, D 34–37) successively used the two-parameter method for the systematic investigation of thorium chelates with some organic reagents; Rudenko and Starý (R 24–26, S 99) used it in their study of metal chelates with β-diketones.

2.6.3. *Average number method*

Rydberg (R 42, R 43) showed that the slope of the distribution curve $\log q$ versus pA is proportional to the ligand number $\bar{n}$, i.e. to the average number of ligands in the chelate per central metal atom. This can be expressed as follows:

$$\bar{n} = N - d(\log q)/d(\mathrm{pA}) \tag{53}$$

$\bar{n}$ can be obtained as a function of pA by graphical differentiation of the curve of $\log q$ versus pA.

According to Bjerrum (B 61) the average number of ligands can be calculated from the following equation:

$$\bar{n} = \frac{\displaystyle\sum_{n=0} n[\mathrm{MA}_n]}{\displaystyle\sum_{n=0} [\mathrm{MA}_n]} = \frac{\displaystyle\sum_{n=0} n\beta_n[\mathrm{A}]^n}{\displaystyle\sum_{n=0} \beta_n[\mathrm{A}]^n} \tag{54}$$

After transformation of eq. (54) we obtain:

$$\bar{n} + \beta_1[\mathrm{A}](\bar{n} - 1) + \beta_2[\mathrm{A}]^2(\bar{n} - 2) + \ldots \beta_N[\mathrm{A}]^N(\bar{n} - N) = 0 \tag{55}$$

By choosing corresponding values of $\bar{n}$ and [A], equations are obtained which can be solved for β_n by the use of determinants (55). By choosing the values of [A] at $0\cdot5$, $1\cdot5$, $2\cdot5$, etc., preliminary values of β_n can be calculated. These values can be refined by successive approximation so that the distribution curve calculated from the values of constants and eq. (42) fits the experimental points.

Using the average ligand number method Rydberg (R 42–43, R 49, R 51) determined the stability constants of some metal acetylacetonates. This method is not very suitable for determination of stability constants from distribution data as the calculations are not carried out directly from experimental values of q.

2.6.4. *Least squares method*

The methods described above for the calculation of stability constants are generally graphical in nature. A more accurate procedure is to treat the data according to the principle of least squares (R 52, R 53), which leads to the best values especially if high-speed electronic computers are available.

Rydberg and Sullivan (R 52, R 53) transformed eq. (42) into the form:

$$Z = \sum_{n=0} a_n[A]^n \qquad (56)$$

where $Z = q^{-1}[A]^N$, and $a_n = \beta_n/p_N\beta_N$. This form is most suitable for calculations using electronic computers.

By using the least squares method the stability constants of thorium, uranium, and plutonium acetylacetones were determined.

2.6.5. *Method of continuous variations*

Korenman (K 57–59) showed that two variants of Job's method of continuous variations (J 11) can be adapted to the investigation of the composition of an extractable chelate.

In the first variant various volumes of organic phase, containing the reagent, and aqueous phase, containing the metal investigated, are equilibrated, and the concentration of the metal in the organic phase is measured spectrophotometrically or radiometrically. The concentration of the organic reagent and that of the metal must be the same, and the sum of the volumes of both phases in any one series of experiments must be kept constant.

In the second variant equal volumes of organic phase and aqueous phase are equilibrated followed by measuring the concentration of metal in the organic phase. The concentration of the reagent in the organic phase and the concentration of the metal investigated in the aqueous phase are now different but their sum must be kept constant.

The number of ligands bound in the metal chelate is equal to the ratio of the volumes of organic and aqueous phases (or to the ratio of the concentrations of the reagent and metal) at which the highest amount of metal is extracted.

The determination of the composition of mercury dithizonates by the method of continuous variations is illustrated in Fig. 7. A primary dithizonate $Hg(HDz)_2$ is formed at pH 4·1 and a secondary dithizonate $HgDz$ at pH 9·8.

The method of continuous variations has been used for the determination of the composition of many metal chelates, especially dithizonates (I 13, K 57–59, D 19, C 47, etc.). It cannot be used if more complicated complexes (e.g. additive complexes with the organic reagent) are formed.

2.7. COMPLEXES OF THE TYPE $MB_u(OH)_v$

All the equations given above are only strictly valid if the anions present in the aqueous phase are such as not to be capable of forming a stable complex with the metal investigated. If a complexing agent, H_nB, is present in the aqueous phase (e.g. oxalate, tartrate, citrate, cyanide, complexonate, etc.) which can form a non-extractable complex of the type $MB_u(OH)_v$, the distribution of metal between the organic phase containing the reagent HA

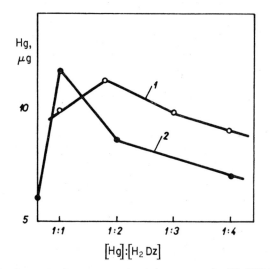

FIG. 7. Amount of mercury extracted versus ratio $[Hg]/[H_2Dz]$ at: (1) pH = 4·1; (2) pH = 9·8.

and the aqueous phase containing the masking agent H_nB now follows eq. (57):

$$q_c = \frac{[MA_N]_{org}}{\sum\limits_{n=0}\sum\limits_{p=0}[MA_n(OH)_p] + \sum\limits_{u=1}\sum\limits_{v=0}[MB_u(OH)_v]}$$

$$= \frac{\beta_N p_N[A]^N}{\sum\limits_{n=0}\sum\limits_{p=0}\beta_{n,p}[A]^n[OH]^p + \sum\limits_{u=1}\sum\limits_{v=0}\beta_{u,v}[B]^u[OH]^v} \tag{57}$$

where $\beta_{0,0} = 1$.

At constant pH and $[HA]_{org}$ and with the same organic solvent the following equation can be obtained from eqs. (33) and (57):

$$\frac{q}{q_c} = \frac{\sum\limits_{n=0}\sum\limits_{p=0}\beta_{n,p}[A]^n[OH]^p + \sum\limits_{u=1}\sum\limits_{v=0}\beta_{u,v}[B]^u[OH]^p}{\sum\limits_{n=0}\sum\limits_{p=0}\beta_{n,p}[A]^n[OH]^p} \tag{58}$$

The values $\beta_{n,p}$ can be calculated by the method of limiting values or by the least squares method from the distribution curve of $\log q$ versus pH at various $[HA]_{org}$ (see Section 2.4). However, if the slope of the distribution curve equals N, then the concentration of hydroxycomplexes $MA_n(OH)_p$

in the aqueous phase can be neglected in comparison with the concentration
of free metal cations and eq. (58) reduces to:

$$\frac{q}{q_c} - 1 = \sum_{u=1} \sum_{v=0} \beta_{u,v}[B]^u[OH]^p \qquad (59)$$

From eq. (59) it can be seen that the stability constant of complexes such as
$MB_u(OH)_v$ can easily be calculated from the distribution of metal at various
pH and [B]. The last concentration is calculated from the total concentration
of the complexing agent and from its dissociation constant (see Section 3.3).

If no hydroxycomplexes are formed, i.e. if q/q_c measured at constant [B]
does not depend on pH, eq. (59) reduces to:

$$\frac{q}{q_c} - 1 = \sum_{u=1} \beta_u[B]^u \qquad (60)$$

By using the above equations Connick and McVey (C 42, C 43) determined
the stability constants of zirconium with various complexing agents on the
basis of the distribution of zirconium between a solution of thenoyltrifluoracetone in benzene and an aqueous phase in the presence and in the
absence of complexing agents. This method requires constancy of pH and
the determination of q-values which should be very large and thus difficult
to determine. For this reason this method can be adapted for only a few
extraction systems (D 2, M 25, S 139).

However, Starý (S 101, S 102, S 105) showed that if the value of q is calculated from the extraction constant (see eq. (62)), eqs. (59) and (60) can then
be used successfully for most extraction systems. By using this method the
composition and stability constants of many metal complexes with tartaric,
oxalic, nitrilotriacetic, ethylenediaminetetraacetic and 1,2-diaminocyclo-
hexanetetraacetic acid have been determined (S 106).

An analogous method was also used for determining the stability of
yttrium complexes with various complexing agents (P 2).

CHAPTER 3

THEORY OF THE SOLVENT EXTRACTION OF METAL CHELATES

ALTHOUGH the solvent extraction of metal chelates had been used for a long time for separation procedures for many metals it was not until 1941 that Kolthoff and Sandell (K 53) gave the first quantitative description of the extraction process.

The first theoretical treatment of the solvent extraction of metal chelates was given by Irving (I 9, I 12, I 33) and later by Dyrssen (D 38), Starý (S 98), Ringbom (R 16), Morrison and Freiser (M 99) and other authors.

3.1. INFLUENCE OF ACIDITY ON THE EXTRACTION OF METAL CHELATES

In the previous part it was stated that the solvent extraction of metal chelates can be described in general as follows: the metal ion M^{N+} reacts with the organic reagent HA, giving an uncharged chelate MA_N which is distributed between two phases according to the equation:

$$M^{N+} + N(HA)_{org} = (MA_N)_{org} + NH^+ \qquad (61)$$

The equilibrium constant of the above reaction, called the extraction constant K, is defined by eq. (62):

$$K = \frac{[MA_N]_{org}[H]^N}{[M][HA]_{org}^N} \qquad (62)$$

The extraction constant for a given system at a specified temperature depends only on the ionic strength of the aqueous phase (seldom on the ionic strength of the organic phase).

Under certain conditions eq. (62) expresses directly the distribution ratio of metal, which is the main interest for separation procedures. Assuming that the concentration of metal chelate species $MA_n (n = 1, 2, \ldots, N)$ and of hydroxycomplexes $M(OH)_p$ can be neglected with comparison of the concentration of free metal cations, we have:

$$K = q([H]^N / [HA]_{org}^N) \qquad (63)$$

where q is the distribution ratio of the metal between the two immiscible phases. It can be seen from eq. (63) that, provided the reagent concentration is maintained constant, the distribution of the metal is a function of pH alone. From the known value of the extraction constant K it is therefore possible to calculate the q-value for every value of $[HA]_{org}$ and pH.

Equation (63), originally published by Kolthoff and Sandell (K 53), was first experimentally verified on the extraction of zinc by dithizone solution (S 10) and on the extraction of metal cupferrates (F 33).

From the analytical point of view a more important value than q is the percentage of the metal extracted E, which is related to the distribution ratio according to eq. (64):

$$E = \frac{100q}{q + (V/V_{org})} \tag{64}$$

where V, V_{org} represent the volumes of aqueous and organic phase respectively.

Expressing eqs. (63) and (64) in the equivalent logarithmic form (I 9), we obtain:

$$\log q = \log K + N\mathrm{pH} + N \log [HA]_{org} = \log EV/V_{org} - \log (100 - E) \tag{65}$$

or

$$-(\log K)/N = \mathrm{pH} - (\log q)/N + \log [HA]_{org} = (\mathrm{pH}_{1/2})_{1\cdot0} \tag{66}$$

Equations (65), (66) represent a family of symmetrical sigmoid curves the position of which along the pH axis depends only on the magnitude of K, and the slope of each depends uniquely on N, i.e. on the charge of the metal ion (I 9).

From eq. (66) it is evident that the value of $-(\log K)/N$ equals the pH-value at which 50 per cent of the metal is extracted ($q = 1$) at $1\cdot00$ M equilibrium concentration of the reagent in the organic phase, provided that the volumes of organic and aqueous phase are equal. This pH-value is called $(\mathrm{pH}_{1/2})_{1\cdot0}$.

In Table 1 the values of per cent of metal extracted, E, (for $V = V_{org}$) and the corresponding values of q are given, calculated from eqs. (63) and (64) for monovalent ($N = 1$), divalent ($N = 2$), trivalent ($N = 3$), and tetravalent ($N = 4$) metal ions. An increase of one unit in the pH will increase the distribution ratio tenfold in the case of univalent metal ions, but

TABLE 1

	$N = 1$		$N = 2$		$N = 3$		$N = 4$	
	E	q	E	q	E	q	E	q
$\mathrm{pH}_{1/2} - 1\cdot0$	9·1	0·1	1·0	0·01	0·1	0·001	0·01	0·0001
$\mathrm{pH}_{1/2} - 0\cdot5$	24·1	0·32	9·1	0·1	3·1	0·032	1·0	0·01
$\mathrm{pH}_{1/2}$	50·0	1·0	50·0	1·0	50·0	1·0	50·0	1·0
$\mathrm{pH}_{1/2} + 0\cdot5$	75·9	3·2	90·9	10·0	96·9	32	99·0	100
$\mathrm{pH}_{1/2} + 1\cdot0$	90·9	10	99·0	100	99·9	10^3	99·99	10^4

100-, 1,000- and 10,000-fold for divalent, trivalent, and tetravalent metal ions respectively. From this reason it is evident that the extraction curves (E versus pH) are of great analytical importance.

The distribution of the metal given in Table 1 can be achieved for all extraction systems if the following two conditions are fulfilled:

1. The metal chelate should be very slightly soluble in water so that its partition coefficient p_N has a large value. In this case the concentration of both charged and uncharged chelated metal species (where $n = 1 \ldots N$) in the aqueous phase can be neglected for the lower values of q.

2. The formation of hydroxycomplexes $M(OH)_p$ can be neglected at the pH investigated.

The above two conditions are approximatively fulfilled for the extraction of silver, lead, lanthanum, and thorium by 8-hydroxyquinoline solution in chloroform and therefore the experimental extraction curves (see Fig. 8) do

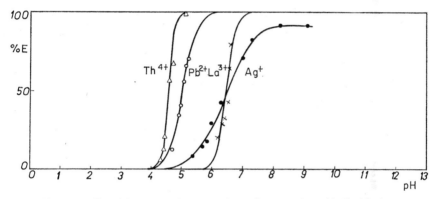

FIG. 8. Effect of pH on the extraction of monovalent (Ag^+), bivalent (Pb^{2+}), tervalent (La^{3+}) and tetravalent (Th^{4+}) metal ions by 0·10 M 8-hydroxyquinoline in chloroform.

not differ substantially from the theoretical ones calculated according to eqs. (63) and (64). Only silver–oxinate extraction forms an exception, because of their low p_N-value.

However, if the p_N-values are not too high, or if various other metal species are present in the aqueous phase (e.g. MA_n, or $M(OH)_p$), the experimentally found extraction curves differ from those predicted theoretically.

When hydroxycomplexes $M(OH)_p$ are formed in the aqueous phase, the distribution ratio q decreases according to eq. (67):

$$q = \frac{[MA_N]_{org}}{[M] + [M(OH)] + [M(OH)_2] + \ldots} = \frac{K[HA]_{org}^N}{(1 + \beta_1[OH] + \beta_2[OH]^2 + \ldots)[H]^N}$$

$$(67)$$

In the previous part it was stated that the slope of the distribution curve
equal the average charge on the metal ion species present in the aqueous phase.
For this reason the distribution curves of the easily hydrolysed metal-ions
have a lower slope than corresponds to the metal ion charge. For instance,
bismuth is present in aqueous solution at pH 1–2 as hydroxycations $BiOH^{2+}$
and $Bi(OH)_2^+$ and the slope of the distribution curves equals 2 or 1 in this
pH-region (see Fig. 36).

The formation of higher hydroxycomplexes and/or decreasing the equilibrium concentration of the reagent in the organic phase leads to a decrease
in the partition coefficient of the metal at higher pH-values.

If the metal concentration can be neglected in comparison with the total
reagent concentration, c_{HA}, the equilibrium concentration $[HA]_{org}$ can be
calculated according to eqs. (37), (39–41) from the relation:

$$\log [HA]_{org} = \log c_{HA} - \log \{1 + p_{HA}^{-1}(1 + K_{HA}[H]^{-1} + K_{H_2A}^{-1}[H]\} \quad (68)$$

In Fig. 9 is given the dependence of $\log [HA]_{org}$ for some organic reagents

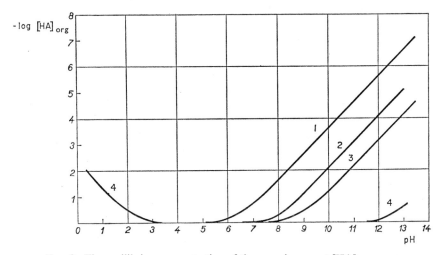

FIG. 9. The equilibrium concentration of the organic reagent $[HA]_{org}$ versus
pH for: (1) cupferron–chloroform system; (2) diethyldithiocarbamate–
carbon tetrachloride system; (3) dithizone–carbon tetrachloride system;
and (4) 8-hydroxyquinoline–chloroform system.

on the pH-values calculated from eq. (68) using the known values of partition coefficient p_{HA} and dissociation constants K_{HA} and K_{H_2A} of the reagent
(see Appendix).

By using eq. (67) it is thus possible to calculate the distribution ratio (or
the percentage of metal extracted) for any pH-value and organic reagent
concentration if the extraction constant and stability constants of hydroxycomplexes (or the relevant hydrolysis constants) are known.

For instance, the extraction constant K for the zinc–dithizone–carbon tetrachloride systems equals approximately 200 and the stability constants of the hydroxycomplexes $Zn(OH)_3^-$ and $Zn(OH)_4^{2-}$ are equal to $10^{14\cdot4}$ and $10^{15\cdot4}$ respectively. For the total dithizone concentration $c_{HA} = 10^{-4}$ M and zinc concentration $c_{Zn} \ll 10^{-5}$ M at pH $= 4$ more than 99 per cent of zinc can be extracted ($q = 200 \times 10^{-8}/10^{-8} = 200$), but at pH $= 14$ only 0·03 per cent of zinc can be extracted:

$$ q = \frac{200 \times (10^{-9\cdot2})^2}{(1 + 10^{14\cdot4} + 10^{15\cdot4})(10^{-14})^2} = 3 \times 10^{-4} $$

The decrease of the extraction at high pH-values may be expected especially for metals forming stable anions under these conditions (e.g. molybdenum (VI), tungsten (VI), uranium (VI), vanadium (V), etc.).

3.2. INFLUENCE OF THE CONCENTRATION OF THE ORGANIC REAGENT

It may be noted from eq. (65) that the extractability of a metal with a given reagent and organic solvent depends heavily upon the concentration of the organic reagent. The higher $[HA]_{org}$ is, the higher is the distribution ratio, and the extraction curve is shifted to the acid side, permitting extraction from more acidic solutions. The use of high reagent concentration is thus advantageous especially for the extraction of metals which are easily hydrolysed. Practical considerations often limit the permissible variations in the magnitude of the latter parameter. The upper limit is set by the solubility of the reagent in the organic solvent used, which is often small (see Appendix); the lower limit is given by the formation of non-extractable hydroxycomplexes. Besides, in the case where the metal chelate is determined spectrophotometrically a large excess of the reagent would be undesirable if it has an appreciable extinction coefficient at the wavelength used for measurements.

Where a chelate of general type MA_N is formed, a tenfold increase in the equilibrium reagent concentration will decrease the value of $pH_{1/2}$ by one unit in pH (see eq. (66)). For an organic reagent with a high partition coefficient, p_{HA}, the equilibrium concentration $[HA]_{org}$ is practically equal to the total concentration c_{HA} if no dissociation of the reagent occurs (see eq. (68)) and if the total metal concentration, c_M, can be neglected in comparison with c_{HA}.

Figure 10 shows the extraction of manganese (II) ($c_M = 10^{-4}$ M) by 0·100 M and by 0·010 M solutions of 8-hydroxyquinoline in chloroform. The experimental values found for $pH_{1/2}$, viz. $(pH_{1/2})_{0\cdot1} = 5\cdot66$ and $(pH_{1/2})_{0\cdot01} = 6\cdot66$, are in full agreement with the theory (S 106).

When an additive complex with the reagent is formed, the extraction constant is expressed as follows:

$$K = \frac{[MA_N(HA)_r]_{org}[H]^N}{[M][HA]_{org}^{N+r}} = q\frac{[H]^N}{[HA]_{org}^{N+r}} \qquad (69)$$

or

$$-\frac{1}{N}\log K = pH - \frac{1}{N}\log q + \frac{N+r}{r}\log [HA]_{org} \qquad (70)$$

From the above equations it is evident that a tenfold decrease in $[HA]_{org}$ reduces $pH_{1/2}$ by 1·5 units for $r = 1$ and by 2·0 units for $r = 2$, etc., for divalent metals ($N = 2$).

For instance, cobalt (II) forms an additive complex of the type $CoA_2(HA)_2$ with 8-hydroxyquinoline, and the experimental values of $pH_{1/2}$ are $(pH_{1/2})_{0·1} = 3·21$ and $(pH_{1/2})_{0·01} = 5·08$ respectively (see Fig. 10).

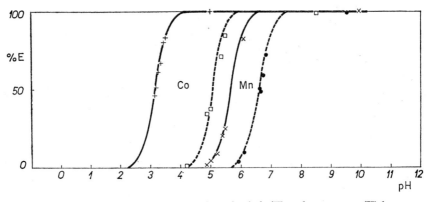

Fig. 10. Effect of pH on the extraction of cobalt (II) and manganese (II) by 8-hydroxyquinoline in chloroform.

When complexes of the type $MA_N(HA)_r(OH)_p$ are formed, the extraction curves for various concentrations of organic reagent become more complicated. Figure 11 shows the percentage of uranium (VI) extracted by 0·20, 0·10, 0·05, and 0·02 M solutions of benzoylacetone in carbon tetrachloride as a function of pH (S 100).

In all separation procedures described up to now an excess of organic reagent was used to ensure quantitative reaction. The use of a smaller amount of the organic reagent than corresponds stoicheiometrically to the amount of metal to be determined (i.e. substoicheiometry) will be discussed separately (see Section 4.2).

3.3 INFLUENCE OF MASKING AGENTS

Although masking agents have been used for a long time in many selective extraction procedures the systematic studies of their influence have only recently been carried out (A 32, S 31, S 106).

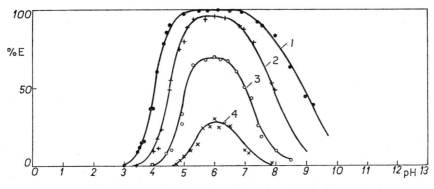

FIG. 11. Effect of pH on the extraction of uranium (VI) by benzoylacetone in carbon tetrachloride 0·20 M (curve 1); 0·10 M (curve 2); 0·05 M (curve 3); 0·02 M (curve 4).

In a previous section (2.7) it was shown that the distribution ratio of metal in the presence of the masking agents H_nB (e.g. oxalic acid, tartaric acid, complexionates, etc.) that form non-extractable complexes MB_u is diminished according to the equation:

$$q_c = \frac{[MA_N]_{org}}{[M] + [MB] + [MB_2] + \ldots} = \frac{K \cdot [HA]_{org}^N}{[H]^N(1 + \beta_1[B] + \beta_2[B]^2 + \ldots)} \tag{71}$$

where β_u is the stability constant of metal complex MB_u.

From the above equation it is evident that the distribution of a particular metal at various values of pH and $[HA]_{org}$ can be calculated from the known value of the extraction constant K and from the stability constants of metal complex with the masking agent. The equilibrium concentration of the anion B can easily be calculated from the total concentration of masking agent c_{H_nB} and from its dissociation constants.

The plots of log [B] versus pH for the same masking agents (tartaric, oxalic, hydrocyanic, nitrilotriacetic, ethylenediaminetetraacetic and 1,2-diamino-cyclohexanetetraacetic acids) are shown in Fig. 12 ($c_{H_nB} = 1·00$ M). Stability constants of metal complexes with these agents are summarized in Table 2 (B 62, S 106, Y 6).

TABLE 2. STABILITY CONSTANTS OF METAL-ION COMPLEXES WITH SOME MASKING AGENTS

(NTA—nitrilotriacetic acid. EDTA—ethylenediaminetetraacetic acid. HEDTA—1,2-diaminocyclohexanetetraacetic acid)

Metal ion	Oxalates				Tartrates		Cyanides			NTA		EDTA	HEDTA
	$\log \beta_1$	$\log \beta_2$	$\log \beta_3$	$\log \beta_4$	$\log \beta_1$	$\log \beta_2$	$\log \beta_2$	$\log \beta_4$	$\log \beta_6$	$\log \beta_1$	$\log \beta_2$	$\log \beta_1$	$\log \beta_1$
Ag^+	0						21			5.2		7.1	8.2
Al^{3+}	7.3	13	15.6			9.6				9.5		16.1	17.6
Am^{3+}	2.3	11.3	12.1			6.8						18.0	8.0
Ba^{2+}					<2					4.8		7.8	10.8
Be^{2+}	4.1				2.9	11.3				7.1		9.3	
Bi^{3+}												26	
Ca^{2+}	3				1.8					6.4	11.6	10.7	12.5
Cd^{2+}	3.7	5.7			2.7		10.6	18		9.5	15.5	16.9	19.2
Ce^{3+}	6.5	10.5	11.3							10.7		16.0	16.8
Cf^{3+}												19.1	
Cm^{3+}												18.4	
Co^{2+}	4.7	6.8			2.8				19	10.8	14.3	16.6	18.9
Cu^{2+}		10.5			3.0	5.1		25?		13.0		18.9	21.6
Dy^{3+}										11.6		18.1	19.7
Er^{3+}												18.8	20.7
Eu^{3+}												17.4	18.6
Fe^{2+}	4.7	6.9				4.8			24	8.8		14.3	
Fe^{3+}	9.4	16.2	20.5			11.9			31	15.9	24.6	25.1	
Ga^{3+}			18.0			9.8				11.4		20.3	22.9
Gd^{3+}												17.1	18.8
Hf^{4+}	10	20	28	36									
Hg^{2+}					<4			41.4				21.8	24.3
Ho^{3+}												18.1	
In^{3+}					4.5						24.4	25.0	16.8
La^{3+}			14.7			6.7				10.4	17.2	15.3	
Lu^{3+}												19.8	21.5
Mg^{2+}	2.4	4.4			1.4					5.4		8.7	10.3
Mn^{2+}	3.8	5.2			2.9					7.4		12.9	14.7

TABLE 2 (*continued*)

Metal ion	Oxalates				Tartrates		Cyanides			NTA		EDTA	HEDTA
	$\log \beta_1$	$\log \beta_2$	$\log \beta_3$	$\log \beta_4$	$\log \beta_1$	$\log \beta_2$	$\log \beta_2$	$\log \beta_4$	$\log \beta_6$	$\log \beta_1$	$\log \beta_2$	$\log \beta_1$	$\log \beta_1$
Mn^{3+}	10	16·6	19·3		7·7								
H_2MoO_4	7·4												
Nd^{3+}	7·2	11·5	13·5							11·1		16·8	17·7
Ni^{2+}		7·9						22		11·5		18·4	19·7
Np^{4+}	8·5	17·7	24·0	27·4		5·4							
NpO_2^+	3·3	7·1			2·3								
Pb^{2+}		6·6			2·9	4·3		10		11·5		18·3	19·5
Pd^{2+}												18·5	
Pr^{3+}										10·9		16·2	17·3
Pu^{4+}	9·6	16·4	21·6	27								25·8	
PuO_2^{2+}	6·6	11·4											
Ra^{2+}												7·1	
Sc^{3+}			16·3		1·2	12·5				11·4	24·1	23·0	25·4
Sm^{3+}										5·0		16·9	18·4
Sr^{2+}	2·5				1·6							8·6	
Tb^{3+}												17·8	19·5
Th^{4+}		10·7		23·6								23·2	
TiO^{2+}	< 2					9·7				12·3		17·5	19·9
Tl^+								35				6·6	
Tl^{3+}			16·9									23·2	
Tm^{3+}												19·3	21·0
U^{4+}		16·8	22·8	27·8									
UO_2^{2+}	8·6	11·1				9·7		19				18·8	19·4
VO^{2+}	6·4	9·0											
VO_2^+													
Y^{3+}	6·5	9·3	11							11·4		18·0	19·2
Yb^{3+}	7·3	10·1	13·9							12·1		18·7	21·1
Zn^{2+}	4·9	7·6			2·7					10·4		16·3	18·7
Zr^{4+}	11·1	20·3	26·9	32·9									

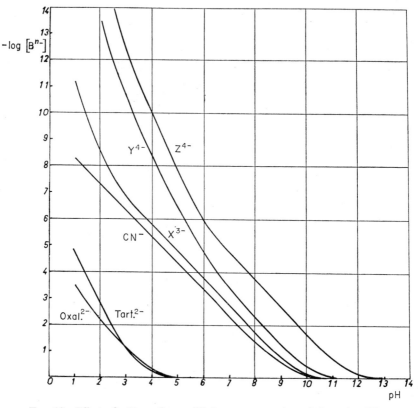

FIG. 12. Effect of pH on the equilibrium concentration of the anion B^{n-} (H_2Oxal = oxalic acid, H_2Tart = tartaric acid, HCN = hydrocyanic acid, H_3X = nitrilotriacetic acid, H_4Y = ethylenediaminetetraacetic acid, and H_4Z = 1,2-diaminocyclohexanetetraacetic acid).

For instance, the distribution ratio of copper (II) between 0·010 M 8-hydroxyquinoline solution in chloroform and 0·010 M EDTA solution at pH = 4·0 equals:

$$q = \frac{10^{1·77}(0·01)^2}{(10^{-4})^2(1 + 10^{18·9} \times 10^{-10·3})} = 0·003$$

i.e. only 0·3 per cent of copper (II) can be extracted; but in the absence of EDTA practically complete extraction of copper takes place under these conditions.

In Fig. 13 are given the extraction curves of copper (II) by 0·01 M 8-hydroxyquinoline solution in chloroform in the presence of various complexing agents. All these curves completely fulfil eq. (71) (S 106). The same results were obtained also for many other metal chelate systems (S 106).

3.4. INFLUENCE OF THE DISSOCIATION CONSTANT, K_{HA}, AND THE PARTITION COEFFICIENT p_{HA} OF THE ORGANIC REAGENT

Introducing the expressions for dissociation constant K_{HA} (see eq. (40)) and partition coefficient p_{HA} (see eq. (39)) of the organic reagent into eq. (62) we obtain:

$$-\frac{1}{N}\log K = pK_{HA} + \log p_{HA} - \frac{1}{N}\log \beta_N p_N = (pH_{1/2})_{1\cdot 0} \qquad (72)$$

where β_N and p_N are the stability constant and partition coefficient respectively of the metal chelate MA_N.

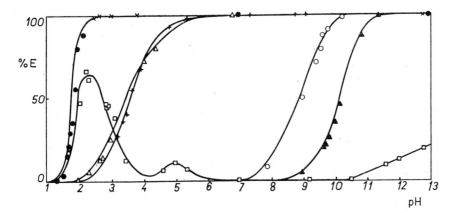

Fig. 13. Effect of pH on the extraction of copper (II) by 0·01 M 8-hydroxy-quinoline in chloroform; ● in the absence of complexing agent, △ in the presence of 0·01 M oxalic acid, × in the presence of 0·01 M tartaric acid, □ in the presence of 0·01 M hydrocyanic acid, + in the presence of 0·01 M nitrilotriacetic acid, ○ in the presence of 0·01 M ethylenediaminetetraacetic acid, and ▲ in the presence of 1,2-diaminocyclohexanetetraacetic acid.

From the above equation it is evident that the higher the value of $(pK_{HA} + \log p_{HA})$ the more alkaline the solution required in general for the extraction of the metal; i.e. the value of $(pH_{1/2})_{1\cdot 0}$ must be higher. Since the value of the stability constant β_N can be correlated with that of K_{HA}, and that of the partition coefficient p_N of the metal chelate with that of the reagent, p_{HA}, the influence of the term involving the product $\beta_N p_N$ will be more complicated. However, it may be expected that in general the extraction of metals by solutions of dithizone in carbon tetrachloride ($\log p_{HA} + pK_{HA} = 8\cdot 8$) or by one of cupferron in chloroform ($\log p_{HA} + pK_{HA} = 6\cdot 4$) will occur in more acidic solutions than those of solutions of acetylacetone in benzene ($\log p_{HA} + pK_{HA} = 10\cdot 2$) or by 8-hydroxyquinoline dissolved in chloroform ($\log p_{HA} + pK_{HA} = 12\cdot 3$).

A relation between values of $\frac{1}{N}\log\beta_N$ and pK_{HA} for a series of closely related compounds (e.g. β-diketones, 8-hydroxyquinolines, etc.) can be expressed as:

$$\frac{1}{N} - \log\beta_N = pK_{HA} + \text{const}' \tag{73}$$

This relation (S 80, S 81, S 107; see also Section 3.7) implies that for constant pK_{HA}, β_N will be also constant.

An analogous relation may also be found between the partition coefficient of a metal chelate p_N and that of the organic reagent p_{HA} (S 80, S 81, S 98, S 107):

$$\frac{1}{N}\log p_N = \log p_{HA} + \text{const}'' \tag{74}$$

From eq. (74) it can be seen that the higher the value of p_{HA}, the higher the value of p_N. By an appropriate modification of an organic reagent, e.g. by substituting a hydrogen atom by a hydrocarbon radical or an aromatic ring, the partitition coefficient, p_{HA}, increases and there will be a higher value too for p_N so that more complete extraction of the metal chelate can be easily achieved. On the contrary, by substituting a $-CH_3$ group by a hydrophilic group such as $-CF_3$, p_{HA} and the corresponding value of p_N decrease.

Equation (74) was confirmed by a systematic study of the solvent extraction of metal acetylacetonates, benzoylacetonates and dibenzoylmethanates; values of $\frac{1}{N}\log p_N$ for metal benzoylacetonates and dibenzoylmethanates are approximately at 2·4 and at 4·6 units higher than those of metal acetylacetonates (2·4 and 4·6 is the difference between values of $\log p_{HA}$ for the corresponding organic reagents). From this reason, by using benzoylacetone or dibenzoylmethane it is possible to achieve quantitative extraction even for those metals that are only partially extracted by acetylacetone solutions.

By combining eqs. (73) and (74) we obtain:

$$\log\beta_N p_N = N(\log p_{HA} + pK_{HA}) + \text{const}''' \tag{75}$$

By comparing eq. (75) with eq. (72) it will be obvious that only a slight change in the value of $\log K$ or of $(pH_{1/2})$ can be anticipated as a consequence of a variation in p_{HA} or pK_{HA} in a series of closely related organic reagents for which the value of the const''' is practically the same. This is true for many 1-phenyl-3-methyl-4-acylpyrazolones (see Table 3) and for 8-hydroxyquinolines, dithizones, etc.

From the above mentioned it is also evident that new derivatives of a known organic reagent will not be substantially different in their extraction properties from those of the parent compound.

TABLE 3. VALUES OF $\log K$ FOR SOME 1-PHENYL-3-METHYL-4-ACYLPYRAZOLONATES (S 81)
(Chloroform was used as a solvent)

Substituent	pK_{HA}^+ $\log p_{HA}$	log K					
		Th (IV)	U (VI)	La (III)	Pb (II)	Zn (II)	Be (II)
Acetyl	7·10	0·4	−0·3	−7·8	−4·6	−5·2	−4·0
Propionyl	7·55	0·0	0·0	−8·0	−4·3	−5·3	−4·9
Butyryl	8·17	−0·8	−1·0	−7·5	−4·3	−6·0	−6·5
Valeryl	8·74	−0·5	−0·5	−8·5	−4·5	−5·3	−6·7
Capronyl	9·4	1·0	−1·4	−9·4	−4·6	−5·6	−7·7
Ethoxycarbonyl	7·95		−2·0	−7·5	−4·6		−5·0
Chloroacetyl	5·7	−0·2	−1·3	−6·9	−3·2		−3·7
Trifluoroacetyl	5·6		−1·6				−3·2
Benzoyl	8·1	−1·6	−2·0	−7·4	−3·7		−5·7
p-Bromobenzoyl	8·8	−1·2	−1·8	−6·9	−3·2		−7·1

3.5. INFLUENCE OF THE SOLUBILITY OF THE METAL CHELATE

It was shown in the introduction (1.2) that the partition coefficient of the metal chelate p_N is approximately equal to the ratio of its solubility in organic and aqueous phases.

From this reason it can be expected that metal chelates readily soluble in the aqueous phase (e.g. all chelates containing hydrophylic groups as oxalates, tartarates, citrates, complexonates, etc.) and practically insoluble in the organic solvents will not be extracted into the organic phase. Metal chelates soluble in both phases can be extracted only partially (e.g. acetylacetonates of zinc, cobalt (II), nickel, manganese (II), lead (II), lanthanides,† etc.) and only chelates practically insoluble in aqueous media but readily soluble in organic solvents (e.g. acetylacetonates of aluminium, gallium, indium, iron (III), beryllium, etc.) can be quantitatively extracted. Thus on the basis of solubility data it is possible to find the most suitable chelate for separations by extraction.

Lacroix (L 2), Sandell (S 14) and recently Oosting (O 10–13) have shown that the value of $\beta_N p_N$ can be calculated from the solubility of the metal chelate, S_{org}, in the organic solvent and its solubility product, L_{MA_N}, in an aqueous phase saturated with the corresponding organic solvent by means of the following equation:

$$\beta_N p_N = \frac{[MA_N]_{org}}{[M][A]^N} = \frac{S_{org}}{L_{MA_N}} \tag{76}$$

By substituting the value of $\beta_N p_N$ into eq. (72) the value of the extraction constant K or $(pH_{1/2})_{1\cdot0}$ can easily be calculated. The values of K found

† The solubility of lanthanide chelates with acetylacetone in organic solvents increases with their atomic number. Partition coefficient p_N increases in the same manner (B 90, E 12).

experimentally for 8-hydroxyquinolates of gallium, indium, aluminium, nickel, copper, etc. (L 2, O 10–13), agree very well with the values calculated according to eqs. (76) and (72) from the solubility data for these chelates.

The evaluation of K from eq. (76) is limited in practice because the direct determination is much simpler than the determination of the solubility product L_{MA_N}.

3.6. INFLUENCE OF THE ORGANIC SOLVENT

The nature of the organic solvent also influences the distribution of both reagent and metal chelate. As mentioned above (cf. eq. (74)), the higher the solubility of the reagent in the organic solvent, the higher also is the partition coefficient, p_{HA}. For example, the solubility of some β-diketones increases in the order: carbon tetrachloride, benzene, and chloroform. The corresponding values of p_{HA} increase in the same order (M 122). Similar correlation has been noted between the solubility and the partition coefficient p_N of metal chelates.

It is evident from eq. (72) that the extent of the solvent extraction of a metal chelate as expressed by the value of K or $pH_{1/2}$ should not depend strongly on the nature of the solvent because the increase (or decrease) of both the parameters (p_{HA} and p_N) is partially compensating (see eq. (74)). This is true, as was shown by Alimarin and Zolotov (A 31, Z 16), only in the extraction of coordinatively saturated compounds (see Section 2.3). If the coordination number of the central atom is more than twice its charge, then this chelate may contain free coordination positions which can be occupied by molecules of water. The hydrated coordinatively unsaturated chelates are normally poorly extracted. In order to make the extraction more effective, it is necessary to displace the water molecules with molecules of the organic reagent (additive complexes of type $MA_N(HA)_r$) or of the organic solvent (complexes of type $MA_N S_S$). Oxygen-containing solvents are capable of readily displacing the water molecules and therefore they extract coordinatively unsaturated chelates better than solvents devoid of oxygen.

In this way the dependence of the extraction of thallium (I)- and barium (II)-8-hydroxyquinolinates, or of cobalt (II) and neptunium (V)-thenoyltrifluoracetonates on the nature of the organic solvent can be explained (A 31, Z 15).

3.7. INFLUENCE OF THE STABILITY OF METAL CHELATES

From eq. (72) it can be seen that the higher the stability constant β_N of the metal chelates MA_N, the higher also is the extraction constant K, and the extraction can be carried out from more acidic solutions.

For instance, the stability of metal acetylacetonates decreases in the following order (B 62, Y 6): palladium, iron (III), beryllium, copper (II), indium and scandium, aluminium, uranium (VI), thorium, nickel, cobalt, zinc, lanthanum, manganese, and magnesium. Values of $(pH_{1/2})_{0.1}$ decrease in a similar order (S 107): palladium, iron (III), beryllium, gallium and copper, scandium, aluminium, indium, uranium (VI), thorium, nickel, lanthanum, cobalt, zinc, manganese, and magnesium (S 107). Analogous dependence was observed also for values of $(pH_{1/2})_{1.0}$ for other β-diketones, 8-hydroxyquinolates, cupferrates, etc. (S 106, S 107, S 109). It is therefore possible to predict the extraction behaviours of many metals if the stability constants of metal chelates with the organic reagent investigated are known.

In recent years, many stability constants of chelates formed between metal ions and various organic reagents have been measured. On the basis of these investigations numerous qualitative and semiquantitative relationships between the stability of the metal chelate and the properties of the metal ions and of the organic reagents have been discussed. In favourable cases stability constants of many chelates that have not yet been studied experimentally may be predicted on the basis of relationships discussed below.

For example, the empirical relationship between the dissociation constant of the reagent K_{HA} and the stability constants of complexes formed by the same metal ion with various organic reagents has been described by a number of authors (C 2, I 15, M 31, S 26, V 7, V 8); see also eq. (73). These relationships are not universally valid for they are usually applicable only to a very limited series of closely related ligands (β-diketones, 8-hydroxyquinolines, etc.). In some cases the stability of metal chelates is found to be substantially lower than expected from the dissociation constants of the corresponding reagent. These deviations have been explained in terms of steric hindrance, and the number of rings, etc. (I 8, I 19).

Irving and Rossotti (I 24) found a linear relationship between the stability constants for complexes of two metal ions M′ and M″ with a series of organic reagents HA′, HA″, HA‴, etc.:

$$\frac{\log \beta_{M'A'}}{\log \beta_{M''A'}} = \frac{\log \beta_{M'A''}}{\log \beta_{M''A''}} = \frac{\log \beta_{M'A'''}}{\log \beta_{M''A'''}} = \ldots \tag{77}$$

An analogous relationship was found for complexes of a pair of organic reagents HA′ and HA″ with a series of metal ions M′, M″, M‴, etc.:

$$\frac{\log \beta_{M'A'}}{\log \beta_{M'A''}} = \frac{\log \beta_{M''A'}}{\log \beta_{M''A''}} = \frac{\log \beta_{M'''A'}}{\log \beta_{M'''A''}} = \ldots \tag{78}$$

From eqs. (77) and (78) it is evident that it is possible to determine the fourth value of β_N if three other stability constants are known.

Many authors have found empirical relationships between the stability constant of metal chelates and the properties of the corresponding metal ions (C 1, I 16, I 19, M 46, etc.). For instance, it was shown (D 38) that the free energy of the formation of a complex between a metal ion and organic reagent may be expressed as:

$$-\Delta G = \text{const.} \times N/r \qquad (79)$$

where N is the charge and r the crystal radius of the metal ion.

This relationship was used by Dyrssen (D 38) to explain the dependence of values of $(\log K)/N$ or of $(pH_{1/2})_{0.1}$ for acetylacetonates and β-isopropyl-tropolonates (D 43) on those of N/r for the corresponding metal ions.

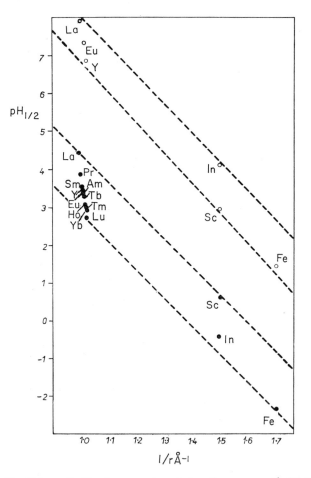

Fig. 14. Values of $pH_{1/2}$ for some tervalent cations versus $1/r$ (● 0·10 M β-isopropyltropolone in chloroform; ○ 0·10 M benzoylacetone in benzene).

Figure 14 shows how the values of $(pH_{1/2})_{0\cdot1}$ for metal β-isopropyltro-polonates (D 43) and benzoylacetonates (S 107) decrease with decrease in ionic radii.

3.8. INFLUENCE OF KINETIC FACTORS

The quantitative description of solvent extraction of metal chelates discussed in the previous sections (3.1–3.7) rests on the assumption that the organic and aqueous phases are in equilibrium. The rate of achievement of equilibrium depends on two factors: (1) the rate of the formation of the extractable species; (2) the rate of transfer of the various species from one phase to the other.

Because the rate of transfer is in practically all cases sufficiently high (a few seconds), the rate of attainment of the extraction equilibrium depends primarily on the rate of formation of the metal chelate.

According to the general kinetic equation for the formation of metal chelates given by Irving (I 9), the rate R of reaching the extraction equilibrium is given by:

$$R = \text{const. } [M][A]^N = \text{const. } [M] \left(\frac{K_{HA}[HA]_{org}}{[H]p_{HA}} \right)^N \tag{80}$$

The experimental verification of eq. (80) shows that it is not strictly valid (R 24, S 106, S 107). However, it can be used for the qualitative discussion of various factors influencing the extraction equilibrium.

The constant in eq. (80) depends first of all on the metal chelate system, i.e. on the nature of the metal ion and organic reagent. Fortunately, from the practical point of view, the formation of most metal chelates requires only a few minutes or less to attain equilibrium. Strongly hydrated ions, as nickel and cobalt, react slowly with the organic reagent, and chromium (III) forms chelates with some β-diketones or 8-hydroxyquinolines only by heating (S 106, S 107).

Many authors have noted a correlation between the rate of equilibration and the extraction constant K. The higher the value of K, the more rapid is the rate of extraction (S 54).

From eq. (80) it is evident that the rate depends very strongly on the concentration of the anion of the organic reagent; the higher its concentration, the shorter the time in general required for reaching equilibrium. For instance, when using pure acetylacetone (i.e. a 10 M solution) the equilibrium for most extraction systems is reached in some seconds; but if 0·1 M acetyl-acetone solutions are used the equilibrium is only reached after some minutes (R 24, S 106).

The pH has also a great influence. The rate at which the metal chelate is formed and extracted into the organic phase decreases rapidly as the pH is reduced (S 54, S 106, S 107, etc.). The partition coefficient of the organic reagent also influences the rate of extraction. The higher the value of p_{HA}, the longer is the time required for reaching equilibrium. For instance, under the same conditions of pH, $[HA]_{org}$, solvent, etc., extraction equilibrium is reached within a few minutes when using solutions of acetylacetone in benzene ($\log p_{HA} = 0.76$). Equilibrium in the extraction of metal by benzoylacetone solution ($\log p_{HA} = 3.14$) is usually achieved by shaking for less than one hour, and using dibenzoylmethane solutions ($\log q_{HA} = 5.35$) some hours are required for reaching the equilibrium.† Analogous behaviour was observed also for metal–dithizone extraction: the rate of extraction is more rapid with carbon tetrachloride ($\log p_{HA} = 4.04$) and also the corresponding K-values are higher than with chloroform solutions of dithizone ($\log p_{HA} \sim 5$). (Cf. I 7, I 13.)

Equation (80) also predicts the influence of the dissociation constant of the organic reagent. For related organic reagents, the lower the value of pK_{HA} the more rapid will be the rate of extraction expected.

The rate of extraction is substantially reduced in the presence of masking agents forming very stable complexes with the metal investigated. This fact can be easily explained from eq. (80) as the free metal concentration in the aqueous phase decreases. It is therefore evident that since EDTA, for instance, does not affect the rate of extraction of molybdenum (VI), uranium (VI), tungsten (VI), vanadium (V), and beryllium (II), etc., the stability of the corresponding complexonates must be relatively low. However, with tri- and tetra-valent metal ions, which form very stable complexonates, very long times (in some cases many days even) are required for reaching equilibrium (S 106).

The masking agents which do not form very stable complexes with the metal investigated (e.g. oxalates, tartrates, citrates, etc.) have in general only a slight effect on the rate of extraction.

† However, in more alkaline solutions the extraction is much more rapid.

CHAPTER 4

ANALYTICAL APPLICATIONS OF THE SOLVENT EXTRACTION OF METAL CHELATES

THE extraction of metal chelates plays a very important role in analytical chemistry because of its speed, versatility, simplicity, and selectivity. The amount of metal separated can be determined either absorptiometrically (if the complex is coloured) or by some other analytical method after back extraction. The element to be determined must be separated selectively and quantitatively. The latter condition is achieved by using an excess of the organic reagent and by choosing a suitable choice of organic reagent, masking agent, and pH-value.

Recently a new analytical method—substoicheiometry—has been developed in which a smaller amount of the reagent is used than corresponds to the amount of metal to be determined. The main advantage of this method compared with all other analytical methods is that the element to be determined need not be isolated quantitatively, as its amount can be calculated from the activity isolated. The greatest importance of this method lies in the field of trace metal analysis.

4.1. SEPARATION OF METALS BY MEANS OF SOLVENT EXTRACTION

For many metal chelate systems the partition coefficient p_N of the neutral complex is so high that quantitative isolation of a desired metal can be reached under conditions in one or in a few extraction steps. For this reason only such simple devices as a separatory funnel or mixer-settler is needed for most separation procedures. Continuous extractors have been rarely used for the isolation of metals in the form of their chelates (M 43, R 14).

Each organic reagent forms extractable chelates only with a certain number of metals. In general it may be expected (K 85, P 40) that the organic reagent which possesses an —OH group (e.g. β-diketones, tropolones, etc.) will react especially well with metals that form stable hydroxycomplexes (e.g. zirconium, hafnium, uranium (IV), plutonium (IV), etc.); reagents with an —SM group (e.g. dithizones, diethyldithiocarbamates, etc.) will react predominantly with metals that form stable and insoluble sulphides (e.g. mercury, silver, copper, etc.). It is therefore evident that a metal that forms an extractable chelate can be isolated from any excess of other metals that form non-extractable chelates or from metals that do not react with the reagent at all. For instance, the metals that form extractable dithizonates (e.g. mercury, silver, copper, zinc, cadmium, etc.) can easily be separated from any excess of metals that are not extractable by dithizone solutions (e.g. aluminium, chromium (VI), molybdenum (VI), uranium (VI), rare earths, etc.). After all the metals that can form dithizonates have been removed, the remaining metals can be extracted by using another organic reagent. Thus, for example, many interfering metals for the absorptiometric determination of aluminium as its tris-8-hydroxyquinolinate can be removed by preliminary extraction as dithizonates, diethyldithiocarbamates, 5-methyl-8-hydroxy-quinolinates, etc. (see Section 5).

A useful method of increasing the selectivity of solvent extraction of metal chelates involves a modification of the oxidation states of the interfering metal ions present in solution. Thus, for instance, platinum (IV), tin (IV), and thallium (III) are not extracted by dithizone solutions and therefore do not interfere in the extractive separation of the metals by dithizone. After reduction to platinum (II), tin (II), and thallium (I) these metals can be selectively removed by using the same reagent. The same principle has also been recommended for the selective separation of arsenic, antimony, and tin using diethyldithiocarbamate as the organic reagent (see Section 5).

A selective extraction of a particular metal can be worked out, however, even when it is present with metals which also form extractable chelates with the reagent employed.

From the extraction constants of various metal chelate systems the best conditions for the separation of many metals can easily be calculated. In the absence of complexing (or masking) agents the separation factor, F, is related to the individual distribution ratios, q' and q'', as follows:

$$F = \frac{q'}{q''} = \frac{K'[HA]_{org}^{(N'-N'')}}{K''[H]^{(N'-N'')}} \tag{81}$$

Thus it can be seen that the metal chelate with the higher value of K can be selectively separated from all other metal chelates with the lower K-value. For this reason, the very selective separation of mercury by dithizone (only palladium has a higher K-value) or molybdenum by oxine (only palladium will interfere) may be expected (see Table 4).

For the simplest case where the charges on the two metal ions to be separated are equal (i.e. $N' = N''$), eq. (81) reduces to the form:

$$F = q'/q'' = K'/K'' \tag{82}$$

As may be seen from this equation, the ratio K'/K'' must be higher than 10^4 for the quantitative separation of one metal M' from an interfering metal M'' present originally at the same concentration. For in order that more than 99 per cent of the desired metal is extracted we must have $q' > 100$, and in order that less than 1 per cent of the interfering metal is co-extracted q'' must be < 0.01. If the concentration of the interfering metal M'' is ten times greater than that of M', the ratio K'/K'' must be greater than 10^5, etc.

Equation (82) shows that the separation factor F for metal ions with the same charge is independent of pH. However, from the practical point of view the most suitable pH value for separation is that for which the product $q'q''$ is approximately equal to unity. Thus, for instance, for the separation of copper from zinc using a 0.100 M solution of benzoylacetone in benzene the separation factor $F = 4 \times 10^6$ (see Table 4). The values of K for copper and zinc benzoylacetonates are $10^{-4.17}$ and $10^{-10.79}$ respectively. At pH $= 4$ about 99 per cent of the copper is extracted ($q' = 10^{-4.17} \times 10^{-2}/10^{-8} = 68$) whereas under these conditions only about 0.001 per cent of the zinc will be extracted ($q'' = 10^{-10.79} \times 10^{-2}/10^{-8} = 10^{-4.8}$).

Although practically all separation procedures are based on the change in pH, in some cases (especially if additive complexes are formed with the organic reagent) a good separation can be achieved by changing the concentration of the organic reagent while keeping the pH constant. Thus, for example, at pH $= 4$, nickel can be separated from cobalt by using a 0.01 M solution of 8-hydroxyquinoline in chloroform ($q_{Ni} = 10^{-2.18} \times 10^{-4}/10^{-8} = 66$, corresponding to 98.5 per cent extraction; $q_{Co} = 10^{-2.16} \times 10^{-8}/10^{-8} = 0.007$, corresponding to 0.7 per cent extraction). Cobalt can then be extracted at the same pH by using a 0.1 M solution of 8-hydroxyquinoline in chloroform ($q_{Co} = 10^{-2.16} \times 10^{-4}/10^{-8} = 69$, or 98.5 per cent extracted).

The selectivity of the separation may be increased by using a masking agent, H_nB (C 12), which forms a non-extractable complex with the interfering metals. For this case, eq. (81) is transformed into

$$F = \frac{q'_c}{q''_c} = \frac{q'(1 + \beta''_u[B]^u)}{q''(1 + \beta'_u B^u)} \tag{83}$$

where β'_u and β''_u are the stability constants of the metal complexes $M'B_u$ and $M''B_u$ respectively. From the known value of the stability constants β'_u and β''_u (see Table 2) it is therefore possible to find the most effective masking agent.

From eq. (83) it is evident that the higher the value of $q'(1 + \beta''_u[B]^u)$ compared to $q''(1 + \beta'_u[B]^u)$ the more selective the separation that can be carried out.

Thus, for instance, beryllium cannot be separated from copper by extraction with acetylacetone in the absence of masking agents for the separation factor F only equals 14 (see Table 4). In the presence of a 0.01 M solution of EDTA at pH $= 6$ the value of the separation factor according to eq. (83) will be:

$$F = 14 \times \frac{1 + 10^{18.9} \times 10^{-8.6}}{1 + 10^{7.1} \times 10^{-8.6}} = 2.7 \times 10^{11}$$

TABLE 4. EXTRACTION CONSTANTS, K, AND VALUES OF $pH_{1/2}$ FOR METAL ION CHELATES
(Acetylacetone (HAA), benzoylacetone (HBA), dibenzoylmethane (HBM), thenoyltrifluoroacetone (HTTA), oxine (HOx), cupferron (HCup) and dithizone (H_2Dz))

Metal ion	HAA (benzene)[a]		HBA (benzene)[a]		HBM (benzene)[a]		HTTA (benzene)[b]		HOx (chloroform)[a]		HCup (chloroform)[c]		H_2Dz (carbon tetrachloride)[d]	
	log K	$pH_{1/2}$	log K	$pH_{1/2}$	log K	$pH_{1/2}$	log K	$pH_{1/2}$	log K	$pH_{1/2}$	log K	$pH_{1/2}$	log K	$pH_{1/2}$
Ac^{3+}								4·6	−4·51[e]	6·51				
Ag^+	N		−7·81	8·9	−8·58	9·9	−5·23	2·48	−5·22	2·87			7·18	−3·2
Al^{3+}	−6·48	3·30	−7·60	3·60	−8·92	4·00	−7·46	3·22			−3·50	2·51	N	
Am^{3+}	N												N	
Ba^{2+}			N			12	−14·4	8·0	−20·9[f]		N		N	
Be^{2+}	−2·79	2·45	−3·88	2·94	−3·46	2·73	−3·2	2·33	−9·62	5·81	−1·54	2·07	N	
Bi^{3+}	N			9·2		10·5		1·8	−1·2	2·13	5·07	−0·4	9·98	0·7
Bk^{3+}								3·0						
Ca^{2+}	N		−18·28	10·1	−18·0	9·9	−6·8		−17·89[e]	10·38	N		N	
Cd^{2+}	N		−14·11	8·1	−13·98	8·0	−12·0	6·7	−5·29[f]	4·65			2·14	2·9
Ce^{3+}							−9·43	3·88					N	
Cf^{3+}							−7·1	3·1						
Co^{2+}	−3·93	2·90	−11·11	6·60	−10·78	6·40	−6·7	4·1	−2·16[f]	3·21	−3·56	3·18	N	
Cu^{2+}			−4·17	3·00	−3·80	2·90	−1·32	1·38	1·77	1·51	2·66	0·03	1·53 10·53	3·2 1·3
Dy^{3+}							−7·03	3·08						
Er^{3+}							−7·2	3·1						
Eu^{3+}			−18·9	7·3			−7·66	3·29						
Fe^{3+}	−1·39	1·60	−0·50	1·20	−1·93	1·70	3·3	−0·24	4·11	1·00	9·8	−2·0	N	
Fm^{3+}							−7·1	3·1						
Ga^{3+}	−5·51	2·90 4	−6·34	3·10	−5·76	2·90	−7·57	3·26	3·72	1·07	4·92	−0·3	−1·3	3·6
Hf^{4+}							7·8	−1·5		1·3		0	N	
Hg^{2+}				3·7		3·9			−3		0·91	0·85	26·85	−9·4
Ho^{3+}							−7·25	3·15						
In^{3+}	−7·20	3·95	−9·30	4·10	−7·61	3·60	−4·34	2·20	0·89	1·54	2·42	0·50	4·84	2·4
La^{3+}			−20·46	7·96	−19·46	7·42	−10·51	4·24	−16·37	6·46	−6·22	3·4	N	
Lu^{3+}							−6·77	2·99						
Mg^{2+}		9·4	−16·65	9·38	−14·72	8·50			−15·13	9·61			N	
Mn^{2+}			−14·63	8·30	−13·71	7·80			−9·32	5·66			N	
H_2MoO_4							−1		9·88				N	

Metal ion	HAA (benzene)[a]		HBA (benzene)[a]		HBM (benzene)[a]		HTTA (benzene)[b]		HOx (chloroform)[a]		HCup (chloroform)[c]		H_2Dz (carbon tetrachloride)[d]	
	log K	pH$_{1/2}$	log K	pH$_{1/2}$	log K	pH$_{1/2}$	log K	pH$_{1/2}$	log K	pH$_{1/2}$	log K	pH$_{1/2}$	log K	pH$_{1/2}$
Nd^{3+}							-8·58	3·59	-2·18	2·38			N	
Ni^{2+}							6·72	5					1·18	3·4
Pa^{4+}	-10·15	6·2	-12·12	6·9	-11·02	6·4		-0·94					N	
Pb^{2+}			-9·61	5·6	-9·45	5·6	-5·2	3·34	-8·04	5·04	-1·53	2·06	0·44	3·8
Pd^{2+}		<0	1·2	0·4		1·8			15				>27	
Pm^{3+}							-8·05	3·42						
Po								0·89						
Pr^{3+}							-8·85	3·68					N	
Pu^{3+}							-4·44	2·21					N	
Pu^{4+}							6·85	-0·97					N	
PuO_2^{2+}							-1·82	1·64					N	
Sc^{3+}	-5·83	2·95	-5·99	3·10	-6·04	3·05	-0·77	0·99	-6·64[e]	3·57	3·32	0·2	N	
Sm^{3+}		5		5			-7·68	3·29	-13·41	5·7	N		N	
Sn^{2+}			-20	11·5	-20·9	11·1							2	3
Sr^{2+}							-14·1	7·8	-19·71[f]	12·06			N	
Tb^{3+}							-7·51	3·24					N	
Th^{4+}	-12·16	4·10	-7·68	2·9	-6·38	2·60	0·8	0·48	-7·18	2·91	4·4	0·25	N	
Ti^{4+}				2·4		2·5				1·45		<0	N	
Tl^+		1·3								11			-3·3	7·3
Tl^{3+}				4·0		3·8	-5·2	5·9	5	2·05			N	
Tm^{3+}							-6·96	2·78					N	
U^{4+}	5·2	2·7					5·3	3·05					N	
UO_2^{2+}			-4·68[e]	3·82	-4·12[e]	3·56	-2·26	0·58	-1·60[e]	2·60		<0	N	
VO_2^+								1·79	1·67	0·88			N	
Y^{3+}			-16·95	6·86			-7·39	3·3		6			N	
Yb^{3+}							-6·72	3·2					N	
Zn^{2+}			-10·79	6·50	-10·67	6·4		2·79	-2·41[f]	3·30	7·4		2·3	2·8
Zr^{4+}		3·4		3·4		3·3	9·15	-1·5		1·01		<0	N	

[e] Complexes of type $MA_N(HA)$ are formed.

[f] Complexes of type $MA_N(HA)_2$ are formed.

N, no extraction occurs.

a [HA]$_{org}$ = 0·10 M.

b [HA]$_{org}$ = 0·20 M.

c [HA]$_{org}$ = 0·05 M.

d [HA]$_{org}$ = 0·0001 M.

It is evident, therefore, that beryllium can be easily separated even from a great excess of copper by using EDTA as a masking agent. Similarly cyanide can be used as a suitable masking agent for separation of lead or bismuth from many other ions when using dithizone.

Equations (81)–(83) are valid, of course, only for the equilibrium state. But as previously stated (see Section 3.8), equilibrium is reached very slowly in the presence of masking agents that form very stable complexes, and therefore the separation factor becomes more favourable than would be expected on the basis of eq. (83).

In some cases differences in the extraction rate can be used for the separation of some metals. For example, chromium (III) practically does not react at room temperature with solutions of 8-hydroxyquinoline in chloroform. By a preliminary extraction at this temperature, many interfering metals can be removed.

If the separation factor is lower than 10^4, the extraction procedure must be repeated several times to ensure the quantitative separation of two metals. Craig (C 50) developed a method which is based on carrying out many individual extractions rapidly and in sequence. This technique has not, however, been extensively used up to the present time for separating metals in the form of their chelates.

Another promising and a simpler method for the separation of closely related metals with similar values of K is partition chromatography. Preobrazhenskij and Katylkin (P 51) used a 0·5 M solution of thenoyltrifluoroacetone adsorbed on grains of teflon (fluoroplast 3 and 4) for the separation of niobium and zirconium: a mixture of hydrochloric acid and hydrofluoric acid was used as the eluting agent.

Reviews of the literature on the separation of metal chelates by liquid–liquid extraction have been given by Irving (I 12, I 33), Morrison and Freiser (M 99–102, F 23), West (W 10–19), Babko (B 3, B 6–8), Alimarin (A 18), Kuznetsov (K 84), Martin and Holt (M 32), Vdovenko (V 11), Zolotov (Z 18), and other authors (M 16, N 17, S 35).

4.2. SUBSTOICHEIOMETRIC DETERMINATIONS

In practically all separation procedures published up to the present time an excess of the organic reagent is commonly used to ensure the quantitative separation of the desired metal. Only two analytical methods (activation analysis, isotope dilution analysis) exist by which use it is possible to carry out the determination of a metal without its quantitative isolation from the analysis sample. For these two methods the new substoicheiometric principle is applicable.

As will be shown below, it is necessary for a successful determination to isolate always exactly the same amount of the element in question from the solutions of standard and analysis sample respectively in which it is present in different amounts. This can be achieved by using equal amounts of the organic reagent for producing an extractable chelate, with the proviso that these amounts must be smaller than corresponds stoicheiometrically to the amount of the metal to be determined and present in both solutions.

By using the substoicheiometric principle in activation analysis the selectivity of separation increases and with isotope dilution analysis the sensitivity of this method is substantially increased.

4.2.1. *Theory of substoicheiometric determinations*

From the theory of substoicheiometric determinations given by Růžička and Starý (R 31, R 35), conditions can be calculated at which the organic reagent reacts quantitatively with the excess of the metal ion M^{N+} to give an extractable chelate MA_N. The pH-values at which the substoicheiometric determination can be carried out are calculated from the expression for the extraction constant K.

The equilibrium concentration of the chelate MA_N in the organic phase is determined from the condition that more than 99·9 per cent of the reagent HA has been used up in forming the chelate MA_N: i.e.

$$[MA_N]_{org} V_{org} \geqslant 0\cdot999 \; c_{HA} V_{org}/N \tag{84}$$

where c_{HA} denotes the total concentration of the reagent and V_{org} is the volume of the organic phase. This condition guarantees the isolation of the same amount of metal with a precision of better than 0·1 per cent.

The equilibrium concentration of the metal M is determined from the relation:

$$[M]V = c_M V - c_{HA} V_{org}/N \tag{85}$$

where V is the volume of the aqueous phase and c_M is the total concentration of the metal in the aqueous phase.

For the equilibrium concentration of the organic reagent it is found that:

$$[HA]_{org} V_{org} \leqslant 0\cdot001 \; c_{HA} V_{org} \tag{86}$$

By substituting eqs. (84), (85), and (86) into the expression for the extraction constant K (see eq. (62)), the value of the threshold pH is:

$$\text{pH} \geqslant \frac{1}{N} \log \frac{c_{HA}}{N} - \frac{1}{N} \log \left\{ c_M - \frac{c_{HA} V_{org}}{NV} \right\} - \frac{1}{N} \log K - \log 0\cdot001 \; c_{HA} \tag{87}$$

Equation (87) is precisely valid only if the dissociation of the organic reagent in the aqueous phase may be neglected at the threshold pH, i.e. for

$$\text{pH} < pK_{HA} + \log p_{HA} + \log (V_{org}/V).$$

From an analysis of the relationship (87) it is evident that the first two terms on the right-hand side have relatively little influence on the value of the threshold pH. If, for example, the amount of organic reagent is half what would correspond to the stoicheiometric ratio, the sum of these two terms for $V_{org} = V$ is zero; if the amount of organic reagent is ten times lower, it is equal to $-1/N$, etc.

A far greater influence on the value of threshold pH is exerted by the last two terms of eq. (86), which will be discussed below in Sections 4.2.2 and 4.2.3.

In the presence of a masking agent, H_nB, used to increase the selectivity, the threshold pH can be calculated from the following equation:

$$pH > \frac{1}{N} \log \frac{c_{HA}}{N} - \frac{1}{N} \log \left\{ c_M - \frac{c_{HA}V_{org}}{NV} \right\} - \frac{1}{N} \log K - 0.001\, c_{HA} +$$

$$+ \frac{1}{N} \log (1 + \beta_u[B]^u) \quad (88)$$

where β_u is the stability constant of the complex MB_u.

The selectivity of the separation can easily be determined from the concentration ratio of the metal M′ and M″ in the organic phase:

$$\frac{[M'A_{N'}]_{org}}{[M''A_{N''}]_{org}} = \frac{K'[HA]_{org}^{(N'-N'')}[M']}{K''[H]^{(N'-N'')}[M'']} \quad (89)$$

As may be seen from eq. (89) for a quantitative separation (i.e. for $[M'A_{N'}]_{org}/[M''A_{N''}]_{org} \geqslant 100$) of metal M′ from an interfering metal M″ having the same total concentration and charge (i.e. $N' = N''$), the ratio K'/K'' has to be higher than 200 for the case when only half the amount of metal M′ reacts quantitatively with the organic reagent (i.e. $c_M = Nc_{HA}/2$) forming the extractable chelate MA_N. The selectivity of the separation using a substoicheiometrical amount of the reagent is thus higher than when using an excess of the reagent. Furthermore, for $N' = N''$, the efficiency of separation does not depend on the pH.

The selectivity of the separation may be further increased by adding a suitable masking agent as stated previously in Section 4.1.

4.2.2. *Substoicheiometric determination in activation analysis*

The amount of the element to be determined by activation analysis can be calculated from the activity of its radioisotopes which are formed from the element in question during irradiation (H 24), e.g. by the (n, γ) reaction with slow neutrons in a nuclear reactor. During the irradiation a great number of other radioisotopes are also formed. From this mixture it is necessary to isolate only radioisotopes of the metal to be determined and in a radiochemically pure form. This isolation is usually carried out in the following manner: to the dissolved irradiated sample a known amount of an inactive isotopic carrier (i.e. milligram amounts of the element to be separated) is added and many separation steps are carried out by which the desired metal is isolated in a radiochemically pure form. The separation steps need not to be quantitative as the total activity of the element to be determined which was induced by the irradiation can be calculated from the relation:

$$A = A^* X/M \tag{90}$$

where A^* is the activity of the recovered fraction of the weight M, and X the amount of carrier added.

The same relation is valid for a standard sample irradiated simultaneously with the analysed sample:

$$A_s = A_s^* X_s/M_s \tag{91}$$

where the index s denotes the standard sample.

Because the analysis sample which contained an unknown amount, Y, of the element to be determined and the standard sample which contained a known amount, Y_s, of the same element have been irradiated simultaneously, the following equation is valid:

$$Y/Y_s = A/A_s \qquad \text{or} \qquad Y = Y_s A/A_s \tag{92}$$

Thus from the chemical yields and activities A^*, A_s^* of the analysis and standard sample respectively it is possible to calculate the amount of metal to be determined in the analysis sample from eq. (92). Destructive activation analysis, i.e. one involving separation procedures, is commonly carried out in this way.

A substoicheiometric determination depends on the isolation of exactly the same amounts of the element to be determined from both the analysis and the standard sample (i.e. $M = M_s$). If furthermore the amount of carrier added to both standard and analysis sample is the same (i.e. $X = X_s$), eq. (92) can be simplified to:

$$Y = Y_s A^*/A_s^* \tag{93}$$

Thus the necessity of determining the chemical yield is avoided. Moreover, as was shown in the theory of the substoicheiometric determination (4.2.1), the selectivity of the separation is greatly increased.

The best conditions for the substoicheiometric determination can be chosen from eq. (87) or (88). The amount of carrier added in activation analysis is usually 1 to 0·1 mg/ml; this corresponds approximately to 10^{-2} to 10^{-3} M solutions. The total concentration of the reagent c_{HA} must be of the same order. For this case, eq. (87) can be simplified to

$$pH \geqslant 6 - (\log K)/N \tag{94}$$

From eq. (94) it is evident that the threshold pH can easily be calculated from the value of extraction constant K. In Table 5 are given threshold pH-values for substoicheiometric determination of some metals extractable as dithizonates into carbon tetrachloride.

TABLE 5. THRESHOLD pH-VALUES FOR DETERMINATION OF SOME METALS AS DITHIZONATES BY SUBSTOICHEIOMETRIC DETERMINATION

Metal	$(\log K)/N$	Threshold pH for		
		$c_{HA} = 10^{-3}$ M	$c_{HA} = 10^{-5}$ M	$c_{HA} = 10^{-7}$ M
Hg (II)	13·4	−7·4	−5·4	−3·4
Ag (I)	7·2	−1·2	0·8	2·8
Cu (II)	5·3	0·7	2·7	4·7
Bi (III)	3·3	2·7	4·7	6·7
In (III)	1·6	4·4	6·4	8·4
Zn (II)	1·2	4·8	6·8	8·8

By using the above method traces of silver in germanium dioxide and metallic lead (R 36), traces of copper (Z 2), zinc (Z 2) and indium (R 37) in germanium dioxide were determined under the conditions given in Table 5. The selective substoicheiometric determination of molybdenum has been worked out for oxine as the organic reagent (S 108).

4.2.3. *Substoicheiometric determination in isotope dilution analysis*

Isotope dilution analysis depends on determining the change of specific activity caused by mixing a radioactive and a nonradioactive isotope of the element to be determined. The greatest advantage of this method, the foundations of which were laid down by Hevesy (H 24) and Starik (S 94) more than 25 years ago, is that in order to carry out the analysis only a part of the component to be analysed need to be isolated in a pure state, as only the *change* in the isotopic composition of this part is actually measured.

The amount of the nonradioactive element to be determined, Y, can be calculated from the relationship:

$$Y = Y_s(S_s - S)/S \qquad (95)$$

where Y_s is the amount of radioisotope added to the analysis sample, S is the specific activity of the radioisotope used and S_s is the specific activity of the mixture of the element to be analysed with its radioisotope. Specific activity is equal to the absolute activity divided by the weight of the element to be determined. The necessity of determining this weight accurately limits the sensitivity of the determination and thus isotopic dilution cannot be used in trace analysis.

By using a substoicheiometric determination the sensitivity and selectivity of the method can be greatly increased, as will be evident from the following. If we always isolate the same amounts of the element to be determined both from the standard solution and from the solution obtained by dilution with the inactive element to be determined (i.e. if $M_s = M$), then in eq. (95) the specific activities of S_s and S may be replaced directly by the relative activities of the extracts, provided these are measured under the same conditions.

The conditions for always extracting the same amount of metal can be selected by using eq. (87) or (88). Thus for the determination of submicrogram amounts of metals, the concentration of the organic reagent will be of the order of 10^{-5} or less and when there is twice as much metal as this present eq. (87) can be simplified to:

$$pH \geqslant 7 - (\log K)/N \qquad (96)$$

Since the condition $pH < pK_{HA} + \log p_{HA} + \log (V_{org}/V)$ must be fulfilled (see page 45) only those metal chelates for which the value of $(\log K)/N$ is sufficiently high can be used for the determination of traces of metals by this method. The necessary conditions are best fulfilled by certain dithizonates, cupferrates, etc. (see Table 4).

For example, mercury (II) has been determined very selectively in amounts of 10^{-6} to 10^{-9} g/ml by extraction from 0·5–5 per cent sulphuric acid with a solution of dithizone in carbon tetrachloride (R 32, S 149). Traces of silver (10^{-7} g/ml) were determined by using the same reagent at pH 5 in the presence of EDTA as a masking agent (S 150). Copper in amounts up to $2·5 \times 10^{-10}$ g/ml and zinc in amounts up to $3·2 \times 10^{-9}$ g/ml were determined by extraction with dithizone dissolved in carbon tetrachloride at pH values of about 5, and 8 to 9 respectively (see Table 5). Potassium iodide and diethyldithiocarbamate were used as very suitable masking agents for the selective isolation of copper and zinc respectively (R 33, S 103). Traces of iron (up to 5×10^{-10} g/ml) were determined substoicheiometrically with a solution of cupferron in chloroform (S 110).

4.2.4. *Extractive titration*

In an extractive titration the aqueous phase containing the metal to be determined is equilibrated with a small volume of a solution of the organic reagent insufficient to react with all the metal present. The organic phase is separated and the process repeated with successive small volumes of the reagent solution until the end-point is reached, as shown by a change in colour of the organic phase (if the reagent and/or the metal chelate is coloured) or by a change in the radioactivity (if the element to be determined is labelled). It is obvious that the organic reagent must react quantitatively and stoicheiometrically with the element to be determined whose concentration then follows from the total volume of reagent solution required and its known concentration.

In the first stages of the titration procedure the amount of the reagent used is smaller than corresponds to the amount of the metal to be determined and therefore the best conditions for the extraction titrations can be calculated from the basic theory of substoicheiometric determinations (see eqs. (87) and (88)).

Extractive titration can in general be used for the determination of many metals that form extractable dithizonates (see I 48, S 90, D 4, etc.).

CHAPTER 5

SYSTEMS

5.1. β-DIKETONES

IN THEIR enolic form β-diketones have a hydrogen atom replaceable by a metal and a ketonic oxygen which can complete a chelate ring:

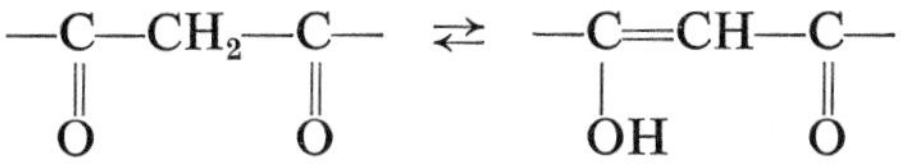

$$-\underset{\underset{O}{\|}}{C}-CH_2-\underset{\underset{O}{\|}}{C}- \;\rightleftarrows\; -\underset{\underset{OH}{|}}{C}=CH-\underset{\underset{O}{\|}}{C}-$$

The most important of the β-diketones are acetylacetone, benzoylacetone, dibenzoylmethane, and thenoyltrifluoracetone.

5.1.1. Acetylacetone (diacetylmethane; 1,4-pentadione)

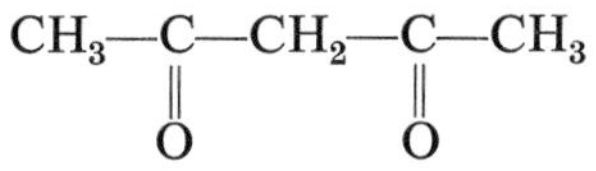

$$CH_3-\underset{\underset{O}{\|}}{C}-CH_2-\underset{\underset{O}{\|}}{C}-CH_3$$

Acetylacetone (HAA; M.Wt. 100·11) is a colourless liquid boiling at 135–137°C (745 mm Hg). It is miscible with chloroform, benzene, and other organic solvents. Acetylacetone is soluble in water to the extent of 17·2 g/100 ml at 20°C (R 24). Its partition coefficient between organic and aqueous phases, equals 3·3, 5·8, and 25 for carbon tetrachloride, benzene, and chloroform respectively (R 24).

In aqueous solution acetylacetone is a weak acid ($pK_{HA} = 8\cdot9$, see Appendix): in alkaline solutions it decomposes to acetone and acetic acid (G 44).

The purest acetylacetone available commercially proved to contain 2–15 per cent of acetic acid and had to be purified before use. An older method (by shaking with diluted ammonia and water, drying, and distillation (M 54)) caused a great loss of acetylacetone and more recently the following method for purification has been recommended (R 41). About 20 ml of impure acetylacetone is dissolved in 80 ml benzene and this solution shaken three times with an equal volume of distilled water. The acetic acid partitions into the aqueous phase, in which it is more soluble, whereas acetylacetone is more soluble in the benzene phase. The purified acetylacetone was kept in the benzene phase and used directly for the extraction procedures. If necessary, the benzene could be removed by distillation.

Acetylacetone is unique in the field of liquid–liquid extraction of metal

3

51

chelates because it can be used both as the solvent and as the organic reagent. Because of the higher reagent concentration ($\sim$10 M) the extractions may be carried out from more acidic solutions. Solutions of acetylacetone in benzene, chloroform, or carbontetrachloride are also widely used in extraction procedures.

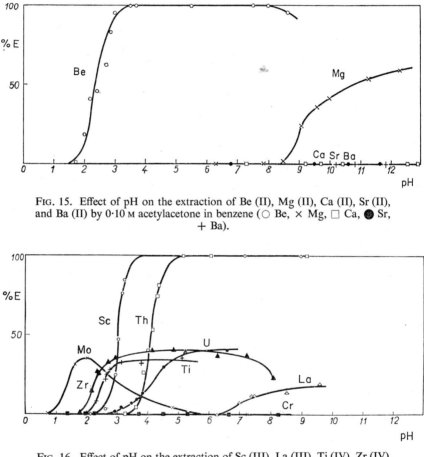

FIG. 15. Effect of pH on the extraction of Be (II), Mg (II), Ca (II), Sr (II), and Ba (II) by 0·10 M acetylacetone in benzene ($\bigcirc$ Be, $\times$ Mg, $\square$ Ca, $\bullet$ Sr, $+$ Ba).

FIG. 16. Effect of pH on the extraction of Sc (III), La (III), Ti (IV), Zr (IV), Th (IV), Cr (VI), Mo (VI), and U (VI) by 0·10 M acetylacetone in benzene ($\bigcirc$ Sc, $\triangle$ La, $+$ Ti, $\blacktriangle$ Zr, $\square$ Th, $\blacksquare$ Cr, $\times$ Mo, $\bullet$ U).

Acetylacetone forms well-defined chelates of the type MA_N with over 50 metals; only uranium (VI) forms an additive complex $UO_2A_2(HA)$ (R 47). These chelates are characterized by unusual thermal stability, volatility, and high solubility (of the order of grams per litre) in organic solvents (E 12, B 90), so that macro- as well as micro-scale separations are feasible.

With pure acetylacetone, extraction equilibrium is reached in some seconds;

when solutions of acetylacetone in organic solvents are used, the extraction rate is smaller (R 24, S 107). Only cobalt (II), nickel (II), molybdenum (VI), and magnesium (II) are exceptions—the extraction equilibrium is reached in some hours (S 107). Chromium (III) reacts only on heating; it can therefore be selectively isolated by extraction with acetylacetone after the preliminary extraction of interfering metals at room temperature.

Acetylacetonates of iron (III), uranium (VI), vanadium (III), cobalt (III), and chromium (III) absorb at the visible region, so that direct absorbtiometric determination of these metals is possible. The chelate of beryllium with

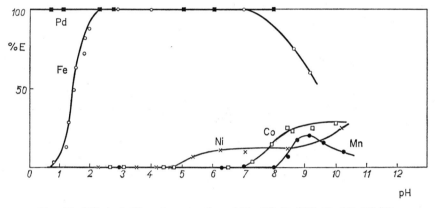

Fig. 17. Effect of pH on the extraction of Mn (II), Fe (III), Co (II), Ni (II), and Pd (II) by 0·10 M acetylacetone in benzene (● Mn, ○ Fe, □ Co, × Ni, ■ Pd).

acetylacetone absorbs at 295 mμ; for the spectrophotometric determination of beryllium the excess of acetylacetone, which also absorbs at this wavelength, must be removed.

Systematic study of the extraction of metals by pure acetylacetone was carried out by Freiser et al. (K 75, K 76, S 113, S 114). Shigematsu and Tabushi (S 66) and Starý and Hladký (S 107) used chloroform and benzene solutions of acetylacetone in their systematic study.

A survey of extraction data of metal acetylacetonates is given in Table 6 and extraction curves for many metals using 0·10 M acetylacetone solution in benzene are shown in Figs. 15–19.

From Table 6 it can be seen that the extractability of metals by a solution of HAA in benzene decreases in the following order: palladium, thallium (III), iron (III), plutonium (IV), beryllium, uranium (IV), gallium and copper (II), scandium, aluminium, indium, uranium (VI), thorium, lead, nickel, lanthanum, cobalt (II) and zinc, manganese, and magnesium. As stated earlier (Section 3.7), the stability constants of metal acetylacetonates decrease in a similar order.

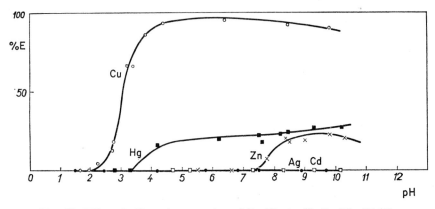

Fig. 18. Effect of pH on the extraction of Cu (II), Ag (I), Zn (II), Cd (II), and Hg (II) by 0·10 M acetylacetone in benzene (○ Cu, ● Ag, × Zn, □ Cd, ■ Hg).

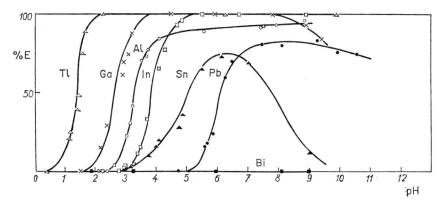

Fig. 19. Effect of pH on the extraction of Al (III), Ga (II), In (III), Tl (III), Sn (II), Pb (II) and Bi (III) by 0·10 M acetylacetone in benzene (○ Al, × Ga, □ In, △ Tl, ▲ Sn, ● Pb, ■ Bi).

5.1.2. *Benzoylacetone (acetylbenzoylmethane)*

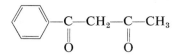

Benzoylacetone (HBA) (M.Wt. 162·18, M.p. 59–60°C) is a crystalline solid having a penetrating and persistent odour. It is difficultly soluble in water, but it is easily soluble in organic solvents such as chloroform, benzene, and carbon tetrachloride.

The dissociation constant of benzoylacetone (pK_{HA} = 8·7) is of the same

TABLE 6. A SURVEY OF THE EXTRACTION DATA OF METALS BY ACETYLACETONE
(HAA)

Metal	Optimum conditions for extraction
Ag (I)	Silver is not extracted at any pH value using 0·10 M HAA in benzene (S 107).
Al (III)	About 90% of aluminium is extracted at pH 3–6 by a single extraction by pure acetylacetone solution ($pH_{1/2}$ = 1·75) (K 76, S 114). Using only a 0·10 M solution of acetylacetone in benzene the maximum of extractability (of about 90%) is reached at higher pH-values, viz. from pH 5 to 9 ($pH_{1/2}$ = 3·30; $\log K$ = −6·48) (S 107). Quantitative extraction of aluminium can be achieved in both cases by repetition of the extraction procedure. Chloroform (S 66, S 115), carbon tetrachloride (A 4, A 5) and ethyl ether (M 58) have also been used for the extraction of aluminium acetylacetonate.
As (V)	Arsenic (V) was found not to be extractable by pure HAA solution at pH 3 (J 4).
Au (III)	Only 2% of gold (III) can be extracted by pure HAA solution at pH 3 (J 4).
Ba (II)	Barium cannot be extracted by HAA in benzene or other solvents at any pH (S 107).
Be (II)	Beryllium can be practically completely extracted at pH 1·5–3 by pure HAA ($pH_{1/2}$ = 0·67, $\log K$ = −3·3) (K 76, S 113). Quantitative extraction of beryllium was obtained at pH 3·5–8·0 with a 0·100 M solution of HAA in benzene ($pH_{1/2}$ = 2·45, $\log K$ = −2·79) (B 93, S 107). Chloroform, carbon tetrachloride, diethyl ether and other solvents can also be used for the extraction of beryllium acetylacetonate (A 16, H 58, K 28). The selectivity of separation may be increased by using EDTA as a masking agent (K 28, A 14, M 50, S 62, S 63). The beryllium chelate absorbs strongly in the ultraviolet region. The molar extinction coefficient at 295 mμ is $3·16 \times 10^4$ using chloroform as the solvent. For the spectrophotometrical determination of beryllium the excess of HAA must be removed by shaking two successive portions of 0·1 M sodium hydroxide (A 8, S 67). Extraction with HAA has been used for the isolation of beryllium from iron (A 14), manganese (K 28), alloys (A 16, A 46, S 63), fission products (A 16, A 46, S 62, S 63), sediments (M 50) and biological material (S 67, T 33, T 34).
Bi (III)	Bismuth is not extracted by 0·10 M HAA in benzene at any pH (S 107).
Ca (II)	Calcium is not extracted by 0·10 M HAA in benzene at any pH (S 107).
Cd (II)	Cadmium is not extracted by 0·10 M HAA in benzene at any pH (S 107).
Ce	At pH 8–9 about 80% of cerium can be extracted by a 0·10 M solution of HAA in benzene or isoamyl alcohol (Z 17). Suzuki (S 151) reported that in the presence of 0·65 M sodium bromate and 0·61 M acetylacetone about 95% cerium is extracted by benzene at pH 5–6. The reaction is accelerated by heating. By using a 2 M solution of HAA in benzene, carbon tetrachloride, or xylene more than 98% of carrier-free [144]Ce can be extracted and thus separated from the short-life daughter [144]Pr, which is not extracted (S 152).

TABLE 6 (*continued*)

Metal	Optimum conditions for extraction
Co (II)	Less than 30% of cobalt (II) is extracted by 0·10 M HAA in benzene at pH 7–10. The extraction equilibrium is only reached after some hours (S 107). With isobutyl alcohol or cyclohexanone as the organic solvent, maximum extraction of cobalt acetylacetonate (60%) is reached at pH 8·1–8·4 (Z 16, Z 17).
Co (III)	On being boiled in the presence of hydrogen peroxide at pH 6–7 cobalt (II) forms with acetylacetone a very stable cobalt (III)-acetylacetonate which can be extracted practically completely (95 to 99·5% by a single extraction) by pure HAA at pH −0·3 to 2·0. All interfering ions can be removed by a preliminary extraction with HAA at room temperature and at a pH lower than 4 (M 5).
Cr (III)	At room temperature chromium (III) is not extracted at any pH by pure HAA or by solutions of HAA in benzene (M 5, S 107). Chromium (III) acetylacetonate which is formed only on boiling in the presence of excess of HAA at pH approximately 6 can be quantitatively extracted ($> 99\%$) from pH −0·8 to pH 6 (M 7). The procedure is very selective as the interfering metals can be removed by a preliminary extraction with HAA at room temperature.
Cu (II)	At pH 2–5 about 80% of copper is extracted by pure HAA ($pH_{1/2} = 1·10$, $\log K = -4·2$) (K 76, S 113). Maximum extraction of copper ($\sim$90%) using 0·10 M HAA in benzene is reached at pH 4–10 ($pH_{1/2} = 2·90$, $\log K = -3·93$) (S 107). Complete extraction of copper can be achieved by repeating the extraction procedure. Chloroform (S 66) and carbon tetrachloride (S 115) can also be used as suitable solvents.
Dy (III)	About 52% of dysprosium is extracted by pure HAA at pH 6·5 ($pH_{1/2} = 5·8$) (B 90).
Er (III)	At pH 6 about 68% of erbium is extracted by pure HAA ($pH_{1/2} = 4·9$) (B 90).
Fe (III)	By using pure HAA, quantitative extraction of iron (III) (99·9%) was obtained at pH 1 ($pH_{1/2} = 0·07$, $\log K = -3·2$) (K 76, S 114, V 2). With only 0·10 M HAA in benzene the complete extraction of iron (III) was observed at pH 2·5–7 ($pH_{1/2} = 1·60$, $\log K = -1·39$) (S 104, S 107). Carbon tetrachloride (A 4, A 5), chloroform (S 66, S 115, T 3, T 5), methyl-isobutylketone (T 3, T 4), or xylene (K 26) have also been used as organic solvents. Iron (III) acetylacetonate is strongly red coloured (maximum absorbancy at 440 mμ) so that the direct absorptiometric determination of iron in the organic extract is possible (S 115). Thus, iron (III) has been determined in the presence of iron (II), which is not extracted by solutions of HAA (L 13).
Ga (III)	About 97% of gallium can be extracted by pure HAA at pH 6–9 ($pH_{1/2} = 1·20$, $\log K = -6·6$) (K 76, S 114). Complete extraction of gallium with HAA from 6 M hydrochloric acid (W 34) can probably be explained by the formation of the extractable species $HGaCl_4$.

TABLE 6 (*continued*)

Metal	Optimum conditions for extraction
Ga (III) (*cont.*)	With 0·10 M HAA in benzene quantitative extraction was observed at pH 3·5–8 ($pH_{1/2} = 2·90$, $\log K = -5·51$) (S 107).
Gd (III)	At pH 6 about 40% of gadolinium is extracted by pure HAA (B 90).
Ge (IV)	Only 0·2% of germanium was found to be extracted by pure HAA from diluted hydrochloric acid at pH 3 (J 4).
Hf (IV)	At pH higher than 3 about 80% of hafnium is extracted by pure HAA ($pH_{1/2} = 1·75$) (K 76). Approximately the same amount of hafnium was found to be extracted at pH > 3 by 2 M HAA in benzene ($pH_{1/2} = 1·6$) (P 26) or at pH 7 by 0·05 M HAA in chloroform ($pH_{1/2} = 4·7$) (R 50).
Hg (II)	Less than 25% of mercury can be extracted at pH 4–10 by 0·10 M HAA in benzene (S 107).
Ho (III)	At pH 6·5 about 62% of holmium can be extracted by pure HAA ($pH_{1/2} = 5·1$) (B 90).
In (III)	Quantitative extraction of indium (III) by pure HAA was found to take place in the pH region from 3 to 6 ($pH_{1/2} = 1·7$, $\log K = -8·1$) (S 114). With 0·10 M solutions of HAA in carbon tetrachloride, benzene or chloroform quantitative extraction takes place at a pH higher than 5·5 ($pH_{1/2} = 4·15$, 3·95 and 4·55; $\log K = -7·2$, $-7·2$ and $-9·09$ for carbon tetrachloride, benzene and chloroform respectively) (R 24–26). Carrier-free [115m]In can easily be separated from [115]Cd by extraction with HAA as cadmium is not extracted by it (R 25, R 26).
La (III)	At pH 6–10 less than 20% of lanthanum is extracted by 0·10 M HAA in benzene (S 107) and only a few per cent of lanthanum was found to be extracted by 0·10 M HAA in chloroform at pH > 9 (R 50).
Mg (II)	Less than 60% of magnesium can be extracted by 0·01 M HAA in benzene at pH 9–12 ($pH_{1/2} = 9·4$). The extraction rate is very slow—equilibrium is only reached after 24 hours (S 107). If only a few minutes' shaking is used, magnesium is practically not extracted (S 66).
Mn (II)	About 10 to 20% of manganese is extracted at pH 5·5–6·5 by pure HAA (M 5). This reagent can also be used for leaching manganese ores (L 5). With benzene or chloroform as solvents, less than 30% manganese can be extracted at pH 9–10 (S 66, S 107).
Mn (III)	In the presence of oxidizing agent such as hydrogen peroxide the extraction of manganese is almost complete at pH 8–9·5 (S 68).
Mo (VI)	From 96 to 98% of molybdenum (VI) is extracted from 6 N to 0·01 N sulphuric acid by pure HAA (M 5), or by a 1:1 mixture of HAA and chloroform (G 46). By using three portions of organic solvent successively more than 99·8% of molybdenum can be isolated.

58   THE SOLVENT EXTRACTION OF METAL CHELATES

TABLE 6 (continued)

Metal	Optimum conditions for extraction
Mo (VI) (cont.)	The extraction of molybdenum (VI) from a highly acidic medium (e.g. 2 N HCl) is very selective; tungsten (VI) in the presence of citric acid and many other metals does not interfere (M 5). With 0·10 M HAA in benzene less than 35% molybdenum is extracted at pH 1–5 (S 107). The molybdenum chelate with acetylacetone absorbs at 352 mμ (the molar extinction coefficient $\varepsilon = 1630$) so that a spectrophotometric determination is possible (M 5).
Nb (V)	At pH 2–5 about 90% of niobium is extracted by 2·0 M HAA in benzene (pH$_{1/2}$ = 0·8). The extractability is decreased by prolonged shaking, probably owing to hydrolysis. Hydrogen peroxide, oxalic acid, citric acid, or EDTA interfere seriously (S 153). Chloroform, carbon tetrachloride, xylene, and other solvents can also be used for the extraction of the niobium chelate (S 153).
Nd (III)	About 28% of neodymium is extracted at pH 6 by pure HAA (B 90).
Ni (II)	At pH 5–6 less than 20% of nickel is extracted by 0·10 M HAA in benzene. The rate of extraction is extremely slow—equilibrium is only reached after some days' shaking (S 107).
Pa	About 40% of protactinium was found to be extracted from an acetate buffer by a 1:2 mixture of HAA and benzene (M 8). Only 1% of protactinium can be extracted from 1 M acetic acid or from 2 N sodium hydroxide (M 8).
Pb (II)	More than 75% of lead is extracted by pure HAA at pH 6–8 (pH$_{1/2}$ = 5·65, log $K = -13·3$) (K 75). Less than 80% of lead can be extracted at pH 7–10 when using 0·10 M HAA in benzene (pH$_{1/2}$ = 6·2, log $K = -10·15$) (S 107).
Pd (II)	Complete extraction of palladium by 0·10 M HAA in benzene takes place over the pH range 0–8 (pH$_{1/2}$ < 0) (S 107).
Po	Polonium acetylacetonate is soluble in benzene and other organic solvents (S 50).
Pu (IV)	In the pH range from 4 to 7 plutonium (IV) can be completely extracted by 1·0 M HAA in benzene (pH$_{1/2}$ = 2·5, log p_N = 2·5) or in chloroform (pH$_{1/2}$ = 1·8) (R 50, R 51).
Ru (III)	Ruthenium forms a red-coloured chelate on heating with HAA which can be partially extracted (~90%, $V = 6V_{org}$) at pH 4–6 into a 1:2 mixture of HAA and chloroform (B 85). Interfering ions such as iron (III), vanadium, aluminium, and titanium can be removed by preliminary extraction with HAA at pH 2 at room temperature. Benzene can also be used as the organic solvent (W 28). The ruthenium (III) chelate absorbs at 505 mμ (B 85).

TABLE 6 (*continued*)

Metal	Optimum conditions for extraction
Sb (III)	Less than 0·05% of antimony is found to be extracted into HAA from diluted hydrochloric acid (J 4).
Sc (III)	Quantitative extraction of scandium (III) by a 0·10 M solution of HAA in benzene was observed in the pH region from 3·5 to 9 ($pH_{1/2} = 2·95$, $\log K = -5·83$) (S 107).
Sm (III)	At pH 6 about 33% of samarium is extracted by pure HAA (B 90). However, by using solutions of HAA in benzene or chloroform only a few per cent of samarium can be extracted at pH > 8 (R 50).
Sn (II)	Divalent tin is partially (< 75%) extracted by a solution of HAA in benzene at pH 3–9 (S 107).
Sr (II)	Strontium is practically not extracted at any pH by 0·1–1·0 M HAA in benzene or chloroform (R 50, S 107).
Tb (III)	At pH 6 about 50% of terbium is extracted by pure HAA (B 90).
Tc	At pH ~4 approximately 55% of technetium is extracted by pure HAA (S 89).
Te (IV)	Only 1% of tellurium is found to be extracted by pure HAA from diluted hydrochloric acid at pH ~3 (J 4).
Th (IV)	It is found that thorium can be completely extracted at pH 5–9 by 0·10 M HAA in benzene ($pH_{1/2} = 4·10$, $\log K = -12·16$, $\log p_N = 2·5$) (P 17, R 43, R 44, S 107). Chloroform can also be used as an organic solvent ($\log p_N = 2·54$) (R 43, R 44).
Ti (IV)	Over the pH range from 0 to 2 the extraction of titanium by pure HAA increases from 10 to 75% (M 3, W 10). By using 0·10 M HAA in benzene about 35% of titanium is extracted at pH 3–5 (S 107).
Tl (III)	Quantitative extraction of thallium (III) by 0·10 M HAA in benzene takes place in the pH range 2·0–10 ($pH_{1/2} = 1·3$) (S 107).
U (IV)	Uranium (IV) is quantitatively extracted at pH > 3 by 0·50 M HAA in benzene or chloroform ($pH_{1/2} = 2·0$ and 2·4 respectively) (R 49, R 50).
U (VI)	More than 95% uranium (VI) is extracted at pH 2–7 by pure HAA ($pH_{1/2} = 1·66$) (K 76). EDTA can be used as a suitable masking agent for bismuth and other metals (K 75). When using chloroform as the organic solvent it is found that uranium (VI) can be extracted as a complex UO_2A_2 ($\log p_N = 0·25$) and as UO_2A_2HA ($\log p_N = 1·52$) (R 44, R 47). Benzene or butyl acetate can also be used as organic solvents (S 107, T 4). The absorption spectra of the uranium chelates are given in ref. (C 41). The extraction of uranium (VI) by HAA in the presence of EDTA has been used for its separation from thorium and mixed fission products (T 2).

TABLE 6 *(continued)*

Metal	Optimum conditions for extraction
V (III)	Vanadium (III) is completely extracted by a 1:1 acetylacetone–chloroform mixture at pH 2·3–3·0 ($pH_{1/2} = 0$). The chelate absorbs at 390 mμ (M 6).
V (IV)	Vanadium (IV) can be extracted to the extent of 80% by a 1:1 HAA–chloroform mixture at pH 2–4 ($pH_{1/2} = 1·4$) (M 6).
V (V)	Only 68% of vanadium can be extracted at pH ~2·1 by 1:1 HAA–chloroform solution ($pH_{1/2} = 1·2$). The complex absorbs at 355 and 450 mμ (M 6).
W (VI)	Tungsten (VI) cannot be extracted by pure HAA in the pH range 0–4·5 (M 5).
Y (III)	In the pH range from 5·5 to 10 little more than 50% of yttrium is extracted by pure HAA ($pH_{1/2} = 5·15$) (S 28, B 90). With chloroform as the solvent only 10% of yttrium can be extracted (S 66).
Yb (III)	At pH 6 about 86% of ytterbium is extracted by pure HAA ($pH_{1/2} = 4·5$) (B 90).
Zn (II)	More than 50% of zinc was found to be extracted by pure HAA at pH 5·5–8 ($pH_{1/2} = 5·3$) (K 76, S 27, S 34, S 113). By using only 0·10 M HAA in benzene, less than 10% of zinc is extracted at pH values from 8 to 10 (S 107).
Zr (IV)	At pH ~2 approximately 70% of zirconium is extracted by pure HAA ($pH_{1/2} = 1·5$) (K 76, W 10). Suzuki (S 153) found that at pH 3–8 about 98% of zirconium can be extracted by 2 M HAA in chloroform. In the presence of hydrogen peroxide (0·2%) [95]Zr can be separated from [95]Nb, which is not extracted at pH ~5. Carbon tetrachloride, benzene, ethyl acetate, and other solvents can also be used for the extraction of the zirconium chelate (S 107, S 153).

order as that of acetylacetone, but its partition coefficients between the organic and aqueous phases are substantially higher (660, 1150, and 2500 for carbon tetrachloride, benzene, and chloroform respectively) (S 95). For the same reason the partition coefficients of neutral metal benzoylacetonates are much higher than those of the corresponding acetylacetonates.

In general, benzoylacetonates of the type MA_N are formed; only uranium (VI) forms with this reagent a complex of the type UO_2A_2HA which is extracted into the organic phase.

Partition equilibrium is reached in 10–30 min with most extraction systems; only beryllium, magnesium, molybdenum, and nickel are extracted very slowly—the attainment of equilibrium requiring several hours (S 107).

A systematic study of the solvent extraction of metal benzoylacetonates has recently been made by Starý and Hladký (S 97, S 107). A survey of the extraction data is given in Table 7 and the extraction of many metals by a

TABLE 7. A SURVEY OF EXTRACTION DATA FOR METAL BENZOYLACETONATES

Metal	Optimum conditions for extraction
Ag (I)	Silver is only partially extracted by 0·10 M HBA in benzene ($pH_{1/2} = 8·9$, $\log K = -7·8$) (S 107).
Al (III)	More than 90% of aluminium is extracted by 0·10 M HBA in benzene ($pH_{1/2} = 3·6$, $\log K = -7·6$) (S 107). The extraction rate is rather slow.
Ba (II)	Barium is virtually not extracted by 0·10 M HBA in benzene below pH 11·5 (S 107).
	Complete extraction of beryllium by 0·10 M HBA is achieved in the pH range from 4 to 10 ($pH_{1/2} = 2·94$, $\log K = -3·88$) (S 107).
Bi (III)	Bismuth begins to extract at pH values higher than 7. Maximum extractability when using 0·10 M HBA in benzene is reached at pH 10–11 ($pH_{1/2} = 9·2$) (S 107).
Ca (II)	At pH higher than 11·5, approximately 95% of calcium is extracted by 0·10 M HBA in benzene ($pH_{1/2} = 10·1$, $\log K = -18·28$) (S 107).
Cd (II)	Practically complete extraction of cadmium ($\log p_N = 2·15$) is obtained at pH 9·5–11 when using 0·10 M HBA in benzene or chloroform ($pH_{1/2} = 8·48$ and 8·93; $\log K = -14·92$ and $-15·83$ for benzene and chloroform respectively) (R 25, R 26). When carbon tetrachloride is used as the organic solvent only 98% extraction of cadmium was observed at pH > 9 with 0·10 M HBA solution ($pH_{1/2} = 8·48$, $\log K = -14·90$) (R 25, R 26).
Co (II)	The quantitative extraction of cobalt (II) by 0·10 M HBA in benzene is observed in the pH range 7·5–11 ($pH_{1/2} = 6·6$, $\log K = -11·11$) (S 107).
Cr (III)	Chromium (III) is not extracted by solutions of HBA in various organic solvents at room temperature at any pH-value (S 107).
Cu (II)	Copper is quantitatively extracted in the pH range 4–9 using 0·10 M HBA in benzene ($pH_{1/2} = 3·0$, $\log K = -4·17$) (S 107).
Er (III)	Erbium can be extracted by 0·10 M HBA in chloroform ($pH_{1/2} = 5·9$) (J 8).
Eu (III)	Quantitative extraction of europium by 0·10 M HBA in benzene was observed at pH > 8·5 ($pH_{1/2} = 7·3$, $\log K = -18·9$) (S 97).
Fe (III)	Iron (III) can be completely extracted at pH 2–7 by using 0·10 M HBA in benzene ($pH_{1/2} = 1·2$, $\log K = -0·5$) (S 107). The chelate absorbs strongly at 420–440 mμ (S 107).
Ga (III)	Quantitative extraction of gallium using 0·10 M HBA in benzene ensues in the pH range 4–8 ($pH_{1/2} = 3·1$, $\log K = -6·3$) (S 107).
Hf (IV)	Hafnium can be incompletely extracted from slightly acid solutions by 0·10 M HBA in benzene ($pH_{1/2} \sim 1·4$) (P 7).

TABLE 7 (*continued*)

Metal	Optimum conditions for extraction
Hg (II)	At pH 5–10 more than 75% of mercury is extracted by 0·10 M HBA in benzene ($pH_{1/2} = 3\cdot7$) (S 107).
In (III)	Quantitative extraction of indium (III) using 0·10 M HBA in benzene ($\log p_N = 5\cdot5$), chloroform ($\log p_N = 5\cdot5$) and carbon tetrachloride ($\log p_N = 4\cdot7$) was reached at pH 5–7 ($pH_{1/2} = 4\cdot14$, 4·6 and 4·13; $\log K = -9\cdot30$, $-10\cdot65$ and $-9\cdot24$ for benzene, chloroform and carbon tetrachloride respectively) (R 25, R 26). Extraction by HBA has been used for the separation of carrier-free [115 m]In from [115]Cd (R 25, R 26).
La (III)	Quantitative extraction of lanthanum is obtained at pH 9 using 0·10 M HBA in benzene, chloroform, and carbon tetrachloride ($pH_{1/2} = 7\cdot96$, 8·41 and 7·95; $\log K = -20\cdot46$, $-21\cdot81$ and $-20\cdot34$ for benzene, chloroform, and carbon tetrachloride respectively) (S 99). At pH 10–11 carrier-free [140]La can easily be separated from [140]Ba (S 99).
Mg (II)	Quantitative extraction of magnesium was obtained after some hours' shaking with 0·10 M HBA in benzene at pH $>$ 10·5 ($pH_{1/2} = 9\cdot4$, $\log K = -16\cdot65$) (S 107).
Mn (II)	Approximately 90% of manganese (II) can be extracted at pH 9–12 by using 0·10 M HBA in benzene ($pH_{1/2} = 8\cdot3$, $\log K = -14\cdot63$) (S 107).
Mo (VI)	Molybdenum (VI) is only partially extracted in the pH range 1–4 by using 0·10 M HBA in benzene (S 107).
Ni (II)	Only 80% of nickel (II) is found to be extracted at pH 7·5–10 after some hours' shaking with 0·10 M HBA in benzene ($pH_{1/2} = 6\cdot9$, $\log K = -12\cdot12$) (S 107).
Pb (II)	Quantitative extraction of lead by 0·10 M HBA in benzene has been obtained between pH 7 and 10 ($pH_{1/2} = 5\cdot7$, $\log K = -9\cdot61$) (S 107).
Pd (II)	Palladium can be completely extracted at pH 1·5–10 by using 0·10 M HBA in benzene ($pH_{1/2} = 0\cdot4$, $\log K = -1\cdot2$) (S 107).
Pu (IV)	At pH $\sim$ 4 approximately 90% of plutonium (IV) is extracted as its benzoylacetonate into benzene. At higher pH values the extraction decreases (H 17).
Sc (III)	Scandium can be completely extracted by 0·10 M HBA in benzene in the pH region 4·5–7 ($pH_{1/2} = 3\cdot10$, $\log K = -5\cdot99$) (S 107).
Sn (II)	Divalent tin is only partially ($<$ 70%) extracted at pH 3–7 by 0·10 M HBA in benzene (S 107).
Sr (II)	Only 50% extraction of strontium by 0·10 M HBA in benzene is found in the pH range 11 to 12 ($pH_{1/2} \sim 11\cdot5$, $\log K = -20\cdot0$) (S 107).

TABLE 7 (*continued*)

Metal	Optimum conditions for extraction
Th (IV)	Quantitative extraction of thorium by 0.10 M HBA in benzene takes place in the pH range 4–8 ($pH_{1/2} = 4.0$, $\log K = -7.68$) (S 107).
Ti (IV)	Titanium (IV) can be quantitatively extracted at pH > 3 when using 0.10 M HBA in benzene ($pH_{1/2} = 2.4$) (S 107).
Tl (III)	Only incomplete extraction of thallium ($< 75\%$) was observed in the pH range 5–10 when using 0.10 M HBA in benzene ($pH_{1/2} = 4.0$) (S 107).
U (VI)	Uranium (VI) forms a chelate with benzoylacetone of the type UO_2A_2HA which is quantitatively extracted at pH 5–7 when using 0.10 M HBA in benzene, chloroform, or carbon tetrachloride ($pH_{1/2} = 3.82$, 3.72 and 4.03; $\log K = -4.68$, -4.44 and -5.06 for benzene, chloroform, and carbon tetrachloride respectively). The uranium (VI) chelate absorbs strongly at 380 mμ (S 100).
Y (III)	Yttrium (III) can be completely extracted ($\log p_N > 3.5$) by 0.10 M HBA in benzene, chloroform, and carbon tetrachloride at pH > 8 ($pH_{1/2} = 6.86$, 7.31 and 6.89; $\log K = -16.95$, -18.3 and -17.04 for benzene, chloroform, and carbon tetrachloride respectively) (S 96). At pH ~ 9, carrier-free ^{90}Y can be easily separated from ^{90}Sr (S 96).
Zn (II)	Quantitative extraction of zinc by 0.10 M HBA in benzene has been observed at pH 7–9 ($pH_{1/2} = 6.5$, $\log K = -10.79$) (S 107).
Zr (IV)	More than 90% of zirconium (IV) was found to be extracted by 0.10 M HBA in benzene at pH 5–6.5 ($pH_{1/2} = 3.4$) (S 107). When using only a 0.05 M solution of HBA the extraction of zirconium decreases. This decrease is probably caused by hydrolysis of the zirconium (P 25).

0.10 M solution of benzoylacetone (HBA) in benzene as a function of pH is shown in Figs. 20–24.

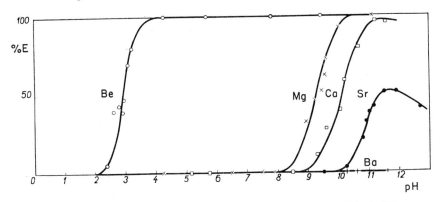

FIG. 20. Effect of pH on the extraction of Be (II), Mg (II), Ca (II), Sr (II), and Ba (II) by 0.10 M benzoylacetone in benzene ($\bigcirc$ Be, $\times$ Mg, $\square$ Ca, ● Sr, + Ba).

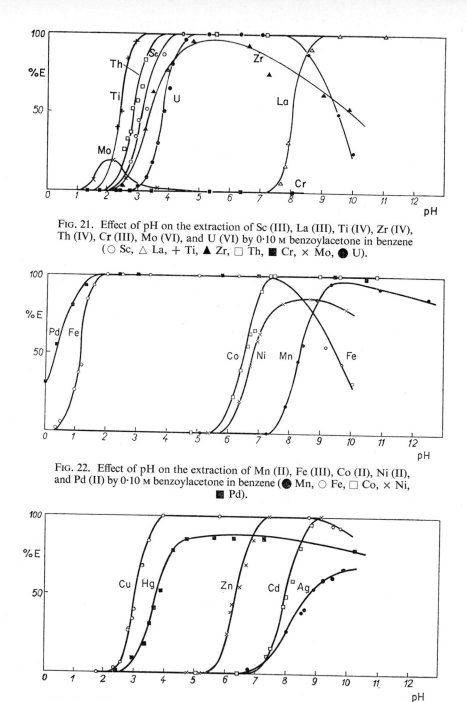

Fig. 21. Effect of pH on the extraction of Sc (III), La (III), Ti (IV), Zr (IV), Th (IV), Cr (III), Mo (VI), and U (VI) by 0·10 M benzoylacetone in benzene (○ Sc, △ La, + Ti, ▲ Zr, □ Th, ▦ Cr, × Mo, ● U).

Fig. 22. Effect of pH on the extraction of Mn (II), Fe (III), Co (II), Ni (II), and Pd (II) by 0·10 M benzoylacetone in benzene (◕ Mn, ○ Fe, □ Co, × Ni, ▦ Pd).

Fig. 23. Effect of pH on the extraction of Cu (II), Ag (I), Zn (II), Cd (II), and Hg (II) by 0·10 M benzoylacetone in benzene (○ Cu, ● Ag, × Zn, □ Cd, ▦ Hg).

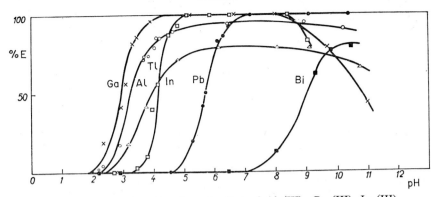

Fig. 24. Effect of pH on the extraction of Al (III), Ga (III), In (III), Tl (III), Pb (II), and Bi (III) by 0·10 M benzoylacetone in benzene (○ Al, × Ga, □ In, △ Tl, ● Pb, ■ Bi).

5.1.3. *Dibenzoylmethane* (1,3-*diphenyl*-1,3-*propanedione*)

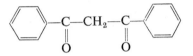

Dibenzoylmethane (M.Wt. 224·25, M.p. 77–78°C) is a crystalline solid, very slightly soluble in water but readily soluble in organic solvents (see Appendix).

Its dissociation constant ($pK_{HA} = 9·35$) is of the same order as that of acetylacetone, but the partition coefficients of dibenzoylmethane are much higher ($\log p_{HA} = 5·35$, 5·40, and 4·51 for benzene, chloroform, and carbon tetrachloride respectively) (M 122).

As expected from theory (see Section 3.4), the extraction constants K of metal dibenzoylmethanates will not differ substantially from those of corresponding acetylacetonates and benzoylacetonates. The partition coefficients of metal dibenzoylmethanates will, however, be much higher owing to the hydrophobic properties of the two benzene rings in the molecule of dibenzoylmethane.

A more widespread use of this reagent is somewhat hindered by the slow rate of establishment of extraction equilibrium, which generally requires some hours; with beryllium, molybdenum (VI), nickel, palladium, mercury, and aluminium, shaking for several days is required before the equilibrium is established. Iron (III), uranium (VI), and copper are extracted relatively quickly—here the attainment of equilibrium requires only a few minutes' shaking (S 107).

Dibenzoylmethane forms strongly coloured chelates with iron (III) and with uranium (VI), and these can be used for the selective determination of the two metals.

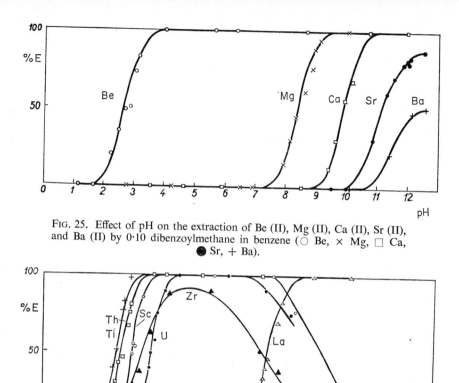

FIG. 25. Effect of pH on the extraction of Be (II), Mg (II), Ca (II), Sr (II), and Ba (II) by 0·10 dibenzoylmethane in benzene (○ Be, × Mg, □ Ca, ● Sr, + Ba).

FIG. 26. Effect of pH on the extraction of Sc (III), La (III), Ti (IV), Zr (IV), Th (IV), Cr (III), Mo (VI), and U (VI) by 0·10 M dibenzoylmethane in benzene (○ Sc, △ La, + Ti, ▲ Zr, □ Th, ■ Cr, × Mo, ● U).

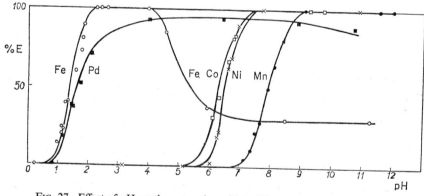

FIG. 27. Effect of pH on the extraction of Mn (II), Fe (III), Co (II), Ni (II), and Pd (II) by 0·10 M dibenzoylmethane in benzene (● Mn, ○ Fe, □ Co, × Ni, ■ Pd).

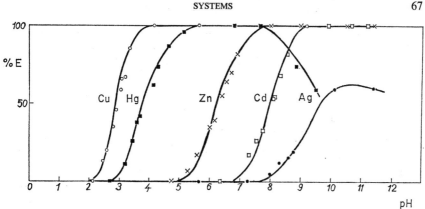

FIG. 28. Effect of pH on the extraction of Cu (II), Ag (I), Zn (II), Cd (II), and Hg (II) by 0·10 M dibenzoylmethane in benzene (○ Cu, ● Ag, × Zn, □ Cd, ■ Hg).

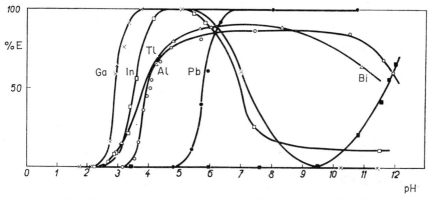

FIG. 29. Effect of pH on the extraction of Al (III), Ga (III), In (III), Tl (III), Pb (II), and Bi (III) by 0·10 M dibenzoylmethane in benzene (○ Al, × Ga, □ In, △ Tl, ● Pb, ■ Bi).

The extraction data for metal dibenzoylmethanates are summarized in Table 8; the extraction curves of many metals when using a 0·10 M solution of dibenzoylmethane (HDM) in benzene are shown in Figs. 25–29.

5.1.4. *Dipivaloylmethane*

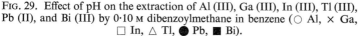

Dipivaloylmethane is a colourless oil which is soluble in diethylether, benzene, chloroform, carbon tetrachloride, and other organic solvents.

TABLE 8. A SURVEY OF EXTRACTION DATA FOR METAL DIBENZOYLMETHANATES

Metal	Optimum conditions for extraction
Ag (I)	Less than 60% of silver is extracted at pH 10–11 when using 0·10 M HDM in benzene ($pH_{1/2} = 9·9$, log $K = -8·6$) (S 107).
Al (III)	At pH 5–10 about 80% of aluminium is extracted by 0·10 M HDM in benzene ($pH_{1/2} = 4·0$, log $K = -8·92$). The equilibrium is only reached after some days' shaking (S 107).
Ba (II)	At pH > 12 more than 50% of barium can be extracted by 0·10 M HDM in benzene ($pH_{1/2} = 12$) (S 107).
Bi (III)	Less than 60% of bismuth can be extracted between pH 9 and 12 ($pH_{1/2} = 10·5$) when using 0·10 M HDM in benzene (S 107).
Ca (II)	Calcium (II) is practically completely extracted at pH > 10·5 when using 0·10 M HDM in benzene ($pH_{1/2} = 9·9$, log $K = -18·0$) (S 107).
Cd (II)	Quantitative extraction of cadmium by 0·10 M HDM in benzene is found at pH 9–11 ($pH_{1/2} = 8·0$, log $K = -13·98$) (S 107).
Co (II)	Cobalt (II) can be quantitatively extracted at pH 7·5–10 when using 0·10 M HDM in benzene ($pH_{1/2} = 6·4$, log $K = -10·78$) (S 107).
Cu (II)	Practically complete extraction of copper by 0·10 M HDM in benzene takes place in the pH range 4–9 ($pH_{1/2} = 2·9$, log $K = -3·8$) (S 107).
Fe (III)	Iron (III) can be completely extracted at pH 2–4 when using 0·10 M HDM in benzene ($pH_{1/2} = 1·7$, log $K = -1·93$) (S 107). Butylacetate can also be used as a suitable solvent (S 64). Solutions of iron (III) dibenzoylmethanate in organic solvents absorb strongly in the visible region. The molar extinction coefficient in butylacetate at 410 mμ is 17,000 (S 64).
Ga (III)	Quantitative extraction of gallium (III) occurs at pH 4–5·5 when 0·10 M HDM solution in benzene is used ($pH_{1/2} = 2·9$, log $K = -5·76$) (S 107).
Hg (II)	Mercury (II) can be quantitatively extracted in the pH range 5·5–7·5 ($pH_{1/2} = 3·9$) (S 107). The extraction rate is very slow.
In (III)	Indium (III) is quantitatively extracted at pH 4·5–5·5 when using 0·10 M HDM in benzene ($pH_{1/2} = 3·6$, log $K = -7·61$) (S 107).
La (III)	Quantitative extraction of lanthanum by 0·10 M HDM in benzene takes place at pH > 9 ($pH_{1/2} = 8·5$, log $K = -19·46$).
Mg (II)	After prolonged shaking magnesium can be completely extracted by 0·10 M HDM in benzene at pH > 9·5 ($pH_{1/2} = 8·5$, log $K = -14·72$) (S 107).
Mn (II)	Quantitative extraction of manganese by 0·10 M HDM in benzene takes place in the pH region 9–12 ($pH_{1/2} = 7·8$, log $K = -13·71$) (S 107).

TABLE 8 (*continued*)

Metal	Optimum conditions for extraction
Mo (VI)	Less than 10% of molybdenum (VI) can be extracted even after prolonged shaking at pH 1–4 when using 0·10 M HDM in benzene (S 107).
Ni (II)	After being shaken for some days nickel (II) can be quantitatively extracted by 0·10 M HDM in benzene at pH 7·5–11 ($pH_{1/2} = 6·4$, $\log K = -11·02$) (S 107).
Pb (II)	Quantitative extraction of lead by 0·10 M HDM in benzene occurs in the pH region 7·5–11 ($pH_{1/2} = 5·6$, $\log K = -9·45$) (S 107).
Pd (II)	The percentage extraction of palladium (II) by 0·10 M HDM in benzene was found to be 90% at pH values ranging from 3 to 11 ($pH_{1/2} = 1·8$). The extraction rate is very slow (S 107).
Sc (III)	Quantitative extraction of scandium by 0·10 M HDM in benzene occurs in the pH range 4–8 ($pH_{1/2} = 3·05$, $\log K = -6·04$) (S 107).
Sr (II)	At pH $\sim$ 12 approximately 80% of strontium can be extracted by 0·10 M HDM in benzene ($pH_{1/2} = 11·1$, $\log K = -20·9$) (S 107).
Th (IV)	Thorium (IV) is quantitatively extracted at pH 3·5–8 when using 0·10 M HDM in benzene ($pH_{1/2} = 2·6$, $\log K = -6·38$) (S 107).
Ti (IV)	Quantitative extraction of titanium (IV) by 0·10 M HDM in benzene takes place at pH > 3 ($pH_{1/2} = 2·6$) (S 107).
Tl (III)	About 80% of thallium (III) can be extracted at pH 5–9 by 0·10 M HDM in benzene ($pH_{1/2} = 3·8$) (S 107).
U (VI)	With HDM uranium (VI) forms a complex of the type UO_2A_2HA which is quantitatively extracted at pH 5–6·5 when using 0·01 M HDM in benzene, chloroform, and carbon tetrachloride ($pH_{1/2} = 3·56$, $3·51$ and $3·74$; $\log K = -4·12$, $-4·02$ and $-4·48$ for benzene, chloroform, and carbon tetrachloride respectively) (M 122). Butyl acetate (S 65), ethyl acetate (P 54), or various ketones (G 37) can also be used as suitable solvents. EDTA or its calcium salt can be used as an excellent masking agent for many interfering metals (P 54, S 65). As is evident from the relevant stability constants, 1,2-diaminocyclohexanetetraacetic acid will be a more suitable masking agent than EDTA (S 102). The uranium (VI) chelate absorbs strongly at 400 mμ ($\varepsilon = 2·10^4$) (S 65, S 107).
Zn (II)	Quantitative extraction of zinc (II) by 0·10 M HDM in benzene takes place in the pH region 8–11 ($pH_{1/2} = 6·4$, $\log K = -10·67$) (S 107).
Zr (IV)	At pH 4–5, approximately 90% of zirconium can be extracted by 0·10 M HDM in benzene ($pH_{1/2} = 3·3$) (S 107).

In aqueous solution dipivaloylmethane is a very weak acid ($pK_{HA} = 11.77$) (G 51). In basic solutions (1 M potassium hydroxide) this reagent forms a chelate with lithium, which is partially extractable into diethyl ether. Small amounts of sodium can also be extracted thus (G 51).

5.1.5. *Thenoyltrifluoracetone*

Thenoyltrifluoracetone (HTTA) (M.Wt. 222·2, M.p. 42·5–43·2°C) is usually obtained as a straw-yellow crystalline solid. It may be purified by vacuum distillation. The reagent is only slightly soluble in water but freely soluble in a variety of organic solvents. Thenoyltrifluoracetone is sensitive to light and should be stored in brown bottles.

The partition coefficient of HTTA between benzene and diluted acids is approximately 40. At higher salt concentrations it is much higher (K 40; see Appendix). In slightly alkaline solution HTTA is converted to an enolate ion, thereby lowering its distribution ratio. At pH ~ 8 ($\log p_{HA} + pK_{HA} = 8$) about half the HTTA is transferred into the aqueous phase. However, if the pH is raised further, above 9, the HTTA cleaves into trifluoroacetic acid and acetylthiophene (C 44).

The dissociation constant of HTTA has been studied by several authors (see Appendix). The best value of pK_{HA} at 25°C appears to be 6·23 (R 7). The trifluoromethyl group increases the acidity of the enol form so that the extractions occur from stronger acid solutions than in the case of other β-diketones (see Table 5). Thus a wide range of metals may be extracted without interference from hydrolysis.

HTTA was introduced as an analytical reagent by Calvin and Reid (R 7). Although the reactivity of HTTA is as general as that of other β-diketones, it has found its greatest use in the separation of the actinide elements.

HTTA forms chelates of the general type MA_N; only strontium (II) (K 51) and uranium (VI) form complexes of the type $MA_N HA$ at higher concentrations of HTTA (P 30).

In extraction procedures the concentration of HTTA in benzene, toluene, xylene, or methylisobutyl ketone is kept in the range 0·1–0·5. With more dilute solutions separations are slow and incomplete (B 79).

De and Khopkar (D 4, D 6) have shown that HTTA can also be used as an absorptiometric reagent for various cations; the reagent itself has its maximum of absorbancy at 330 mμ with the molar extinction coefficient, $\varepsilon = 11,900$. Coloured complexes can be used for the determination of uranium (VI)—yellow, copper (II)—green, iron (III)—bright red, chromium (III)—deep yellow, and cerium (IV)—deep red.

Irving (I 12), and recently Poskanzer and Foreman (P 49) and De (D 6) have made an excellent review of extraction data for many metals. Sheperd and Meinke (S 51) have made a survey of extraction curves of many metals with HTTA (see Figs. 30, 31).

A summary of extraction data for metal thenoyltrifluoracetonates is given in Table 9.

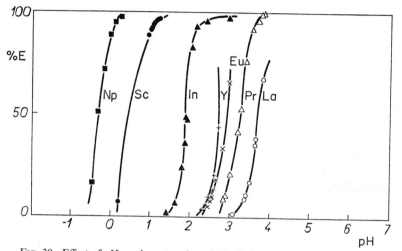

FIG. 30. Effect of pH on the extraction of Np (IV), Sc (III), Y (III), La (III), Eu (III), Pr (III), and In (III) by 0·5 M thenoyltrifluoracetone in benzene (■ Np, ● Sc, + Y, ○ La, × Eu, △ Pr, ▲ In).

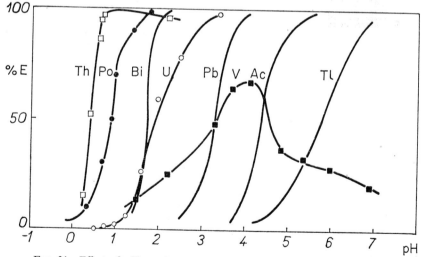

FIG. 31. Effect of pH on the extraction of Th (IV), Po, Bi (III), U (VI), Pb (II), V (V), Ac (III), and Tl (I) by 0·20–0·25 M thenoyltrifluoracetone in benzene (□ Th, ● Po, ○ U, ■ V).

TABLE 9. A SURVEY OF EXTRACTION DATA FOR METAL THENOYLTRIFLUORACETONATES

Metal	Optimum conditions for extraction
	Tervalent actinium can be quantitatively extracted at pH $> 5\cdot5$ by using $0\cdot25$ M HTTA in benzene ($pH_{1/2} = 4\cdot6$) (H 4).
Al (III)	Quantitative extraction of aluminium by $0\cdot10$ M HTTA in 4-methyl-2-pentanone has been observed at pH $5\cdot5$–6 ($pH_{1/2} = 3\cdot5$–$4\cdot5$ depending on the concentration of acetate) (E 15). Benzene can also be used as the organic solvent ($\log K = -5\cdot23$) (B 79).
Am (III)	Benzene can be used as the organic solvent for the extraction of americium (III)-thenoyltrifluoracetonate ($\log K = -7\cdot46$) (P 49). With toluene $\log K = -8\cdot6$ (M 15) and with cyclohexane $\log K = -6\cdot62$ (I 31).
Ba (II)	Barium can be extracted by HTTA in benzene ($\log K = -14\cdot4$) (P 49).
Be (II)	The extraction of beryllium by HTTA in benzene takes place from neutral solutions ($\log K = -3\cdot2$) (B 79). At pH ~ 4 the extraction rate is rather slow. By using $0\cdot5$–$1\cdot0$ M HTTA in xylene the extraction of beryllium is complete even in slightly acid solutions (pH < 4) (D 9). HTTA extraction has been used for the separation of carrier-free beryllium (B 79).
Bi (III)	Bismuth can be quantitatively extracted by $0\cdot25$ M HTTA in benzene at pH $> 2\cdot5$ ($pH_{1/2} = 1\cdot7$) (H 4).
Bk (III)	About 80% of berkelium can be extracted at pH $\sim 3\cdot4$ by $0\cdot2$ M HTTA in toluene ($\log K = -7\cdot5$) (M 15).
Ca (II)	Traces of calcium can be quantitatively extracted by $0\cdot05$ M HTTA in methyl-isobutylketone ("hexone") at pH ~ 8 (K 34). Benzene can also be used as the organic solvent ($\log K = -12\cdot0$) (B 79).
Cd (II)	Cadmium can be extracted by $0\cdot10$ M HTTA in chloroform ($\log p_N = 1\cdot5$, $pH_{1/2} = 6\cdot7$, $\log K = -11\cdot4$) (S 33).
Ce (III)	Benzene can be used as the solvent for the extraction of cerium (III)-thenoyltrifluoracetonate ($\log K = -9\cdot43$) (P 49).
Ce (IV)	At pH 4–6 more than 80% of cerium (IV) is extracted with $0\cdot15$ M HTTA in benzene ($pH_{1/2} = 2\cdot9$). The orange-red chelate has a maximum absorbancy at 410 mμ ($\varepsilon = 2485$) (K 33). This method is not very suitable for the determination of cerium as it requires an accurate adjustment of the pH. By using $0\cdot5$ M HTTA solution in xylene, radiocerium can be extracted from 1 M sulphuric acid; potassium dichromate and sodium bromate must be present (S 83).
Cf (III)	About 70% of californium (III) can be extracted by $0\cdot2$ M HTTA in toluene ($\log K = -7\cdot8$) (M 15).

TABLE 9 (*continued*)

Metal	Optimum conditions for extraction
Cm (III)	Curium (III) can be extracted by 0·2 M HTTA in toluene ($\log K = -8·6$) (M 15).
Co (II)	At pH 7·6–8·8 more than 97% of cobalt (II) can be extracted by 0·1 M HTTA in isobutyl alcohol or methylethylketone (Z 16, Z 17). The above solvents are found to be much better than benzene ($\log K = -6·7$) (P 49) or chloroform. However, in the presence of acetone (the optimum acetone:benzene ratio is 3:1–2:1) cobalt (II)-thenoyltrifluoracetonate can be quantitatively extracted at pH 5·1–6·8 (D 7, M 18). The chelate absorbs at 430 mμ (D 7).
Cr (III)	More than 80% of chromium (III) is extracted by 0·15 M HTTA in benzene at pH 5–6 (pH$_{1/2} \sim 4$). The molar extinction coefficient at 430 mμ is $\varepsilon = 421·5$ (M 19).
Cu (II)	Quantitative extraction of copper by 0·15 M HTTA in benzene was found at pH 3–6 (K 30); $\log K = -1·32$ (B 79). The molar extinction coefficient of the green chelate at 430 mμ is $\varepsilon = 218·3$ (K 30).
Dy (III)	About 85% of dysprosium can be extracted at pH ~ 3 using 0·5 M HTTA in benzene (pH$_{1/2} = 2·7$ (I 12); $\log K = -7·03$ (P 49)). Hexone can also be used as a suitable solvent (R 2).
Er (III)	Erbium (III) can be extracted at pH 5·5 by 0·10 M HTTA in methylisobutylketone (hexone) (R 2).
Es (III)	About 60% of einsteinium (III) is extracted at pH $\sim 3·4$ by 0·2 M HTTA in toluene ($\log K = -7·9$) (M 15).
Eu (III)	Europium (III) can be extracted by 0·5 M HTTA in benzene (pH$_{1/2} = 2·9$ (I 12); $\log K = -7·66$ (P 49)). Cyclohexane can also be used as the organic solvent ($\log K = -7·66$) (I 31).
Fe (III)	More than 99% of iron (III) is extracted by 0·15 M HTTA in benzene at pH ~ 2 (pH$_{1/2} = 1·0$) (K 31). The extraction rate is rather slow and 12 hours' shaking at room temperature is necessary for reaching equilibrium ($\log K = 3·3$) (P 49). Quantitative extraction of iron (III) by 15% HTTA in xylene is found to take place from 2 M nitric acid containing 9 M ammonium nitrate (T 27). By using 0·5 M HTTA in xylene about 90% of iron can be extracted from 10 M nitric acid. By washing the organic phase with a mixture containing 0·25 M hydrofluoric acid and 0·25 M hydrochloric acid the selectivity of separation is greatly increased (M 91). The iron (III)-chelate in the organic phase absorbs at 460–510 mμ. The molar extinction coefficient is approximately 4900 (K 31, T 27).
Fm (III)	About 70% of fermium (III) can be extracted by 0·2 M HTTA in toluene at pH $= 3·4$ ($\log K = -7·7$) (M 15).
Gd (III)	More than 75% of gadolinium can be extracted by 0·5 M HTTA in benzene at pH > 3 (pH$_{1/2} = 2·9$, $\log K = -7·58$) (S 51, P 49).

TABLE 9 (*continued*)

Metal	Optimum conditions for extraction
Hf (IV)	Hafnium (IV) can be extracted from acid solutions by HTTA in benzene ($\log K = 7\cdot8$; aqueous phase, 2 M perchloric acid) (H 41, L 8); ($\log K = 8\cdot18$; aqueous phase, 4 M perchloric acid) (H 42) or in dichlorobenzene ($\log K = 7\cdot28$; aqueous phase, 4 M perchloric acid) (H 42).
Ho (III)	Holmium (III) can be extracted by $0\cdot2$ M HTTA in benzene at pH > 3 ($pH_{1/2} = 3\cdot15$, $\log K = -7\cdot25$) (S 51, P 49).
In (III)	Indium (III) can be quantitatively extracted by $0\cdot005$ M HTTA in benzene at pH > 4 ($pH_{1/2} = 2\cdot8$; aqueous phase, 3 M sodium perchlorate) (R 21). When using a $0\cdot5$ M HTTA solution complete extraction of indium was found at pH $2\cdot5$–$3\cdot5$ ($pH_{1/2} = 1\cdot9$, $\log K = -4\cdot34$) (P 49, S 140).
Ir (III)	Tervalent iridium can be extracted by HTTA in benzene at pH > 7 (P 49).
La (III)	Lanthanum (III) can be extracted by $0\cdot5$ M HTTA in benzene at pH $> 3\cdot5$ ($pH_{1/2} = 3\cdot7$, $\log K = -10\cdot51$) (P 49, S 51). When using $0\cdot1$ M HTTA in methylisobutylketone as solvent quantitative extraction of lanthanum was observed at pH ~ 5 ($pH_{1/2} = 1\cdot7$, aqueous phase, $0\cdot5$ M acetate; $pH_{1/2} = 3\cdot3$, aqueous phase, $1\cdot0$ M acetate) (M 49, R 2).
Li	Lithium is not extracted by $0\cdot2$ M HTTA in benzene at pH $< 7\cdot5$ (P 49).
Lu (III)	Lutecium can be extracted by HTTA in benzene ($\log K = -6\cdot77$) (P 49) or in methylisobutylketone (R 2).
Nb (V)	About 95% of niobium can be extracted by $0\cdot5$ M HTTA in xylene from 10 M nitric acid (M 91).
Nd (III)	Neodymium is extracted at pH > 3 by $0\cdot5$ M HTTA in benzene ($pH_{1/2} = 3\cdot12$, $\log K = -8\cdot57$) (P 49, S 51).
Ni (II)	Nickel (II) can only be extracted with difficulty by HTTA in benzene. However, in the presence of acetone (the optimum benzene:acetone ratio is 1:3) nickel can be quantitatively extracted by $0\cdot15$ M HTTA in benzene from aqueous solution of pH from $5\cdot5$ to $8\cdot0$ ($pH_{1/2} = 3\cdot8$). The molar extinction coefficient $\varepsilon = 868$ at 410 mμ (D 8).
Np (IV)	Tetravalent neptunium can be quantitatively extracted by HTTA in benzene ($\log K = 5\cdot6$) (S 139). Practically complete extraction (i.e. $> 99\%$) of neptunium (IV) from 1 M hydrochloric acid can also be achieved by using $0\cdot5$ M HTTA in xylene (M 87, M 90). Neptunium can be back-extracted from the organic phase into 10 M nitric acid. Protactinium and zirconium remain in the organic phase (M 11, M 87, M 90, S 19). The selectivity of the separation may be further increased by a preliminary extraction of neptunium (VI) from nitric acid with methylisobutyl ketone (M 11). Cyclohexane can also be used as the organic solvent ($\log K = 5\cdot15$) (I 30). Extraction by HTTA was used for the isolation of neptunium from metallic plutonium (S 82).

TABLE 9 (*continued*)

Metal	Optimum conditions for extraction
Np (V)	At pH 7–9 about 90% of neptunium (V) can be extracted by 0·01 M HTTA in isobutyl alcohol. When using cyclohexanone, ethyl acetate or methylethylketone as solvents, the percentage of extraction of neptunium (V) is lower (Z 16, Z 17). When solutions of 0·01 M HTTA in nonpolar solvents such as benzene, chloroform, or carbon tetrachloride were used, no extraction of neptunium (V) was observed over a wide pH region (Z 16, Z 17).
Pa (IV)	About 90% of protactinium (IV) is extracted from 6 N hydrochloric acid containing Cr^{2+} ions by 0·3–1·0 M HTTA in benzene ($\log K = 6·72$) (B 82).
Pa (V)	About 90% of protactinium (V) is extracted from 2–6 M hydrochloric acid with 0·5 M HTTA in benzene. The yellow chelates obey Beer's law at 430–440 mμ (M 128, M 129). When using only 0·2 M HTTA in benzene, quantitative extraction can be obtained from more dilute hydrochloric acid (0·2 M) ($pH_{1/2} = -0·73$) (P 49). Lead can be completely extracted at pH $\sim$ 5 using 0·25 M HTTA in benzene ($pH_{1/2} = 3·2$, $\log K = -5·2$) (H 4).
Pm (III)	Promethium can be extracted by 0·5 M HTTA in benzene ($pH_{1/2} = 3·0$, $\log K = -8·05$) (P 49, S 51).
Po	Quantitative extraction of polonium by 0·25 M HTTA in benzene was observed at pH $\sim$ 2 ($pH_{1/2} = 0·9$) (H 4).
Pr (III)	At pH > 4 praseodymium was completely extracted by 0·1–0·5 M HTTA in benzene ($\log K = -8·48$ (K 22) or $-8·85$ (S 51)).
Pu (III)	The extraction constant for plutonium (III)-thenoyltrifluoracetonate is $3·6 \times 10^{-5}$ ($\log K = -4·44$) for benzene and 3×10^{-5} ($\log K = -4·70$) for cyclohexane respectively (P 49, I 31).
Pu (IV)	Plutonium (IV) is quantitatively extracted from dilute nitric acid (0·5–1·0 M) by 0·5–1·0 M HTTA in benzene (M 88). When using only a 0·1 M solution of HTTA the quantitative isolation of plutonium (IV) can only be achieved by repeating the extraction procedure (P 9) ($\log K = 6·85$, aqueous phase, 1 M sodium perchlorate (P 49); $\log K = 6·34$, aqueous phase, nitric acid (P 49, C 53, C 54)). Plutonium (IV) can be back-extracted from the organic phase into 0·3 M hydrofluoric acid or 10 M nitric acid (after the solution of HTTA has been diluted to 0·05 M) (P 9, M 88). Carbon tetrachloride ($\log K = 5·0$, aqueous phase, 1 M nitric acid (C 53)), cyclohexane ($\log K = 6·37$, aqueous phase, 1·0 M nitric acid (I 30, L 12)) or xylene (M 88) can also be used as suitable organic solvents. Extraction by HTTA has been used for isolating the microgram quantities of plutonium occurring naturally in ores (P 9).
Pu (VI)	Plutonium (VI) can be extracted by HTTA in benzene ($\log K = -1·82$ (P 49)), or in cyclohexane ($\log K = -1·54$ (I 29, I 32)).
Ra (II)	Radium is not extracted in the pH range 2–6 by 0·25 M HTTA in benzene (H 4).

TABLE 9 (continued)

Metal	Optimum conditions for extraction
Ru	Less than 5% of ruthenium can be extracted by 0·05 M HTTA in methylisobutylketone at pH $\sim$ 8 (K 34), and less than 1% by 0·2 M HTTA in benzene from 1 N nitric acid (C 54).
Sc (III)	More than 95% of scandium can be extracted by 0·5 M HTTA in benzene at pH $>$ 1·6 (pH$_{1/2}$ = 0·5, log K = −0·77) (P 49, S 51). Methylisobutylketone can also be used as the organic solvent (R 2).
Sm (III)	Samarium can be extracted by 0·5 M HTTA solution in benzene (pH$_{1/2}$ = 2·9, log K = −7·68) (P 49, S 51).
Sr (II)	At pH 9–13 about 80% of strontium is extracted by 0·2 M HTTA in benzene (pH$_{1/2}$ = 8·0, log K = −14) (K 51, B 79). When using 0·2 M HTTA in methylisobutylketone more than 99% of strontium can be extracted in the pH range 10–12 (pH$_{1/2}$ = 6) (K 51). When using only 0·05 M HTTA in methylisobutylketone, cyclohexanone, ethyl acetate, or isoamyl acetate, etc., quantitative extraction of strontium can be reached at pH 8–10 by repeating the extraction procedures (K 34, K 35, S 149).
Tb (III)	Terbium can be extracted by solutions of HTTA in benzene (log K = −7·51) (P 49).
Tc	Technetium is virtually not extracted by solutions of HTTA either from dilute nitric acid (pH = 3) or from alkali (pH = 11) (S 89).
Th (IV)	More than 98% of thorium can be extracted at pH $>$ 1 by 0·25–0·45 HTTA in benzene (H 4, P 10, W 1). Log K = −0·8 (H 4, W 1), −0·9 (P 10, Z 1), and −1·4 (D 2). Thorium can be back-extracted with 2 M nitric acid (M 43). Carbon tetrachloride (log K = −1·0 (G 18, M 48)), methylisobutylketone (log K = −1·0 (G 18, G 19)), chloroform (R 3), or xylene (M 89) can also be used as organic solvents. Extraction with HTTA has been used for the isolation of thorium from urine (P 10).
Tl (I)	More than 95% of thallium can be extracted at pH $\sim$ 7 by 0·25 M HTTA in benzene (pH$_{1/2}$ = 5·8, log K = −5·2) (H 4). When using 0·025 M HTTA in benzene, ethyl acetate, isobutyl acetate, or methylisobutylketone only 50–80% extraction of thallium (I) was observed at pH 7–10 (B 13).
Tl (III)	At pH $\sim$ 4 thallium (III) can be practically quantitatively extracted by 0·25 M HTTA in benzene (pH$_{1/2}$ = 2·6) (H 4).
Tm (III)	Thulium can be extracted by 0·5 M HTTA in benzene (pH$_{1/2}$ = 3·05, log K = −6·96) (P 49, S 51).
U (IV)	Tetravalent uranium can be extracted from acid solutions by HTTA in benzene (log K = 5·3, aqueous phase, perchloric acid and sodium perchlorate, μ = 2·0 (B 57); log K = 4·18, aqueous phase, nitric acid (P 49)).

TABLE 9 (*continued*)

Metal	Optimum conditions for extraction
U (VI)	Uranium (VI) can be quantitatively extracted at pH 3·5–8 by 0·15 M HTTA in benzene (K 29, K 32). When only a 0·01 M solution of HTTA is used the pH range for complete extraction of uranium (IV) is narrower (H 30). Log $K = -2·26$, aqueous phase, lithium perchlorate and perchloric acid, $\mu = 2·0$ (D 3, P 49); $\log K = -2·0$, aqueous phase, 0·05 M perchloric acid, $\mu = 2·0$ (D 3). At higher concentrations of HTTA additive complexes of the type UO_2A_2HA are probably formed (P 30). In the presence of EDTA ($\sim 0·01$ M) the extraction of uranium (VI) becomes specific (K 29, K 32). The uranium (VI) chelate in the benzene phase absorbs at 430 mμ ($\varepsilon = 1954$). Cyclohexane can also be used for extraction ($\log K = -2·8$, aqueous phase, 0·01 M nitric acid) (I 26, I 29).
V (IV)	The extraction of vanadium (IV) by 0·25 M HTTA in benzene passes through a maximum at pH about 4 (F 32, S 51).
Y (III)	At pH 6–9 more than 95% of yttrium is extracted by 0·10 M HTTA in benzene (S 149). Log $K = -7·39$ (S 51, P 49). Methylisobutylketone can also be used as the organic solvent (K 34). Extraction with HTTA has been used for the separation of carrier-free ^{90}Y from ^{90}Sr (S 149).
Yb (III)	Ytterbium can be extracted by a solution of HTTA in benzene ($\log K = -6·72$ (P 49)), or in toluene ($\log K = -7·3$ (M 15)).
Zr (IV)	More than 95% of zirconium can be isolated by a single extraction from 2 M nitric acid with 0·5 M HTTA in benzene (A 10, H 15). Log $K = 9·00–9·15$, aqueous phase, 2 M perchloric acid (C 42, H 41, L 8); $\log K = 9·59$, aqueous phase, 4 M perchloric acid (H 42). Under these conditions hafnium (IV), plutonium (IV), neptunium (IV), uranium (IV), protactinium (III), and niobium (V) are also extracted. Peroxycomplexing of niobium and protactinium is particularly effective in achieving clear separation of these elements from zirconium (M 86). After washing the organic phase with 2 M nitric acid containing 0·01% hydrogen peroxide, zirconium can be back-extracted into 40% hydrofluoric acid (H 15). This method has been used for the preparation of radiochemically pure ^{95}Zr and ^{95}Nb (H 15). By using 0·5 M HTTA in xylene, about 99% of zirconium can be extracted from 2 M hydrochloric or nitric acid. Zirconium can be back-extracted into a mixture of dilute hydrofluoric and hydrochloric acids (0·25–0·50 M) (H 22, M 30, M 86). Dichlorobenzene can also be used as the organic solvent ($\log K = 8·49$), aqueous phase, 4 M perchloric acid (H 42).

5.1.6. *Furoyltrifluoracetone*

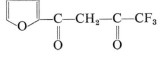

In its analytical properties furoyltrifluoracetone (HFTA) is very similar to thenoyltrifluoracetone. A survey of extraction data for HFTA is given in Table 10.

TABLE 10. A SURVEY OF EXTRACTION DATA FOR METAL FUROYLTRIFLUORACETONATES

Metal	Optimum conditions for extraction
Co (II)	With HFTA cobalt (II) forms a yellow chelate extractable into methylisopropylketone (M 4).
Cu (II)	Green copper-furoyltrifluoracetonate can be extracted at pH 7 into methylisopropylketone (M 4). The absorbancy of the chelate can be measured at 660 mμ (B 52).
Fe (II)	Purple iron (II)-furoyltrifluoracetonate can be extracted into 1-butanol (M 4).
Fe (III)	Iron (III) forms a red chelate with HFTA extractable into methylisobutylketone (M 4).
Hf (IV)	Hafnium (IV) can be extracted from acid medium into a solution of HFTA in benzene (log $K = 7\cdot26$, aqueous phase, 2 M perchloric acid) (L 8).
Mn (II)	A yellow manganese chelate with HFTA can be extracted by methylisopropylketone (M 4).
Ni (II)	Nickel (II) forms a green chelate with HFTA extractable with methylisopropylketone (M 4).
Pd (II)	A yellow chelate with HFTA is extractable into 1-butanol (M 4).
U (VI)	The yellow uranium (VI) chelate with HFTA can be extracted into 1-butanol (M 4).
Zr (IV)	Zirconium (IV) can be extracted from acid solutions by a solution of HFTA in benzene (log $K = 8\cdot65$, aqueous phase, 2 M perchloric acid) (L 8).

5.1.7. Other β-diketones

Trifluoracetylacetone was used by Schultz (S 23) for the partial separation of zirconium (IV) from hafnium (IV).

Pyrroyltrifluoracetone (L 8) and selenoyltrifluoracetone (P 36) have been studied as organic reagents for the separation of zirconium (IV) from hafnium (IV).

Selenoylacetone has been proposed for the extraction of thorium (P 19) and zirconium (IV).

1-Phenyl-3-methyl-4-acyl-pyrazolones have been used by Skytte (S 80, S 81) for a detailed study of the influence of the physical and chemical properties of an organic reagent on its behaviour as an extractant (see Section 3.4, Table 3).

5.2. TROPOLONE AND ITS DERIVATIVES

Tropolones have a hydrogen atom replaceable by a metal and an oxygen atom which can complete a five-membered chelate ring:

The most important of the tropolones is β-isopropyltropolone, whose extraction properties have been systematically studied by Dyrssen (D 43).

5.2.1. *Tropolone*

A solution of tropolone in chloroform was used by Dyrssen (D 34) for the extraction of thorium (IV), uranium (VI), lanthanum (III), and yttrium (III).

Thorium (IV) was found to be quantitatively extracted ($\log p_N = 3\cdot16$) at pH 2–8 when using a $0\cdot05$ M solution of the reagent in chloroform (pH$_{1/2} = 1\cdot0$, $\log K = 2\cdot0$). Complete extraction of uranium (VI) and yttrium (III) takes place at a pH higher than 2 and $5\cdot5$ respectively when using the same concentration of the reagent in chloroform. Lanthanum (III) is only partially extracted at pH > 5 (D 34).

Extraction by tropolone has been used for the separation of uranium (VI) and thorium (IV) from the rare earths (D 34).

5.2.2. *β-Isopropyltropolone*

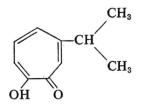

β-Isopropyltropolone (HIPT) is a more stable compound than tropolone itself. The reagent can easily be isolated from cedar wood or thuja. This wood may contain as much as 4 per cent of HIPT.

HIPT is somewhat soluble in water and readily soluble in chloroform. Its distribution coefficient between chloroform and an aqueous phase at 25°C ($\mu = 0\cdot1$) is rather high ($\log p_{HA} = 3\cdot37$) (D 43). The dissociation constant of HIPT, determined by potentiometric titration at 25°C, is $9\cdot1 \times 10^{-8}$ whence $pK_{HA} = 7\cdot04$ (D 41, D 43).

With nickel (II), copper (II), zinc (II), iron (III), indium (III), praseodymium (III), and thorium (IV) HIPT forms extractable chelates of the type MA_N, while with calcium (II), strontium (II), barium (II), uranium (VI), europium (III), holmium (III), ytterbium (III), and lutecium (III) additive complexes of the type $MA_N HA$ are formed. In the presence of sodium ions, zinc and nickel can be extracted as $NaZnA_3$ and $NaNiA_3$ respectively. The solubility of the extractable chelates in organic solvents is low (10^{-4} to 10^{-3} M) and this restricts its use for the extraction of large quantities of metals. In some cases (e.g. copper (II), iron (III), and uranium (VI)) the extraction coefficients of the extractable chelates are very high at 400–450 mμ, where HIPT itself does not absorb, so that absorptiometric determinations are possible (D 43).

In Table 11, a survey of extraction data obtained by Dyrssen is given.

5.3. 8-HYDROXYQUINOLINE AND ITS DERIVATIVES

8-Hydroxyquinolines have a hydrogen atom replaceable by a metal and a heterocyclic nitrogen which forms with this metal a five-membered chelate ring:

Among this group of organic reagents the most important are 8-hydroxy-quinoline and 8-hydroxyquinaldine.

5.3.1. *8-Hydroxyquinoline (8-quinolinol, 'oxine')*

8-Hydroxyquinoline (Mol.Wt. 145·15, M.p. 75–76°C), which has the trivial name "oxine", recrystallizes from a mixture of water and alcohol in

TABLE 11. A SURVEY OF EXTRACTION DATA FOR METAL β-ISOPROPYLTROPOLONATES
A 0·1 M solution of the reagent in chloroform was used unless stated to the contrary

Metal	Optimum conditions for extraction
Ag (I)	At about pH 10 approximately 50% of silver is extracted ($pH_{1/2} = 9·7$, $\log K = -8·7$).
Al (III)	Aluminium can be extracted by HIPT in chloroform probably as a complex AlA_2ClO_4.
Am (III)	Quantitative extraction of americium was observed at pH > 4 ($pH_{1/2} = 3·41$).
Ba (II)	More than 50% of barium can be extracted at pH > 10 ($pH_{1/2} = 9·5$).
Ca (II)	More than 99% of calcium can be extracted at pH $> 8·5$ by a 0·5 M solution of HIPT in chloroform. When using only 0·10 M HIPT in chloroform the maximum extractability was obtained at pH $> 9·5$ ($pH_{1/2} = 8·19$).
Cd (II)	At pH 8–10 about 99% of cadmium is extracted ($pH_{1/2} = 5·05$).
Co (II)	Cobalt (II) is oxidized by HIPT to cobalt (III) which is quantitatively extracted ($\log p_N = 2·35$) at pH 8–10.
Cu (II)	Quantitative extraction of copper ($\log p_N = 4·12$) was observed at pH 2–4 ($pH_{1/2} = 0·2$, $\log K = 1·7$). The chelate absorbs at 435 mμ.
Eu (III)	Europium can be quantitatively extracted as a complex EuA_2HA at pH > 4 ($pH_{1/2} = 3·41$, $\log K = -6·24$).
Fe (III)	Iron (III) can be extracted by 0·10 M HIPT in chloroform ($pH_{1/2} = -2·33$, $\log K = 10·0$). The chelate absorbs at 410 mμ ($\varepsilon = 13,900$). The extraction rate is unusually slow in acid medium (1–4 days).
Ho (III)	Holmium reacts with HIPT to give a complex HoA_3HA which can be extracted into chloroform ($pH_{1/2} = 3·08$, $\log K = -6·13$).
In (III)	Indium can easily be extracted by a 0·1 M solution of HIPT in chloroform ($pH_{1/2} = -0·34$, $\log K = 4·01$).
La (III)	Quantitative extraction of lanthanum was observed at pH $> 5·5$ ($pH_{1/2} = 4·44$, $\log K = -10·3$).
Lu (III)	HIPT forms a complex of the type LuA_3HA with lutecium. Quantitative extraction was obtained at pH $> 3·5$ ($pH_{1/2} = 2·76$, $\log K = -4·27$).
Ni (II)	Nickel can be extracted in the form NiA_2 or $NaNiA_3$. In the pH range 6·5–8 about 99% of nickel ($\log p_N = 2·1$) is extracted ($pH_{1/2} = 4·86$).
Pr (III)	Praseodymium can be extracted ($pH_{1/2} = 3·83$, $\log K = -8·49$).
Sc (III)	Quantitative extraction of scandium was obtained at pH $> 1·5$ ($pH_{1/2} = 0·65$, $\log K = 1·08$).

TABLE 11 (*continued*)

Metal	Optimum conditions for extraction
Sm (III)	Samarium (III) can be quantitatively extracted at pH > 4.5 (pH$_{1/2}$ = 3.52, $\log K = -2.52$).
Sr (II)	At pH 9·0–9·5 about 97% of strontium is extracted by 0·5 M HIPT in chloroform. When using only a 0·10 M solution the extractability of strontium is somewhat decreased (pH$_{1/2}$ = 8·58).
Tb (III)	Terbium can be extracted (pH$_{1/2}$ = 3·38).
Th (IV)	Quantitative extraction of thorium ($\log p_N = 5$) takes place at pH > 1 (pH$_{1/2}$ = 0·16, $\log K = 6·2$).
Tm (III)	Thulium can be extracted from neutral solutions (pH$_{1/2}$ = 3·04).
U (VI)	Uranium (VI) can be extracted quantitatively in the form UO_2A_2HA at pH > 1 (pH$_{1/2}$ = 0·2, $\log K = 2·63$).
Y (III)	Yttrium can be extracted (pH$_{1/2}$ = 3·46).
Yb (III)	Ytterbium is extracted in the form of the additive complex YbA_2HA (pH$_{1/2}$ = 3·46, $\log K = -4·89$).
Zn (II)	From the distribution data it is evident that zinc can be extracted in the form ZnA_2 ($\log p_N = 2·25$) or as $NaZnA_3$ ($\log p_N = 3·97$). When using 0·10 M HIPT in chloroform the extraction is practically complete in the pH range from 5·5 to 11 (pH$_{1/2}$ = 4·13).

almost colourless needles. It is sparingly soluble in cold water ($3·6 \times 10^{-3}$ M at 20–25°C), but readily soluble in mineral acids and in dilute alkalis to form yellow solutions. The increase of solubility in acidic solutions is caused by the formation of hydroxyquinolinium ions, H_2Ox^+; in alkaline solutions oxinate ions, Ox^-, are formed.

The following constants have been determined for oxine at 25°C ($\mu = 0·1$) (D 26, I 11):

$$K_{HA} = [H^+][Ox^-]/[HOx] = 10^{-9·66}; \quad K_{H_2A} = [H^+][HOx]/[H_2Ox]^+ = 10^{-5·00}$$

Oxine is freely soluble in absolute alcohol, chloroform, benzene, and other organic solvents. The partition coefficient of the neutral compound between chloroform and aqueous phase at pH 6–9 is 460 at 25°C (D 26). Because of its amphoteric nature the partition of oxine is diminished under pH 6 and over pH 9 (see Fig. 9).

In general 0·01–0·10 M solutions of oxine in chloroform are used for extraction procedures. Benzene, toluene, or xylene can also be used in place of the chloroform. For the extraction of alkaline earths more concentrated solutions ($0\cdot5$–$1\cdot0$ M) are used.

In some cases oxine is dissolved in acetic acid or alcohol and precipitate of metal chelate is then extracted by suitable solvents.

The reagent is somewhat sensitive to light and its solutions should be stored in brown bottles.

Oxine, one of the most versatile of organic reagents, is known to react with at least 50 metals. Generally there are the same metals forming hydroxy- and amminocomplexes.

Most metal-oxinates are extremely soluble in chloroform and can be completely extracted into this solvent, forming yellow solutions; only iron (III), vanadium (V), cerium (IV), and ruthenium (II) form green or greenish-black coloured chelates. Oxine itself absorbs at 318 mμ and only feebly above 375 mμ in which region most oxinates have an absorption band. A direct photometric determination can be based on the fact that Beer's law is obeyed up to at least 100 ppm of the metal. At higher metal concentration deviations become considerable.

Some oxinates (e.g. those of aluminium, gallium, indium, etc.) fluoresce in the chloroform phase (C 38, G 24, H 1, I 34–37). Since extremely small quantities of the metals are sufficient to cause a very strong fluorescence, this property has been utilized for their detection and determination.

Microamounts of calcium (G 30), titanium, gallium, and indium (G 32), copper, manganese (G 31), cobalt, nickel (G 33), and vanadium (G 34) can also be determined by flame photometry wherein these metals are converted into their oxinates and the extracted chelates are sprayed into an oxy-hydrogen flame. The sensitivity could be increased 5–15 times above that realized for aqueous solutions.

Spectrographic methods (G 23, M 69, P 43) and polarographic methods can also be used for the determination of many metals after their extraction as oxinates.

Systematic study (S 107) of the solvent extraction of metal oxinates has shown that Be^{2+}, Mg^{2+}, La^{3+}, TiO^{2+}, ZrO^{2+}, Th^{4+}, VO_2^+, Mn^{2+}, Fe^{3+}, Pd^{2+}, Cu^{2+}, Al^{3+}, Ga^{3+}, In^{3+}, and Pb^{2+} are extracted as chelates of the type MA_N; Ca^{2+}, Sc^{2+}, Co^{2+}, UO_2^{2+}, and Sr^{2+} are extracted as MA_NHA, and Ba^{2+}, Zn^{2+}, Cd^{2+}, and Ni^{2+} form extractable complexes of the type $MA_N(HA)_2$. Molybdenum (VI) (when present as H_2MoO_4) and probably tungsten (VI) also are extracted as MoO_2A_2 and WO_2A_2 respectively.

From the values of the extraction constants (see Table 12) it is evident that the extractability of metal ions by oxine in chloroform decreases in the following order: Pd^{2+}, H_2MoO_4, W (VI), VO_2^+, Tl^{3+}, Fe^{3+}, ZrO^{2+}, Ga^{3+}, Cu^{2+}, TiO^{2+}, In^{3+}, Bi^{3+}, Ni^{2+}, UO_2^{2+}, Al^{3+}, Th^{4+}, (Hg^{2+}), Co^{2+}, Zn^{2+}, Sc^{3+}, Cd^{2+}, Pb^{2+}, Mn^{2+}, Be^{2+}, La^{3+}, Ag^+, Mg^{2+}, Ca^{2+}, Sr^{2+}, and Ba^{2+}.

Reviews of the extraction of metal oxinates have been given by many

84   THE SOLVENT EXTRACTION OF METAL CHELATES

TABLE 12. A SURVEY OF EXTRACTION DATA FOR METAL OXINATES

Metal	Optimum conditions for extraction
Ag (I)	At pH 8–9·5 about 90% of silver (I) can be extracted by a 0·10 M solution of oxine in chloroform as the complex AgA_2HA ($pH_{1/2} = 6·51$ (S 106), $\log K = -4·51$ (S 106); $pH_{1/2} = 6·9$, $\log K = -4·8$ (S 30)). Benzene ($(pH_{1/2})_{0·1} = 6·8$, carbon tetrachloride $(pH_{1/2})_{0·1} = 7·2$, toluene $(pH_{1/2})_{0·1} = 7·4$, or chlorbenzene $(pH_{1/2})_{0·1} = 6·5$ can also be use das organic solvents (S 30).
Al (III)	Complete extraction of aluminium (III) by 0·01–0·10 M oxine in chloroform is obtained in the pH range 4·5–11 (($pH_{1/2})_{0·01} = 3·77$, $\log K = -5·22$) (A 11, G 11, G 12, L 2, R 13, R 14, S 106). At pH 6·5–8 the extraction is complete only after prolonged shaking (G 11, G 12). Quantitative extraction of aluminium can also be achieved by the precipitation of aluminium oxinate followed by its extraction with chloroform (A 49, B 78, G 35, M 92, M 93, M 113, O 7). Benzene (M 52, R 1), toluene, xylene, chloroform, or carbon tetrachloride (S 113) can also be used as organic solvents. From the extraction constants of metal oxinates it is evident that many metals are coextracted with aluminium. In the presence of 0·3 M cyanide, copper, nickel, zinc, cobalt, and cadmium are masked (G 11). The interference by iron (III) can be overcome by reduction and conversion into ferrocyanide (G 11, G 12), by masking with 1,10-phenanthroline (G 36, S 91), or by a preliminary extraction as thiocyanate (S 86) or cupferrate (C 24, V 15, Z 9). Thorium can be masked by 6 M acetate solution or by 4-sulpho-benzene-arsenic acid (M 28), and the addition of quinalizarine–sulphuric acid prevents the extraction of zirconium as oxinate at pH 4·5 (R 15). The use of nitrilotriacetic acid (G 17) as masking agent cannot be recommended, for the extraction of aluminium is itself decreased (S 106). Very selective isolation of aluminium can be obtained after removing interfering ions by a preliminary extraction as diethyldithiocarbamates (G 17, K 20, R 17, T 44) or as 8-hydroxyquinaldinates (A 40, C 24, H 43, R 15). Only uranium (VI) interferes (R 14) but it can be masked at pH 9·5–10 by saturated ammonium carbonate solution (A 40). Fluoride ions interfere and their indirect determination is thus possible (W 24). Aluminium oxinate absorbs at 390 mμ (L 14, M 79, S 106), but oxygen and light cause rapid decomposition of this complex (L 14). The aluminium complex gives a strong fluorescence so that a fluorometric determination of aluminium is possible (R 6). Extractions with oxine have been used for the isolation and/or determination of aluminium in iron (R 17), in metallic nickel (Y 9), in thorium (M 28), in thorium oxide (G 17), in tungsten oxide (G 11), in lead, antimony, tin and their alloys (R 18), in high purity magnesium (M 114), in calcium (S 91), in high purity chromium (K 20), in uranium (A 40), in rare earths (T 44), in alkalis (K 27), in high purity acids and in silica (R 6), in steel (A 49, C 24, K 2, K 8, M 55, W 22), in heat-resistant alloys (Z 9), in nonferrous alloys (K 43), in sea water (M 92, M 93), in industrial waters (G 36), in silicic materials (V 15), in silica and carbonate materials (R 15), in polyethylene (B 78), and in glass (C 24).

TABLE 12 (*continued*)

Metal	Optimum conditions for extraction
As (III)	Tervalent arsenic is not extracted by solutions of oxine in chloroform (G 12).
Ba (II)	Barium can be partially extracted as the complex $BaA_2(HA)_2$ at pH > 10 by using $0 \cdot 5$–$1 \cdot 0$ M oxine in chloroform. Log $K = -20 \cdot 9$ (S 106, U 8). The complex absorbs at 380–400 mμ (S 106). The extraction of barium can be increased by adding n-butylamine due to the formation of a complex $(C_4H_9NH_3^+)_2BaA_4^{2-}$ (U 8).
Be (II)	At pH 6–10 about 87% of beryllium (log $p_N = 0 \cdot 85$) can be extracted by $0 \cdot 5$ M oxine in chloroform (pH$_{1/2}$ = $5 \cdot 11$; log $K = -9 \cdot 62$) (S 106). The chelate absorbs at 380 mμ (S 106). Methylisobutylketone can also be used as the organic solvent (K 3). Extraction with oxine has been used for the determination of beryllium in alloys (K 37).
Bi (III)	Quantitative extraction of bismuth by $0 \cdot 1$ M oxine in chloroform occurs in the pH range $2 \cdot 5$–11 (pH$_{1/2}$ = $2 \cdot 13$, log $K = -1 \cdot 2$) (S 106). When using only $0 \cdot 01$ M solution quantitative extraction takes place in the pH range 4–$5 \cdot 2$ (M 75). The complex absorbs at 390–395 mμ (M 75).
Ca (II)	Calcium can be quantitatively extracted at pH > $10 \cdot 7$ using $0 \cdot 5$ M oxine in chloroform (S 106, U 6, U 8). At this concentration the complex CaA_2HA is extracted into the organic phase (S 106). The complex absorbs at 380–400 mμ (U 6). By using 2% oxine with 2% n-butylamine in chloroform more than 90% of calcium is extracted at pH 10–11 (U 6). Methylisobutylketone can also be used as the organic solvent for the extraction of calcium oxinate (G 30).
Cd (II)	Complete extraction of cadmium as the complex $CdA_2(HA)_2$ occurs at pH $5 \cdot 5$–$9 \cdot 5$ when using $0 \cdot 1$ M oxine dissolved in chloroform (pH$_{1/2}$ = $4 \cdot 66$, log $K = -5 \cdot 29$) (S 106). The complex absorbs at 380–390 mμ (M 42, U 7). In the presence of polar solvents (e.g. alcohols, alkylamines) cadmium is extracted in the form $CdA_2(ROH)_2$, $CdA_2(H_2O)(RNH_2)$ or $CdA_2(H_2O)(R_2NH)$ (U 7). When using less concentrated solutions of oxine ($0 \cdot 001$–$0 \cdot 01$ M) only 70–97% of cadmium can be extracted into chloroform (R 22, R 23, U 7). However, in the presence of $0 \cdot 2$ M n-butylamine the extraction becomes quantitative at higher pH values (11–$11 \cdot 6$) (U 7).
Ce	Cerium can be extracted with $1 \cdot 4$ M oxine in chloroform at pH $9 \cdot 9$–$10 \cdot 6$ in the presence of citrate and tartrate (W 20). The complex absorbs at 495–500 mμ (A 19); at this wavelength only a few other oxinates, viz. iron (III), vanadium (V), and ruthenium (III), absorb. After conversion of iron into ferrocyanide, cerium can be selectively determined in cast iron and in alloys (W 20). If manganese is present a preliminary separation by cathodic electrolysis is recommended.
Co (II)	Cobalt (II) can be quantitatively extracted as the complex $CoA_2(HA)_2$ at pH $4 \cdot 5$–$10 \cdot 5$ by using $0 \cdot 10$ M oxine in chloroform (pH$_{1/2}$ = $3 \cdot 21$; log $K = -2 \cdot 16$) (S 106). When using less concentrated solutions ($0 \cdot 01$–$0 \cdot 07$ M)

TABLE 12 (*continued*)

Metal	Optimum condition for extraction
Co (II) (*cont.*)	quantitative extraction only occurs at pH > 7 (D 17, J 11, M 75). The complex absorbs at 420 mμ (S 106).
Cr (III)	Chromium (III)-oxinate is only formed on boiling in the presence of the excess oxine (B 63, T 19). The chelate can be completely extracted with chloroform at pH 6–8. It absorbs at 425 mμ (M 75). At room temperature chromium (III) is not extracted by 0·10–0·01 M oxine in chloroform at any pH (S 106).
Cu (II)	Copper can be completely extracted at pH.2–12 with 0·10 M oxine in chloroform (pH$_{1/2}$ = 1·51, log K = 1·77 (S 106), log K = 1·4 (G 12)). When using 0·07 M oxine in chloroform quantitative extraction of copper occurs in the pH range 2·8–14 but at higher pH if tartrate is present (G 12). Benzene, toluene, xylene, or carbon tetrachloride can also be used as organic solvents (S 133). Complexonates and cyanides interfere strongly (S 106). The copper (II)-oxinate has its maximum absorbancy at 410–420 mμ (M 75, M 111, S 106). Extraction with oxine has been used for the determination of copper in uranium (M 116).
Eu (III)	Europium (III) oxinate can be extracted by chloroform (H 1).
Fe (II)	Divalent iron is not extracted as its oxinate at a pH lower than 4. Above this pH it is oxidized and extracted as ferric oxinate (M 109).
Fe (III)	Quantitative extraction of ferric iron using 0·01–0·10 M oxine in chloroform occurs at pH 2–10 (A 11, G 12, M 75, S 73, S 106, T 46). When 0·01 M oxine in chloroform was used pH$_{1/2}$ = 1·50, log K = 4·11 (S 106). Benzene and other solvents can also be used for the extraction of iron (III)-oxinate (K 83, S 134). The chelate absorbs strongly at 470 and at 580 mμ (M 75, S 106). The latter wavelength is generally used for determination of iron (III); at this wavelength only oxinates of vanadium (V), ruthenium (III), and cerium (IV) absorb strongly (H 19, S 106). A spectrophotometric method has been used for the determination of iron in chromium, nickel, and manganese (M 109), in vanadium (H 18) since at higher pH values vanadium is not extracted by oxine dissolved in chloroform, or in sea water (H 19).
Ga (III)	Gallium can be quantitatively extracted at pH 2·2–12 using 0·01 M oxine in chloroform (pH$_{1/2}$ = 1·07 (S 106), pH$_{1/2}$ = 1·0 (L 2, L 3); log K = 3·72 (S 106)). Cyanides do not interfere, but complexonates interfere seriously (S 106). The gallium chelate absorbs at 400 mμ (ε = 6470) (M 76, M 79, S 106) and shows a strong fluorescence (I 37, S 61). A spectrophotometric method has been used for the determination of gallium in germanium (L 22) after preliminary extraction of the gallium from 6 N hydrochloric acid by ether. A fluorometric method has been used for the determination of gallium in aluminium and iron (S 10), bauxites (L 3), silicate rocks (S 11, N 18, N 19), and in various ores (M 69, K 88).
Gd (III)	Gadolinium oxinate can be extracted by chloroform. Its maximum absorbancy is at 370 mμ (ε = 6850) (H 1).

TABLE 12 (*continued*)

Metal	Optimum conditions for extraction
Hf (IV)	Quantitative extraction of hafnium by 0·10 M oxine in chloroform occurs at pH 2 ($pH_{1/2} = 1·3$) (D 28). Hafnium (IV) oxinate, which has been precipitated by an excess of the reagent, can be completely extracted by chloroform at pH 4·5–11 (M 120). The chelate absorbs at 385 mμ ($\varepsilon = 1·4 \times 10^4$) (M 120).
Hg (I)	About 55% of mercury can be extracted at pH 8–10 by using 0·001 M oxine in chloroform. The chelate absorbs at 395 mμ (U 7).
Hg (II)	At pH > 3 mercury (II) can be extracted by 0·10 M oxine in chloroform (S 106). The complex absorbs at 390 mμ ($\varepsilon = 5400$) (U 7).
Ho (III)	Holmium (III) can be virtually completely extracted by 0·10 M oxine in chloroform ($pH_{1/2} \sim 5$) (R 28).
In (III)	Quantitative extraction of indium by 0·01 M oxine in chloroform occurs at pH 3·0–11·5 ($pH_{1/2} = 2·13$) (L 8, S 106), log $K = 0·89$ (S 106). The indium chelate absorbs strongly at 395–400 mμ ($\varepsilon = 6670$) (M 74) and also shows a strong fluorescence (I 35, B 69). Extraction with oxine has been used for the isolation and/or determination of indium in beryllium (M 63), in ores and minerals (M 69), and for isolation of radioindium from irradiated materials (T 25) and from cadmium (L 8, R 22, R 23).
La (III)	Lanthanum (III) can be quantitatively extracted (log $p_N = 2·57$) by 0·10 M oxine in chloroform at pH 7–10 ($pH_{1/2} = 6·46$) (S 106), log $K = -15·66$ (D 28), log $K = -16·37$ (S 106). The complex absorbs at 380 mμ (S 106).
Mg (II)	At pH 9 magnesium is quantitatively extracted by 0·10 M oxine in chloroform; only 1 minute's shaking must be used as magnesium oxinate is decomposed by shaking ($pH_{1/2} = 8·57$, log $K = -15·13$) (S 106). The magnesium chelate dissolves in chloroform (solubility $2·2 \times 10^{-4}$ M) (Z 8) and absorbs at 385 mμ ($\varepsilon = 5300$) (Z 8). In the presence of n-butylamine (2% solution) magnesium can be quantitatively extracted at pH 10·7–13·6 when using 0·1% oxine in chloroform. The complex $[RNH_3]^+[MgA_3]^-$ absorbs at 380 mμ ($\varepsilon = 5600$) (U 1–3). Also in the presence of butylcellosolve (5% solution) (L 20, L 23, J 3) or butyl carbitol (A 47) magnesium can be extracted at pH 10–12 by 0·2–0·3 M oxine in chloroform. Quantitative extraction of magnesium by 0·2 M oxine in chloroform in the presence of ethanol or isoprentyl alcohol has been observed at pH 10·05–10·28 and 10·29–10·33 respectively (J 1). Methylisobutylketone has also been recommended as a suitable solvent for magnesium oxinate (K 3, G 29). Extraction with oxine has been used for the determination of magnesium in calcium minerals, aluminium (G 29) and zirconium alloys (U 3) (interfering ions were removed by a preliminary extraction at lower pH and/or by masking with cyanide), in electrolytic nickel (L 20, L 23), and in uranium (A 47).

TABLE 12 (*continued*)

Metal	Optimum conditions for extraction
Mn (II)	Manganese (II) can be quantitatively removed from an aqueous phase at pH 6·5–10 by extraction with 0·10 M oxine in chloroform (G 12, S 106) ($pH_{1/2} = 5·66$, $\log K = -9·32$) (S 106). The manganese (II) chelate absorbs at 395 mμ (G 12, S 106). At higher pH values oxidation with atmospheric oxygen to manganese (III) oxinate occurs (S 106).
Mo (V)	Molybdenum (V) oxinate is extractable into chloroform (B 106).
Mo (VI)	Molybdenum (VI) can be quantitatively extracted by 0·01 M oxine into chloroform in the pH region 1·0–5·5 ($pH_{1/2} = 0·5$, $\log K = \log [MoO_2A_2]_{org}/[H_2MoO_4][HOx]^2_{org} = 9·88$) (S 106). The extraction of molybdenum from acid medium is highly selective; the last traces of interfering metals can be readily eliminated by washing the organic extract with 0·1 M oxalic acid at pH 1·0. The complex absorbs at 380–385 mμ (E 1, S 106). Extraction with oxine has been used for the specific determination of molybdenum in nuclear reactor and other materials (E 1).
Nb (V)	Niobium (V) can be almost quantitatively extracted from 2·5% tartrate solution at pH 6–9 with a 4% solution of oxine in chloroform (A 13, A 20, A 29, A 33). When using other solvents such as n-butyl alcohol, dichlorobenzene, ethyl acetate, cyclohexane, etc., extraction is not quantitative. Extraction from $\sim$ 2% alkaline citrate solution at pH $\sim$ 9·4 by 0·07 M oxine in chloroform has been recommended for the isolation of niobium (V) from tantalum, tungsten, molybdenum, and vanadium (K 9). Niobium (V) precipitated as oxinate in the presence of excess of the reagent was found to be completely extracted with chloroform at pH 2·8–10·5 (B 50, M 117). The strong absorption of the chelate at 380–385 mμ ($\varepsilon = 1·13 \times 10^4$) (K 9, K 62) can be used for determination of niobium in uranium-base alloys (M 117) or in niobium-bearing steels (K 9). Isotopic dilution analysis has also been used for the quantitative determination of niobium (A 27).
Nd (III)	Neodymium (III)-oxinate can be extracted into chloroform. The molar extinction coefficient at 370 mμ is 5780 (H 1).
Ni (II)	Quantitative extraction of nickel by 0·01 M oxine in chloroform occurs at pH 4·0–10·0 ($pH_{1/2} = 3·16$, $\log K = -2·18$) (S 106). Attainment of extraction equilibrium at low pH values is slow and requires some hours (S 106). After 1 minutes' shaking quantitative extraction of nickel was achieved at pH 4·5–9·5 when using 0·07 M oxine in chloroform (G 12). Benzene, toluene, and other solvents can also be used for the extraction of nickel-oxinate (S 134). The absorption of the organic extract at 390 mμ can be used for the spectrophotometric determination of nickel (S 106).
Np (V)	Neptunium (V) is practically not extracted by 0·10 M oxine in chloroform or in benzene (Z 17). However, when using 0·10 M oxine in isoamyl alcohol or in butyl alcohol about 30% and 70% respectively of the neptunium (V) can be extracted at pH $\sim$ 10 (Z 17).

TABLE 12 (*continued*)

Metal	Optimum conditions for extraction
Pa	About 67% of protactinium can be extracted as oxinate from saturated ammonium carbonate with amyl alcohol (M 8, M 9).
Pb (II)	Lead can be completely extracted by 0·01–0·10 M oxine in chloroform at pH 6–10 ($\mathrm{pH}_{1/2} = 5·04$, $\log K = -8·04$) (S 106). The complex absorbs at 400 mμ (M 113, S 106).
Pd (II)	Quantitative extraction of palladium (II) by 0·01 M oxine in chloroform occurs in the range pH 0–10 ($\log K = 15$). In the very acid media the rate of extraction is slow (S 106). The chelate absorbs at 425–430 mμ (J 3, S 106).
Pm (III)	Promethium can be partially extracted in the presence of tartrate at pH 9·3–9·6 by a dilute solution of oxine in chloroform (I 43).
Po	Polonium forms a complex with oxine that can be partially extracted with chloroform from an acetate buffer of pH 3–4 (I 45, K 39).
Pr (III)	Praseodymium can be extracted as an oxinate into chloroform. The molecular extinction coefficient at 370 mμ is 6020 (H 1).
Pu (IV)	Tetravalent plutonium forms a purple-brown precipitate with oxine, extractable into amyl acetate at pH < 8 (H 17).
Pu (VI)	Plutonium (VI) forms with oxine at pH 4–8 an orange-brown precipitate which can be extracted into amyl acetate (H 17).
Rh (III)	Rhodium (III) forms a yellow precipitate with oxine when heated to 90–100°C which can be completely extracted by chloroform at pH 6–9. The chelate absorbs at 425 mμ (J 3).
Ru (III)	More than 92% of ruthenium (III) can be extracted by 5–15% oxine in chloroform at pH 6·4 (J 3, S 14). The last traces of ruthenium remaining in aqueous phase can be extracted by a mixture of butylcellosolve and chloroform. The chelate has maximum absorbancy at 410 and 570 mμ (S 14).
Sc (III)	Scandium (III) was found to be precipitated in the presence of oxine as a complex ScA$_3$HA (P 46, P 47) and it is also extracted in this form into chloroform (S 106). By using 0·10 M oxine in chloroform, scandium is quantitatively extracted at pH 4·5–10 ($\mathrm{pH}_{1/2} = 3·57$; $\log K = -6·64$) (S 106). With less concentrated solutions (0·002 M oxine), quantitative extraction of scandium was observed in a narrower pH region, viz. 9·7–10·5 (U 4). The scandium oxinate absorbs at 380 mμ ($\varepsilon = 6400$) (H 1, U 4).
Sm (III)	At pH 6–8·5 samarium is quantitatively extracted ($\log p_N = 2·45$) by 0·50 M oxine in chloroform ($\mathrm{pH}_{1/2} = 5·0$; $\log K = -13·31$) (D 28). The chelate absorbs at 370 mμ ($\varepsilon = 6120$) (H 1).
Sn (IV)	At pH 2·5–5·5 tin (IV) can be completely extracted with 0·07 M oxine in chloroform after two minutes' shaking (G 12). Although Teicher and Gordon (T 23) reported they could not reproduce the above experiments, very selective extraction of tin (IV)-oxinate with chloroform was obtained from diluted sulphuric acid (pH = 0·85 ± 0·10) in the presence of halide

TABLE 12 (*continued*)

Metal	Optimum conditions for extraction
Sn (IV) (*cont.*)	(E 1). Extraction by oxine has been used for the isolation and determination of tin in iron and steel (W 4).
Sr (II)	Strontium can be quantitatively extracted by 0·5 M oxine in chloroform at pH > 11·5 as a complex $SrA_2(HA)_2$. $pH_{1/2} = 10·46$, (S 106); $\log K = -19·71$ (S 106), $-20·0$ (D 32). The chelate absorbs at 380–400 $m\mu$ (S 106).
Ta (V)	Only a few per cent of tantalum (V) was found to be extracted at pH 0–7 when using 0·07–0·28 M oxine in chloroform (A 13, K 62). Isoamyl alcohol and other oxygen-containing solvents are more suitable for the extraction of tantalum (V) oxinate (A 13).
Tb (III)	At pH higher than 7 almost complete extraction of terbium occurs when using 0·10 M oxine in chloroform (R 28).
Th (IV)	Quantitative extraction of thorium ($\log p_N = 2·39$) by 0·10 M oxine in chloroform occurs in the pH range 4–10 (D 27, S 106). $pH_{1/2} = 3·1$ (D 27), $\log K = -7·12$ (D 27); $pH_{1/2} = 2·91$ (S 106), $\log K = -7·18$ (S 106). Methylisobutylketone can also be used as a suitable solvent for thorium oxinate (D 27). The absorbancy of the thorium chelate at 380 $m\mu$ apparently does not obey Beer's law (M 81).
Ti (IV)	Titanium (IV) is completely extracted as $TiOA_2$ by 0·10 M oxine in chloroform at pH 2·5–9·0 ($pH_{1/2} = 0·9$, $\log K = -0·90$) (S 106, T 46). The complex absorbs at 380 $m\mu$ (T 46). In the presence of hydrogen peroxide ($\sim 1\%$) quantitative extraction of titanium by 0·07 M oxine in chloroform has been observed at pH 3–5. Titanium is practically not extracted at pH > 8 (G 5, H 18). The complex absorbs at 425 $m\mu$ (M 110, M 113).
Tl (I)	About 60% of thallium (I) can be extracted at pH 12 by 0·05 M oxine in chloroform ($pH_{1/2} = 11·5$). When using isobutyl alcohol approximately 85% of thallium is extracted under the above conditions. Other solvents (methylethylketone, carbon tetrachloride or diethyl ether) are less effective (B 13).
Tl (III)	Quantitative extraction of thallium (III) by 0·01 M oxine in chloroform takes place in the pH range 3·5–11·5 ($pH_{1/2} = 2·05$, $\log K = 5$) (S 106). With less concentrated solutions only 86–98% thallium can be extracted (M 76). Thallium (III) oxinate absorbs at 400 $m\mu$ (M 76).
U (VI)	Uranium (VI) can be quantitatively extracted as the additive complex UO_2A_2HA by 0·10 M oxine in chloroform at pH 5–9 (A 32, B 95, D 28, H 30, S 106) ($pH_{1/2} = 2·6$, $\log K = -1·60$) (D 28, S 106). Methylisobutylketone can also be used as a suitable solvent for the extraction of the uranium chelate (C 30, C 32, D 28). The complex absorbs at 425–430 $m\mu$ (R 30, M 113, S 106). Many interfering ions can be masked by ethylenediaminetetraacetic acid or by 1,2-diaminocyclohexanetetraacetic acid, which form only relatively very weak chelates with uranium (VI) (C 30, S 106).

TABLE 12 (*continued*)

Metal	Optimum conditions for extraction
U (VI) (*cont.*)	In the presence of dimethyldioctylammonium chloride, uranium can be extracted as $[R_4N]^+[UO_2A_3]^-$ with methylisobutylketone (C 32). Extraction by oxine has been used for the isolation and/or determination of uranium in ores after preliminary extraction by tri-n-butylphosphate (M 121), in iron (S 76), or in irradiated thorium (C 30).
V (V)	At pH 2–6 vanadium (V) is quantitatively extracted by 0·10 M oxine in chloroform as a complex VO_2A ($pH_{1/2} = 0·88$, $\log K = 1·67$) (S 106). Vanadium is practically not extracted above pH 9 because the nonextractable anion VO_3 is formed. When using less concentrated solution of oxine (0·003–0·07 M) the pH region for quantitative extraction is narrower (pH 2·3–3·3) (O 5, T 17, T 18). Carbon tetrachloride, benzene, amyl alcohol, amyl acetate and other solvents have also been recommended as suitable solvents (A 41, B 9, N 2, O 5, S 134, S 136). Solutions of the vanadium (V)-oxinate in chloroform absorb at 380 mμ and 580 mμ (N 1, O 5, S 106, T 17). The latter wavelength can be used for the selective determination of vanadium in alkali brines (B 10), in water (N 2, S 137), in rocks (S 6, V 5), or in oils (N 1).
W (VI)	More than 99% of tungsten (VI) can be extracted at pH 2·5–3·5 when using 0·01–0·14 M oxine in chloroform in the presence of 0·01 M EDTA (A 36, S 106). At pH > 7 tungsten is practically not extracted by oxine in chloroform (A 36).
Y (III)	Yttrium can be practically completely extracted at pH 7–10 by 0·20 M oxine in chloroform ($pH_{1/2} \sim 5$) (R 22). With 0·5 M oxine in chloroform complete extraction of yttrium takes place in the pH region 5·5–7 (P 1, P 2). Solutions of yttrium oxinate in the organic phase can be determined spectrophotometrically at 380 mμ (H 1) or fluorometrically (I 34). Extraction with oxine has been used for the separation of carrier-free ^{90}Y from ^{90}Sr (R 22, R 27).
Yb (III)	Quantitative extraction of ytterbium by 0·10 M oxine in chloroform takes place at pH > 8 (R 28).
Zn (II)	Zinc can be quantitatively extracted by 0·10 M oxine in chloroform as the complex $ZnA_2(HA)_2$ in the pH region 4–5 ($pH_{1/2} = 3·3$, $\log K = -2·4$). At higher pH values the chelate is quickly destroyed on shaking, probably by formation of the non-extractable complex $ZnA_2.2H_2O$ (S 106). The chelate absorbs at 380–400 mμ (M 42, S 106). In the presence of n-butylamine (0·08% solution) zinc is found to be completely extracted by 0·001 M oxine in chloroform at pH 10–11 as a complex $ZnA_2 \cdot H_2O \cdot C_4H_9NH_2$ of molar extinction coefficient 5210 at 370 mμ (U 7). Isobutylmethylketone has also been recommended as a suitable solvent for zinc oxinate (K 3).
Zr (IV)	Zirconium (IV) is quantitatively extracted by 0·10 M oxine in chloroform as a complex $ZrOA_2$ at pH 1·5–4·0 ($pH_{1/2} = 1·01$, $\log K = 2·71$) (S 106). At higher pH the extraction is less. The zirconium chelate absorbs strongly at 385 mμ ($\varepsilon = 1·4 \times 10^4$) (M 120).

authors (H 29, F 25, G 12, M 75, M 110, M 113, S 106). The effect of pH on the extraction of many metals by solutions of oxine in chloroform is shown in Figs. 32–37.

5.3.2. 8-*Hydroxyquinaldine* (2-*methyl-8-hydroxyquinoline*)

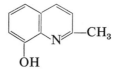

8-Hydroxyquinoline (M.Wt. 159·17, M.p. 74°C), called methyloxine (HMOx) for short, can be recrystallized from alcohol as prisms. It is sparingly

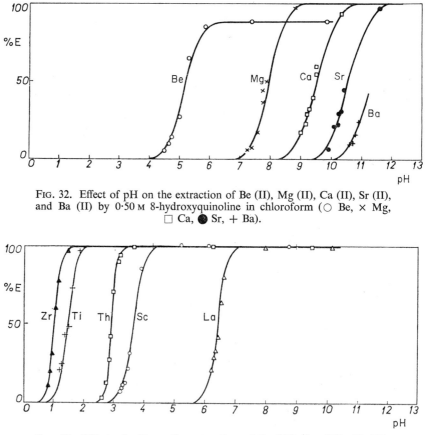

FIG. 32. Effect of pH on the extraction of Be (II), Mg (II), Ca (II), Sr (II), and Ba (II) by 0·50 M 8-hydroxyquinoline in chloroform (○ Be, × Mg, □ Ca, ● Sr, + Ba).

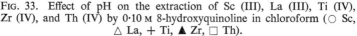

FIG. 33. Effect of pH on the extraction of Sc (III), La (III), Ti (IV), Zr (IV), and Th (IV) by 0·10 M 8-hydroxyquinoline in chloroform (○ Sc, △ La, + Ti, ▲ Zr, □ Th).

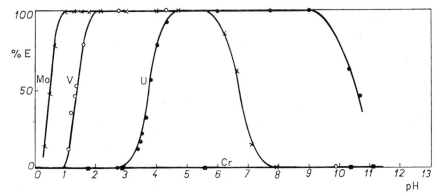

FIG. 34. Effect of pH on the extraction of V (V), Cr (III), Mo (VI), and U (VI) by 0·01 M 8-hydroxyquinoline in chloroform (○ V, ■ Cr, × Mo, ● U).

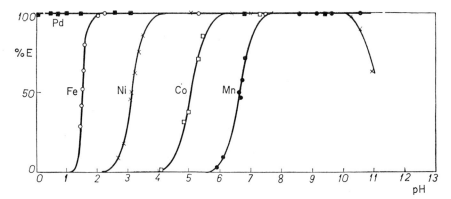

FIG. 35. Effect of pH on the extraction of Mn (II), Fe (III), Co (II), Ni (II), and Pd (II) by 0·01 M 8-hydroxyquinoline in chloroform (● Mn, ○ Fe, □ Co, × Ni, ■ Pd).

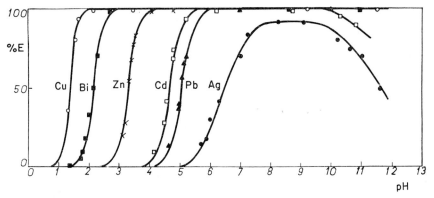

FIG. 36. Effect of pH on the extraction of Cu (II), Ag (I), Zn (II), Cd (II), Pb (II), and Bi (III) by 0·10 M 8-hydroxyquinoline in chloroform (○ Cu, ● Ag, × Zn, □ Cd, ▲ Pb, ■ Bi).

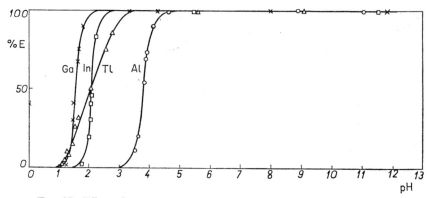

Fig. 37. Effect of pH on the extraction of Al (III), Ga (III), In (III), and Tl (III) by 0·01 M 8-hydroxyquinoline in chloroform (○ Al, × Ga, □ In, △ Tl).

soluble in water but it dissolves in diethyl ether, chloroform, benzene, or dilute alkalis.

In aqueous solutions HMOx is a weak acid with dissociation constants $pK_{HA} = 10·04$ and $pK_{H_2A} = 5·77$ (D 38).

The partition coefficient of the neutral compound between chloroform and water at 25°C (log $p_{HA} = 3·4$) is somewhat higher than that of oxine (D 38).

The reagent is similar to oxine in its analytical properties but seems to be more selective. It is especially noteworthy that HMOx does not precipitate and extract aluminium (B 80, M 51). This fact has been used for removing many metals which obviously interfere in the determination of aluminium.

In general it may be expected (see Section 3) that the pH range of complete extraction of metal-methyloxinates as well as their extraction constants will not differ greatly from that of oxinates, but only few data are available (see Table 13).

Systematic study of the extraction of methyloxinates has been carried out by Motojima and Hashitani (M 113).

5.3.3. 5-Methyl-8-hydroxyquinoline

5-Methyl-8-hydroxyquinoline has been examined for the extraction of thorium. The extraction constant using chloroform as organic solvent was found to be equal to 10^{-10} (log $K = -10·0$) (D 38).

TABLE 13. A SURVEY OF EXTRACTION DATA FOR METAL-METHYLOXINATES

Metal	Optimum conditions for extraction†
Be (II)	Beryllium methyloxinate can be quantitatively extracted with chloroform at pH 7·5–8·5 and determined spectrophotometrically at 380 mμ. Many interfering metals can be removed by a preliminary extraction with oxine at pH 4·5–5 or by mercury cathode electrolysis. Such metals as copper, cadmium, iron (II), nickel and zinc can be masked by cyanide (M 104, M 113). The chloroform extract shows a strong fluorescence and it was found possible to determine 0·3–3 μg of beryllium in 40 ml of solution (M 105, M 115).
Bi (III)	Bismuth forms a precipitate with HMOx which can be extracted at pH $\sim$ 10 into chloroform (R 15).
Cd (II)	Cadmium (II)-methyloxinate can be extracted at pH 10 into chloroform (R 15).
Ce	In the presence of malic acid as a masking agent cerium forms a chelate with HMOx which can be readily extracted at pH $\geqslant$ 10 with carbon tetrachloride and determined at 485 mμ. Iron interferes and must be removed (M 70).
Co (II)	Cobalt (II) can be extracted as a methyloxinate at pH 10 with chloroform (R 15).
Cr (III)	At pH 5·3–9·5 chromium (III) forms with the reagent a precipitate which can be extracted into chloroform and determined at 410 mμ. The content of chromium in uranium has been determined in this way (M 118).
Cu (II)	Quantitative extraction of copper (II)-methyloxinate with chloroform occurs in the pH range 4·2 to 12·5. The maximum absorbancy of the chelate is at 395 mμ (B 64, M 113).
Fe (III)	The iron (III) chelate with the reagent can be extracted with chloroform from a solution of pH 4·5–12·2. The chelate absorbs at 470 and 580 mμ (M 113).
Ga (III)	At pH 5·5–9 gallium (III) forms with the reagent a precipitate extractable into chloroform. Gallium can be determined in the organic extract spectrophotometrically at 380 mμ (M 113), or fluorometrically (S 61, N 18, N 19).
In (III)	Indium (III)-methyloxinate can be extracted at pH 4·6–13 into chloroform (M 113). Benzene has also been recommended as a suitable solvent (I 34).
Mn (II)	The manganese chelate with HMOx can be extracted into chloroform. The complex absorbs at 395 mμ and the content of manganese in uranium and aluminium has been determined in this way (M 121).
Mo (VI)	Molybdenum (VI)-methyloxinate can be extracted with chloroform only in a narrow pH region (3·5–4·5). The complex absorbs at 380 mμ (M 113).

TABLE 13 (*continued*)

Metal	Optimum conditions for extraction†
Ni (II)	Nickel (II) forms a precipitate with HMOx which can be extracted with chloroform in the pH region 8·5–10·7. Maximum absorbancy of the chelate in the organic phase appears to be at 372 mμ (M 113).
Pb (II)	Lead can be determined spectrophotometrically at 385 mμ after extraction as its chelate with HMOx at pH 8·2–11·8 using chloroform as the organic solvent (M 113).
Ti (IV)	Extraction of titanium (IV)-methyloxinate seems to be almost complete over a pH range from 5·0 to 9·3. The absorbancy at 380 mμ is constant in the pH range from 5·0 to 6·0 (M 106, M 107, M 119).
Tl (III)	With excess of the reagent thallium (III) forms a precipitate extractable by chloroform at pH > 4. The complex absorbs at 380 mμ (M 113).
V (V)	The maximum extractability of the vanadium (V) chelate with HMOx occurs at pH 4–4·8 (M 113).

† In general, the extraction procedures were carried out as follows: to 50 ml of aqueous phase, containing the desired metal, 3·0 ml of 1% HMOx solution was added. After adjusting the pH the aqueous phase was equilibrated with 10·0 ml of chloroform (M 113).

5.3.4. *5,7-Dichloro-8-hydroxyquinoline*

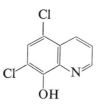

5,7-Dichloro-8-hydroxyquinoline (M.Wt. 214·05, M.p. 179–180°C), called chloroxine for short, forms needle-like crystals from alcohol. It is soluble in alkali ($pK_{HA} = 7·47$) and in acids ($pK_{H_2A} = 2·89$), forming yellow solutions. Chloroform, benzene, or other solvents readily dissolved this reagent (D 36).

The partition coefficient of chloroxine is higher ($\log p_{HA} = 3·8$) than that of oxine (see Appendix) and for this reason it extracts some metals (e.g. rare earths (M 77)) more completely than the parent compound.

In aqueous solution chloroxine is a stronger acid than oxine itself (see Appendix) and the extraction of metal chloroxinates occurs in general in a a more acidic medium than that of metal oxinates.

A solution in chloroform has been used for the extraction of thorium (log $K = -0.88$), uranium (VI) (log $K = -1.26$), and lanthanum (log $K = -13.44$) (D 36).

Gallium and indium can be quantitatively extracted as chloroxinates from slightly acid medium (G 21, M 82, N 19). The gallium and indium chloroxinates in the organic phase absorb strongly at 409 mμ ($\varepsilon = 2540$) and at 412 mμ ($\varepsilon = 2380$) respectively (G 12, M 82). By using solutions of chloroxine in chloroform the extraction of neodymium and erbium was found to be complete at pH 9.4 and 8.3 respectively (M 77).

5.3.5. 5,7-*Dibromo-8-hydroxyquinoline* (*bromoxine*)

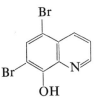

5,7-Dibromo-8-hydroxyquinoline (M.Wt. 302·97, M.p. 196°C), called bromoxine for short, has been used for the extraction of tin (IV) from diluted hydrochloric acid (pH $\sim$ 1) using isobutanol as solvent. The chelate absorbs at 410 mμ (R 29).

Indium and gallium can be extracted with chloroform from slightly acid medium as bromoxinates and determined spectrophotometrically at 410 mμ and 413 mμ respectively (J 12, L 4, M 82). This method has been used for the determination of indium in silicate rocks (M 68). Also uranium (VI) can be determined spectrophotometrically at 420 mμ after extraction as uranium (VI)-bromoxinate (R 30). By using benzene as solvent titanium can be extracted from dilute hydrochloric acid as a bromoxinate (K 81).

5.3.6. 5,7-*Diiodo-8-hydroxyquinoline*

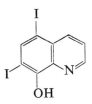

Saturated solutions of the reagent in chloroform extract gallium and indium at pH $\sim$ 4. The chelates absorb at 415 mμ and 416 mμ respectively (G 21, K 81).

5.3.7. *Tributylammonium salt of 7-iodo-8-hydroxyquinoline-5-sulphonic acid (tri-butylammonium salt of ferron)*

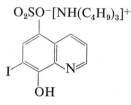

$$O_2SO^-[NH(C_4H_9)_3]^+$$

The extraction of the iron (III) chelate with ferron was studied by Ziegler and co-workers (Z 10–13).

As shown in the introduction, the presence of a sulphonic acid group conveys water solubility; but the above authors utilize ion association with tributylamine to obtain a species readily extractable into isoamyl alcohol. The extraction is constant over the pH range 2·5–7·5 and the absorbancy at $\lambda_{max} = 610$ mμ can be used for the determination of up to 150 μg of iron. Interfering ions can be masked by cyanide and/or by citrate.

This method has been used for the determination of iron in high purity aluminium and zinc.

5.3.8. *7-[α-(o-carbomethoxyanilino)-benzyl]-8-hydroxyquinoline*

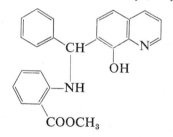

The reagent forms white to yellow, flat crystals, M.p. 133–134°C, readily soluble in chloroform, benzene, and other solvents (U 9). It does not react with ter- and tetra-valent metal ions (steric hindrance), but only with divalent.

The following $pH_{1/2}$ values for the extraction of divalent cations by a 1·0 M reagent solution in chloroform were determined by Umland and Meckenstock (U 9); cadmium, 6·3; cobalt, 3·4; copper, −1·5; mercury, 2·3; magnesium, 8·8; manganese, 5·8; nickel, 4·0; lead, 4·2; zinc, 3·8.

Solutions of the chelates in the chloroform phase absorb strongly at about 380 mμ, so that the spectrophotometric determination of cadmium ($\varepsilon = 6950$), copper ($\varepsilon = 6400$), magnesium ($\varepsilon = 6400$), mercury ($\varepsilon = 4600$), and zinc ($\varepsilon = 7300$) can be carried out (U 9).

The same reagent has been used for the determination of magnesium in minerals (U 10). By using a 0·01 M solution in chloroform magnesium was extracted at pH 12·6 in the presence of tartrates. Cyanide constitutes a suitable masking agent (U 10).

5.3.9. *Other derivatives of 8-hydroxyquinoline*

5-Nitroso-8-hydroxyquinoline

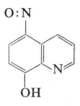

A saturated solution of the reagent in chloroform reacts with gallium at pH 5·0–5·3 to give a yellow complex soluble in organic solvents (G 21).

5,7-Dinitro-8-hydroxyquinoline

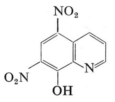

Zirconium can be partially extracted at pH 1–6 by a 0·002 M solution in cyclohexane. In the presence of lactic acid or of acetylacetone the formation of polymeric hydroxy complexes is avoided and the extraction of zirconium is increased (K 86, K 87).

7-(1-piperidylmethyl)-8-hydroxyquinoline

The reagent forms a complex with indium, extractable with chloroform at pH 9–11·5 (P 35).

8-Hydroxycinnoline

Irving (I 22) found that the following metals can be extracted as metal-8-hydroxycinnolinates (the pH region is given in brackets): cadmium (8–12), copper (5–8), cobalt (5–8), gallium (5), indium (5–12), lanthanum (5), nickel (5–12), palladium (5–12), platinum (5–8), thorium (5–8), and zinc (5–12).

8-Hydroxyquinazoline

The following metals were found to be extracted as 8-hydroxyquinazo, linates with chloroform at pH 5–8: cadmium, cobalt, copper (I) and (II), iron (II), gallium, indium, palladium, nickel, and zinc (I 22).

8-Hydroxy-2,4-dimethylquinazoline

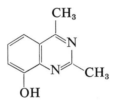

In the pH region from 5–8, silver, copper (I), gallium, indium, rhodium, and zinc can be extracted as complexes with the above reagent. Furthermore, at pH = 5 the extraction of irridium, nickel, and palladium occurs and at pH = 8 manganese can be also extracted (I 22).

1-Hydroxyacridine (neooxine)

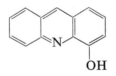

Pure 1-hydroxyacridine is obtained as brownish-yellow needles, slightly soluble in water, but easily soluble in organic solvents such as chloroform.

The dissociation constants of 1-hydroxyacridine (see Appendix) do not differ from those of 8-hydroxyquinoline itself. It is apparent, however, that the permissible pH ranges for metal extraction are narrower than for the oxinates.

1-Hydroxyacridine has been used for the quantitative extraction of copper, nickel, cobalt, and zinc (I 38).

5.4. OXIMES

The oximino group C=N—OH exists in two tautomeric forms:

oxime form   nitrone form

The hydrogen atom of the nitrone form can be replaced by an equivalent of a metal. In order to form a chelate ring the molecule of the oxime must contain another group that is an electron donor as, for example, in the oxime group of dioximes, or one in which the hydrogen atom can also be replaced by a metal, as in acyloin oximes or hydroxyoximes, etc.

The most important organic reagents of this group are dimethylglyoxime, α-furildioxime, benzoinoxime, and salicylaldoxime.

5.4.1. *Dimethylglyoxime*

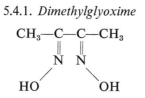

Dimethylglyoxime (M.Wt. 116·12), H_2Dx, is a white crystalline solid. It melts at 238°C with decomposition. The reagent grade should be free from objectional coloured impurities and should sublime on gentle heating without leaving a residue.

The solubility of H_2Dx in water is low and only 0·5 g dissolves in 1 litre of water (5×10^{-3} M solution); the solubility in ammonia is somewhat greater (S 130). Its solubility in chloroform ($3·6 \times 10^{-4}$ M), in toluene ($3·3 \times 10^{-4}$ M) and in xylene (3×10^{-4} M) is also low, but it dissolves to a greater extent in n-butylalcohol ($5·6 \times 10^{-2}$ M) or in isoamyl alcohol ($4·5 \times 10^{-2}$ M) (B 4).

In aqueous solution dimethylglyoxime is a very weak acid with $pK_{HA} = 10·6$ (S 14).

Dimethylglyoxime is preferred for the selective separation and determination of nickel and palladium. Platinum (II) (Y 14) and traces of copper (II) and cobalt† can also be extracted as dimethylglyoximates (S 14).

Nickel. Nickel (II) dimethylglyoximate is slightly soluble in chloroform ($4·8 \times 10^{-4}$ M) and other solvents immiscible with water. Since the solubility of this chelate is less in water ($1·2 \times 10^{-6}$ M), small amounts of nickel

† Cobalt (II) forms a brown water-soluble complex with H_2Dx which is scarcely extracted by chloroform.

can be effectively extracted in this way. The partition coefficient p_N equals 400 (I 46, S 14). The extraction coefficient defined as:

$$K_{ex} = [Ni(HDx)_2]_{CHCl_3}[H^+]^2/[Ni^{2+}][H_2Dx]^2 = 6 \times 10^{-2}$$

can be used for the determination of the distribution ratio of nickel (S 14). At pH > 5, with the aqueous phase saturated with H_2Dx, nickel is practically completely extracted (>99.7 per cent) by chloroform (S 8, S 14, S 19).

The extraction of nickel is usually made from slightly basic solutions (ammoniacal solutions of pH 7–12) in the presence of 1 per cent tartrate or citrate (C 22, N 15) to avoid interference caused by the hydrolysis of tervalent or tetravalent metals. In the presence of manganese plenty of hydroxylamine hydrochloride must be added (O 1, O 2); copper can be masked by thiosulphate (N 14). Traces of cobalt extracted simultaneously with nickel can be removed by washing with diluted ammonia (0.5 M) (S 14), but larger amounts of cobalt must be removed by a preliminary extraction as thiocyanate (H 10). The optimum wavelength for the photometric determination is found to be 366–380 mμ (K 43, N 11, N 13).

A mixture of benzene and amyl alcohol can also be used as the solvent for the extraction of nickel (II)-dimethylglyoximate (C 18). Extraction with dimethylglyoxime has been used for the isolation and/or determination of nickel in copper (N 14), iron and its compounds (N 15, O 2), cadmium (H 27), uranium (S 148), alkali metal halides of high purity (B 66), in silicate rocks and ores (S 8, C 18), and in biological materials and food (S 8, A 12), etc.

Palladium. Palladium (II)-dimethylglyoximate can be quantitatively extracted with chloroform from 0.2–0.3 M hydrochloric acid or from 1 N sulphuric acid (Y 14). Its solubility is 6.4×10^{-4} M and 2.1×10^{-6} M in chloroform and water respectively, so that the partition coefficient, p_N, is 300 (S 14). The complex absorbs at 366 mμ (N 12).

Extraction with H_2Dx has been used for the separation of palladium from gold and platinum which are not extracted under the conditions employed (N 12), and for the isolation of carrier-free palladium from a rhodium target (S 64).

5.4.2. α-Benzildioxime

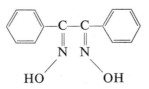

α-Benzildioxime (M.Wt. 240.25) consists of white microcrystalline leaflets which melt at 235–237°C with decomposition. The reagent is almost insoluble in water and is only slightly soluble in alcohol. It dissolves readily in sodium hydroxide and in acetone (W 7).

The reagent permits the spectrophotometric determination of nickel at 275 mμ ($\varepsilon = 5{\cdot}0 \times 10^4$) or at 406 m$\mu$ ($\varepsilon = 1{\cdot}2 \times 10^4$) after extraction as benzildioximate into chloroform at pH 6·0–11·4 (P 24, U 12). When the absorbancy is measured at 275 mμ excess reagent must be removed by washing the extract with alkali. This method has been used for the determination of traces of nickel in high purity indium (P 24).

Palladium (II) can be extracted as benzildioximate with chloroform at pH 2–6. The chelate absorbs at 325 mμ ($\varepsilon = 19{,}600$) (P 60). In the presence of stannous chloride partially reduced rhenium (VII) forms with the reagent in warm 5–9 M sulphuric acid a precipitate which can be extracted into iso-amyl alcohol (T 39).

5.4.3. α-Furildioxime

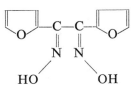

α-Furildioxime (M.Wt. 220·18) consists of white needle-like crystals which melt at 166–168°C. It is very soluble in alcohol and ether.

α-Furildioxime is superior to dimethylglyoxime for the determination both of nickel and palladium, because the wavelength of maximum absorbancy of the nickel- and palladium-furildioximates lies in the visible region (G 3, T 22).

Copper-furildioximate is quantitatively extracted by chloroform but the reaction is rather slow. Maximum absorbancy of the extracted chelate is at 465 mμ (P 13).

Cobalt (II) forms a precipitate with the reagent extractable into chloroform or benzene (P 13).

With excess of the reagent nickel forms an insoluble chelate which is quantitatively extracted by chloroform in the pH range 8·5–9·4 (P 13). This extraction is very selective because cobalt and copper can be backwashed from the organic extract with dilute (1:40) ammonia. The interference of aluminium, indium, and other easily hydrolysed metals can be eliminated by masking with tartrate or citrate (P 13, P 20). The chelate absorbs at 435 mμ ($\varepsilon = 1{\cdot}9 \times 10^4$) (P 24, T 22).

Benzene (P 13), dichlorbenzene (G 3), diethyl ether, or ethyl acetate can also be used as suitable solvents for the nickel chelate (G 3).

The furildioxime method has been used for the determination of nickel in pure aluminium and indium (P 20), and in steel and magnesium alloys (G 3).

Palladium (II) forms with the excess of the reagent a yellow-coloured chelate which is readily extractable into chloroform (M 48, P 22). This extraction procedure is highly selective; platinum group metals and gold do not interfere.

The absorbancy of the chelate can be measured at 380 mμ (M 48) or at 436 mμ ($\varepsilon = 2000$) (P 22).

Benzene, carbon tetrachloride, or isoamyl alcohol can also be used as organic solvents (P 22).

The complex of rhenium with the reagent can be quantitatively extracted from 0·5–1·5 M hydrochloric acid in the presence of stannous chloride by 2–3 portions of chloroform or isoamyl alcohol (P 23).

5.4.4. 1,2-Cyclohexanedionedioxime (nioxime)

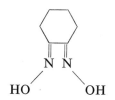

Cyclohexanedionedioxime (M.Wt. 142·14) is a white crystalline compound which melts at 187–188°C.

The reagent has been used for the separation and determination of micro amounts of nickel in the presence of large quantities of foreign cations using chloroform or benzene as organic solvents (M 84).

Palladium also can be determined spectrophotometrically as 280 mμ ($\varepsilon = 13,500$) after extraction of its cyclohexanedionedioximate into chloroform from aqueous solutions of pH from 0·5 to 6·0 (P 60).

The rhenium complex with the reagent absorbs strongly at 436 mμ ($\varepsilon = 68,900$) and at 465 mμ ($\varepsilon = 5800$) (K 10, P 15).

5.4.5. 4-Methyl-1,2-cyclohexanedionedioxime

The reagent reacts with palladium at pH 0·7–5·0 to give a precipitate soluble in chloroform. The chelate has its maximum absorbancy at 280 mμ ($\varepsilon = 1·51 \times 10^4$) (B 40).

Nickel can also be determined spectrophotometrically at 365 mμ ($\varepsilon = 3340$), using this reagent after the extraction of the nickel chelate into toluene from solutions of pH 5·0–5·5; thiogycollic acid has been used as a masking agent for copper (B 68).

5.4.6. 4-Isopropyl-1,2-cyclohexanedionedioxime

The reagent forms with nickel at pH 7–8 (1 M acetate solution) a chelate which can be extracted with various organic solvents such as chloroform, carbon tetrachloride, benzene, toluene, or xylene. Xylene was found to be the most suitable. The chelate absorbs at 383 mμ (M 3).

Iron (II), cobalt, and copper interfere and must be masked. Iron can be masked by fluoride ions, copper by slightly acidic solutions of thioacetamide (M 3).

The above method was used for the determination of nickel in water, lithium chloride, sodium chloride, potassium chloride, reagent grade hydrochloric acid, etc. (M 3).

5.4.7. 1,2-Cycloheptanedionedioxime (heptoxime)

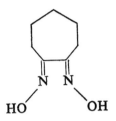

The reagent forms with nickel at pH 3·8–11·7 an orange–red complex extractable into chloroform. Maximum absorbancy was observed at 377 mμ (G 14, P 29).

Only cobalt, copper, and iron (II) give coloured extractable heptoximates. The interference of copper and cobalt in amounts a hundred times that of nickel can be prevented by the use of thiosulphate (P 29). Iron, after oxidation to tervalent state, does not interfere even in the ratio 1000 Fe:1 Ni (P 29).

5.4.8. N,N'-Ethylendi-(4-methoxy-1,2-benzoquinone-1-oxime-2-imine)

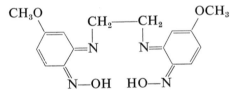

With cobalt (II), iron (II), and palladium (II) the reagent forms extractable chelates in the pH range 2–7 (M 35–38).

5.4.9. Quinoline-5,8-quinone-dioxime

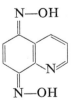

Like other dioximes, the reagent forms extractable chelates with cobalt (II), nickel (II), and palladium (II) (G 22).

5.4.10. α-Benzoinoxime (*cupron*)

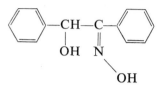

α-Benzoinoxime (M.Wt. 227·25) consists of white crystals which darken on exposure to light. It melts at 149–151°C. The reagent is only slightly soluble in water but dissolves readily in alcohol and aqueous ammonia.

A survey of extraction data for some metals investigated is given in Table 14.

TABLE 14. A SURVEY OF EXTRACTION DATA FOR SOME METALS

Metal	Optimum conditions for extraction
Cr (VI)	Chromium (VI) in acid solutions strongly oxidizes the reagent so that only 1% of chromium can be extracted from 5% hydrochloric acid when using a 0·1% solution of the reagent in chloroform (H 28).
Cu (II)	A green copper chelate with the reagent can be extracted with chloroform from alkaline tartrate solution. The chelate absorbs at 440 mμ (D 20, N 4, M 10). This method has been used for the determination of copper in ferrous alloys (D 20, N 4) or in molybdenum (M 10).
Mo (VI)	More than 98% of molybdenum (VI) can be extracted from 1 M hydrochloric acid with a 0·1% solution of cupron in chloroform after 3 minutes' shaking (G 15, H 28, P 33). By adding fluoride which forms stable complexes with zirconium and niobium, the extraction of both elements is reduced (P 33). Tungsten (VI) (about 40–50%) and technetium (about 5%) are also extracted under these conditions (W 32). Ethyl acetate can also be used as a suitable organic solvent. Cupron has been used for the separation of molybdenum present in steel (H 28) or for separation of [99]Mo from mixed fission products (M 13).
V (V)	Vanadium (V) can be quantitatively extracted at pH 2·2 with several portions of a 0·1% solution of cupron in chloroform (H 28).
(WVI)	Traces of tungsten can be completely extracted from 2 M hydrochloric acid with several portions of 0·25% cupron in chloroform (P 32, P 33, O 3). Greater amounts of tungsten cannot be extracted because of the limited solubility in organic solvents (H 28). Ethyl acetate can also be used as a suitable solvent (M 12). Extraction with cupron has been used for the determination of small amounts of tungsten in steel (P 32).

5.4.11. *Salicylaldoxime*

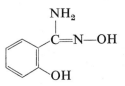

Salicylaldoxime is a white crystalline solid (M.Wt. 137·13) which melts at 57°C. It is only slightly soluble in water but dissolves readily in diethyl ether, benzene, and other organic solvents.

A survey of extraction data for salicylaldoximates is given in Table 15.

5.4.12. *Salicylamidoxime*

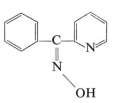

Salicylamidoxime forms a yellow chelate with titanium extractable with isobutanol from an acetate buffer of pH 4·5–7·0. The absorbancy at 400 mμ obeys Beer's law (B 19).

5.4.13. *Phenyl-α-pyridyl ketoxime*

Phenyl-α-pyridyl ketoxime is a white crystalline substance melting at 161°C. The reagent forms coloured precipitates with cobalt (II), copper (II), iron (II), gold (III), nickel (II), and palladium (II) which can be extracted with chloroform (S 43–45).

The reagent has been recommended for the selective determination of palladium (II) (S 43). The palladium complex with the reagent can be completely extracted with 2–3 successive portions of chloroform from aqueous solutions of pH 5–11 and determined by measuring the absorbancy at 410 mμ ($\varepsilon = 3 \times 10^4$). In the presence of EDTA as masking agent only gold interferes (S 43, S 44).

Gold (III) can be selectively determined by extraction of its complex with the reagent into chloroform from aqueous solutions of pH 3–6. EDTA is a

TABLE 15. A SURVEY OF EXTRACTION DATA FOR SALICYLALDOXIMATES

Metal	Optimum conditions for extraction
Ag (I)	Silver forms with the reagent a yellow complex extractable into chloroform (G 25).
Bi (III)	A yellow complex of bismuth with the reagent can be extracted into chloroform (G 25).
Cd (II)	Cadmium can be extracted as a yellow salicylaldoximate into chloroform (G 25).
Co (II)	Cobalt forms with the reagent a brown complex extractable into chloroform (G 25).
Cu (II)	Complete extraction of copper in the pH range 3·5–9·5 can be obtained by using 0·02 M solution of the reagent in n-amyl acetate. The extract exhibits an absorption maximum at 344 mμ which is suitable for the determination of copper (S 1). The method has been used in the analysis of copper in aluminium and zinc-base alloys. Nickel and other metals commonly occurring in these alloys do not interfere below pH 5 (S 1).
Fe (II)	A red-violet complex with the reagent can be extracted into chloroform (G 25).
Mn (II)	Manganese forms with the reagent a brown complex extractable into chloroform (G 25).
Mo (VI)	A yellow molybdenum-salicylaldoximate can be extracted into chloroform (G 25).
Ni (II)	Nickel can be separated from most other elements by a single extraction from a mannitol–aqueous ammonia solution at pH 8·3–10·3 with a 1% solution of the reagent in methylisobutylketone (E 16).
Pb (II)	Lead (II) and salicylaldoxime form a yellow extractable complex (G 25).
Pd (II)	Maximum extractability of the palladium complex with the reagent when using chloroform, carbon tetrachloride, benzene, and other organic solvents can be obtained at pH 3–6 (P 14).
V (V)	A violet complex of vanadium (V) with the reagent can be extracted with chloroform (G 25).
Zn (II)	A yellow zinc (II)-salicylaldoximate can be extracted into chloroform (G 25).

suitable masking agent. The extract shows a very sharp absorption peak at 450 mμ (S 44).

Iron can be determined as a complex with the reagent at 560 mμ ($\varepsilon =$ 15,600) when isoamyl alcohol is used for the extraction. Iron has been determined in this way in strongly alkaline materials and in glass (T 41).

5.4.14. *Quinoline-2-aldoxime*

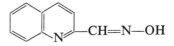

The reagent forms a chelate with copper (I) which can be extracted into isoamyl alcohol: it shows an absorption peak at 478 mμ (O 6).

5.4.15. *Monoxime of di-α-naphthylglyoxal*

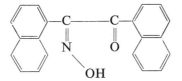

The reagent (M.p. 187–188°C) forms a precipitate with cobalt (II) at pH 5·0–8·5 which can be extracted with chloroform. The molar extinction coefficient at 436 mμ is 3·4 × 10⁴; at this wavelength the reagent is practically transparent (P 16).

The reagent has been used for the determination of cobalt in metallic nickel (P 16).

5.5. NITROSOPHENOLS

Reagents with the *o*-nitrosophenyl grouping form chelate compounds with many metal ions of which the cobalt, iron, and palladium complexes are of chief interest analytically. It is generally accepted that all reagents of this type form complexes with tervalent cobalt and the reagent also serves as oxidizing agent for the change Co (II) to Co (III).

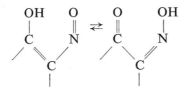

5.5.1. *o-Nitrosophenol*

The simplest reagent of this type is nitrosophenol (M.Wt. 123·11), which is generally used in the form of solutions in petroleum ether.

The reagent gives chelates soluble both in water and in organic solvents such as diethyl ether, but insoluble in petroleum ether with the following metals: copper (II) (red-violet); mercury (II) (red-violet); nickel (II) (red); and iron (II) (green) (C 51, C 52).

The chelates of palladium (II) (green), cobalt (III) (grey), and iron (III) (brown) are distinguished by their extractability by petroleum ether (C 51, C 52).

Methods for the determination of cobalt and iron have been worked out (C 51, C 52) but they appear to find little application (S 14).

5.5.2. o-Nitrosocresol

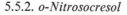
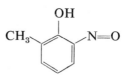

The reagent has been found more statisfactory than o-nitrosophenol, since it is more easily prepared and produces a more intensively coloured cobalt chelate which can be extracted into ligroin (E 9).

This method has been used for the determination of cobalt in biological materials (E 9).

5.5.3. 3-Methoxy-5-nitrosophenol (o-nitrosoresorcinol monomethyl ether)

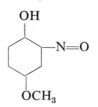

The reagent has been proposed as a colorimetric reagent for ferrous iron and cobalt. The insoluble red-brown complex of cobalt can be extracted at pH 1·5–10 (P 5, T 35, T 36) with benzene, carbon tetrachloride, and other solvents, and measured at 375–380 mμ (P 5). Iron (II) produces a water-soluble green complex with the reagent extractable into isoamyl alcohol or n-butyl alcohol (P 5, P 35, T 36). Maximum absorbancy occurs at 700–710 mμ (P 5).

5.5.4. Isonitrosoacetophenone

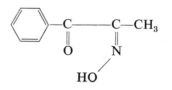

Isonitrosoacetophenone is a white crystalline solid (M.Wt. 149·14; M.p. 126–128°C) which is slightly soluble in water, but soluble in chloroform.

It forms chelates with cobalt (brown), copper (blue), cadmium (yellow), manganese (brown), mercury (yellow), iron and zinc (yellow) which can be extracted into chloroform (K 77).

5.5.5. 3-Nitrososalicylic acid

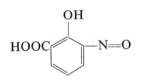

The reagent can be used like nitrosocresol for the determination of nickel in the presence of cobalt (P 12). The brown cobalt chelate is extracted by petroleum ether at pH 5·6–6, whereas nickel is left in the aqueous phase. Ferric ions (but not ferrous) and cupric ions interfere. Cobalt can be determined at 500–550 mμ; the reagent itself does not absorb at this wavelength (P 12).

5.5.6. 1-Nitroso-2-naphthol

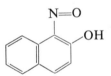

1-Nitroso-2-naphthol (M.Wt. 173·16; M.p. 108–110°C) consists of an orange-brown powder. It is only slightly soluble in water, but it is freely soluble in chloroform, benzene, methylisobutylketone, and other solvents (see Appendix).

The partition coefficient of the reagent between organic solvents and an aqueous phase is rather high (log p_{HA} = 2·97 and 2·55 for chloroform and methylisobutylketone respectively) (D 33).

In aqueous solution 1-nitroso-2-naphthol is a weak acid with pK_{HA} = 7·63 (D 33).

1-Nitroso-2-naphthol forms slightly soluble complexes with a number of metals, which can be extracted into organic solvents. The reagent itself has found its greatest application for determination of cobalt, with which it gives a selective reaction in consequence of the formation of a tervalent cobalt chelate.

A survey of extraction data for the 1-nitroso-2-naphtholates so far investigated is given in Table 16.

TABLE 16. A SURVEY OF EXTRACTION DATA FOR 1-NITROSO-2-NAPHTHOLATES

Metal	Optimum conditions for extraction
Co	The quantitative formation of the cobaltic complex with 1-nitroso-2-naphthol requires a weakly acid medium. Usually a citrate buffer (pH 2·5–5) is used, which prevents the precipitation of metal hydroxides and masks ferric iron so that it does not form an extractable chelate. The reaction is slow but it can be accelerated by heating (N 10); once formed, the complex is very stable to 1–2 N acids or alkali, cyanide, or EDTA (K 54, S 144). The strongly coloured complex can be completely extracted with chloroform (R 12, S 143), benzene (K 14, S 143), carbon tetrachloride (R 12, S 143), ethyl acetate (V 3) and other solvents (S 143). Suzuki (S 143) found that more than 98% of cobalt is extracted by a 1% solution of the reagent in carbon tetrachloride in the pH range 3·5–8. Other metals that are also extracted as nitrosonaphtholates can be back extracted with 2 M hydrochloric acid. The excess of reagent can be removed by washing with 2 M sodium hydroxide so that cobalt can be directly determined by measuring the absorbancy at 530 mμ. Iron (II) and tin (II) interfere and must be oxidized before extraction; palladium must be removed by a preliminary extraction with dithizone or dimethylglyoxime. 1-Nitroso-2-naphthol extraction has been used for the determination of cobalt in steel (K 14), in bismuth (N 7), and in alloys and ores (C 36).
Cu (II)	Copper forms with the reagent a dark brown complex extractable into chloroform, but it can be back extracted into 2 M hydrochloric acid (S 14, S 143).
Fe (II)	Ferrous iron reacts with the reagent in alkaline solution to give a green precipitate extractable into ethyl acetate (V 4). With isoamyl alcohol as solvent it was found that ferric iron after reduction with ascorbic acid can be extracted as a 1-nitroso-2-naphtholate at pH 7·5 ± 0·5 in the presence of tartrates (B 65). The complex absorbs at 680 mμ and at this wavelength cobalt and nickel do not interfere. The above method has been used for the determination of iron in high purity alkali metal halides and tartaric acid (B 65, B 66).
Fe (III)	A ferric complex with the reagent can be extracted at pH $\sim$ 1·5 by using chloroform as the organic solvent. Thus iron can be separated from aluminium and magnesium (B 5).
Ni (II)	Nickel can be partially extracted as a 1-nitroso-2-naphtholate with various solvents, but it can be stripped from the organic extract with 2 M hydrochloric acid (R 12).
Np (V)	More than 90% of neptunium (V) can be extracted by a 1% solution of the reagent in n-butyl alcohol or isoamyl alcohol at pH 9–11. If chloroform or benzene is used as a solvent, only a few per cent of neptunium (V) can be extracted (A 21, A 24).
Pd (II)	Palladium (II) gives a red extractable complex with the reagent (S 14).

TABLE 16 (*continued*)

Metal	Optimum conditions for extraction
Pu (IV)	Plutonium (IV) forms with the reagent a complex which can be extracted at pH $\sim$ 2 with methylisobutylketone (H 17).
Th (IV)	Thorium (IV) can be quantitatively extracted ($\log p_N = 6\cdot75$) with a $0\cdot10$ M solution of the reagent in chloroform ($pH_{1/2} = 1\cdot65$, $\log K = -1\cdot64$) at pH > $2\cdot5$ (D 35, D 44). By using methylisobutylketone as the solvent ($\log p_N = 2\cdot05$) more than 99% of thorium can be extracted at pH > 5 ($pH_{1/2} = 3\cdot2$, $\log K = -4\cdot68$) (D 35).
U (VI)	Uranyl 1-nitroso-2-naphtholate is completely extracted with n-butyl alcohol and ethyl acetate at pH $3\cdot0$–$8\cdot5$ and with isoamyl alcohol at pH $4\cdot5$–$7\cdot5$. With chloroform as solvent the extraction of uranium (VI) is incomplete at any pH value (A 17). In the presence of EDTA as masking agent uranium (VI) can be separated from vanadium and iron (A 17).

5.5.7. 2-*Nitroso-1-naphthol*

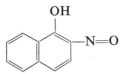

The reagent is a yellow or greenish-yellow crystalline solid (M.p. 147–148°C). It is slightly soluble in water, but it dissolves in various organic solvents (see Appendix).

2-Nitroso-1-naphthol is very similar to the preceding compound in its reactions. It is said to give more sensitive colour reactions with some metals, especially with cobalt. Apparently it oxidizes divalent cobalt in weakly acidic solutions more readily than its isomer.

A survey of extraction data for metal 2-nitroso-1-naphtholates is given in Table 17.

5.5.8. 2-*Nitroso-1-naphthol-4-sulphonic acid*

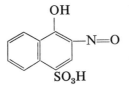

TABLE 17. A SURVEY OF EXTRACTION DATA FOR METAL 2-NITROSO-1-NAPHTHOLATES

Metal	Optimum conditions for extraction
Ag (I)	Silver forms with the reagent a brown precipitate extractable with chloroform (G 25).
Cd (II)	A green precipitate of cadmium (II)-2-nitroso-1-naphtholate can be extracted into chloroform (G 25).
Co	The cobalt complex with the reagent is not formed immediately at room temperature; precipitation is complete only after 24 hours,† but on heating the reaction is rapid. Thus prepared the complex can be extracted with chloroform (C 24, B 84), carbon tetrachloride (B 84, S 77), benzene (B 84, J 17), toluene (B 45), xylene (N 16), amyl acetate (C 29), and other solvents (B 84). The colour of the red cobaltic complex is not destroyed even by shaking the organic phase with 15 M sulphuric or hydrochloric acid, with 10 M sodium hydroxide (B 84), or with cyanide solution (A 35). Under these conditions the excess of the reagent and the other nitrosonaphtholates can be quantitatively stripped into the aqueous phase, and thus a selective separation and determination of cobalt can be carried out at 530–535 mμ (S 77). The interference by tin (II) can easily be eliminated by oxidation, that by iron (III) by masking with citrate (C 24) or fluoride (M 85), and that by manganese by hydrogen peroxide (S 22). Palladium and platinum must be removed by a preliminary extraction with dithizone or dimethylglyoxime. The above method has been used for the determination of cobalt in steel, nonferrous alloys, nickel (C 24), in ingot irons and copper alloys (R 5), in sodium metal (S 77), in soils and rocks (A 35, C 29), and in biological materials (S 22).
Cu (II)	Copper forms with the reagent a brown precipitate extractable with chloroform (G 25).
Fe (II)	A green iron complex can be extracted with chloroform (G 25).
Hg (II)	Mercury forms a yellow complex with the reagent, which can be extracted into chloroform (G 25).
Mn (II)	A red-brown manganese complex with the reagent can be extracted into chloroform (G 25).
Pd (II)	Palladium can be extracted at pH 1·0–2·5 by 0·01% solution of the reagent in benzene or toluene in the presence of EDTA as masking agent (R 19). After removing the excess of the reagent by shaking the organic phase with 1 M sodium hydroxide, the absorbancy of the violet palladium complex is measured at 370–375 mμ (C 7, R 19) or at 550 mμ (C 7). The above method has been used for the determination of palladium in uranium alloys (R 19).
Th (IV)	Quantitative extraction of thorium ($\log p_N = 4\cdot4$) by a 0·05 M solution of the reagent in chloroform takes place at pH > 3 ($\log K = 0\cdot2$) (D 35). When using a 0·10 M solution in methylisobutylketone only 99% of thorium ($\log p_N = 2\cdot1$) can be extracted at pH > 5 ($\log K = -2\cdot48$) (D 35).

† This time can be shortened to 30 minutes by shaking intensively prior to the addition of chloroform (N 16).

The reagent gives a red complex with palladium which can be extracted from 2·8–6 M hydrochloric acid with isoamyl alcohol (K 55).

5.6. NITROSOARYLHYDROXYLAMINES

The nitrosohydroxylamine group can exist in two tautomeric forms:

$$
\begin{array}{ccc}
\mathrm{N{=}O} & & \mathrm{N{-}OH} \\
| & \rightleftarrows & | \\
\mathrm{-N{-}OH} & & \mathrm{-N{=}O}
\end{array}
$$

in which the hydrogen atom can be replaced by an equivalent of a metal and oxygen atom then complete a five-membered ring. The most important reagent of this group is cupferron (L 24).

5.6.1. *Ammonium salt of N-nitrosophenylhydroxylamine (cupferron)*

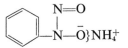

Cupferron, HCup (M.Wt. 155·16), is a white or buff-coloured crystalline powder melting at 163–164°C, soluble in water and alcohol.

In aqueous solution HCup is a weak acid with $pK_{HA} = 4{\cdot}16$ at 25°C (D 26). The partition coefficient of the undissociated acid between chloroform and aqueous phase is rather high ($\log p_{HA} = 2{\cdot}18$ at 25°C) (D 26).

Cupferron is generally used in aqueous solutions. Since both the reagent and its chelates may decompose upon heating to form nitrobenzene, for the best results solutions of cupferron are kept in a refrigerator and extractions are carried out in the cold. The addition of 50 mg of acetophenetide to each 150 ml of reagent solution has been suggested as a stabilizer (M 99). Solutions of the undissociated acid in chloroform seem to be more stable (S 110).

Cupferron was first introduced as a specific reagent for copper (II) and iron (III) but many other metals were later found to form insoluble cupferrates (B 47, H 12). Most of them are soluble in ethyl acetate, diethyl ether, benzene, isoamyl alcohol and other organic solvents, but chloroform is the solvent preferred (B 47).

A review of the uses of cupferron in analytical chemistry has been given by Furman, Mason, and Pecola (F 33) and by other authors (L 24, S 109). A quantitative comprehensive study of cupferron extraction has recently been carried out by Starý and Smižanská (S 109).

A survey of extraction data for cupferrates investigated is given in Table 18; extraction curves for many metals (S 109) are shown in Figs. 38–43.

TABLE 18. A SURVEY OF EXTRACTION DATA FOR CUPFERRATES

Metal	Optimum conditions for extraction
Ag (I)	Silver (I) cupferrate is only slightly soluble in chloroform or other organic solvents. Traces of silver can be partially extracted in the presence of excess of 0·05 M HCup at pH higher than 3·5; the extraction of greater amounts of silver is impracticable (S 109).
Al (III)	Aluminium is completely extracted by a 0·05 M solution of HCup in chloroform at pH 3·5–9·5 (E 15, S 109) ($\log K = -3\cdot50$, $pH_{1/2} = 2\cdot51$) (S 109). Extraction with HCup has been used for the determination of aluminium in steel after iron had been removed by electrolysis (R 18, S 12).
Ba (II)	Barium is not extracted as cupferrate into chloroform at any pH value (S 109).
Be (II)	Beryllium can be quantitatively extracted with chloroform at pH > 3 from a solution containing 0·05 M HCup ($\log K = -1\cdot54$, $pH_{1/2} = 2\cdot07$) (S 109).
Bi (III)	Quantitative extraction of bismuth with chloroform takes place in the pH range 2–12 in the presence of 0·005 M HCup ($\log K = 5\cdot07$, $pH_{1/2} = 0\cdot6$) (S 109). HCup extraction has been used for the separation of bismuth from lead (B 71).
Ca (II)	Calcium is not extracted as cupferrate into chloroform at any pH value (S 109).
Cd (II)	Small amounts of cadmium can be partially extracted by chloroform at pH > 4·5 in the presence of 0·05 M HCup. The extraction of greater amounts is impracticable on account of the limited solubility of cadmium cupferrate in chloroform (S 109).
Ce (III)	Tervalent cerium can be quantitatively extracted at cupferrate at pH 4–5 with three portions of chloroform (K 36).
Ce (IV)	In acidic solutions (0·10–0·15 M sulphuric acid) containing 0·1% HCup tetravalent cerium forms a rust-coloured precipitate extractable into butyl acetate ($\log K = 4\cdot6$) (H 7) or amyl acetate (H 6).
Co (II)	Complete extraction takes place at pH > 4·5 in the presence of a 0·05 M reagent solution. Chloroform was used as organic solvent ($\log K = -3\cdot56$, $pH_{1/2} = 3\cdot18$) (S 109). A 1:1 mixture of isoamyl alcohol and benzene can also be used as a suitable solvent (F 27).
Cu (II)	Copper can be quantitatively extracted with chloroform in the pH region 2–10 in the presence of 0·05 M HCup. $\log K = 2\cdot69$ (F 33); $\log K = 2\cdot66$ (S 109); $pH_{1/2} = 0\cdot03$ (S 109).
Fe (III)	Iron (III) is quantitatively extracted as cupferrate into chloroform at pH 0–12 in the presence of 0·05 M HCup (S 109); $\log K = 9\cdot85$, $pH_{1/2} = -2\cdot0$ (S 12). Amyl acetate or o-dichlorbenzene can also be used as organic solvents (B 49, W 2). The iron (III) chelate absorbs at about 460–485 mμ. HCup extraction is very often used for isolating ferric iron from aluminium and many other metals (F 19, I 2, M 53, P 3, S 71, S 125, T 28).

TABLE 18 (*continued*)

Metal	Optimum conditions for extraction
Ga (III)	Quantitative extraction of gallium cupferrate with chloroform takes place in the pH range 1·5–12, if 0·005 M HCup is present (log K = 4·92, $pH_{1/2}$ = 0·7) (S 109).
Hf (IV)	Hafnium (IV) can be quantitatively extracted from diluted acids with 0·005 M HCup in chloroform (log K > 8) (D 28).
Hg (II)	About 98% of mercury can be extracted as cupferrate with chloroform at pH 2–5 in the presence of 0·05 M reagent solution (log K = 0·91, $pH_{1/2}$ = 0·85) (S 109).
In (III)	Indium (III) is completely extracted with chloroform at pH 3–8 in the presence of 0·005 M HCup solution (log K = 2·42, $pH_{1/2}$ = 1·50) (S 109).
La (III)	Only 90% of lanthanum can be extracted as cupferrate at pH 4–10 in the presence of 0·05 M HCup solution (log K = −6·22, $pH_{1/2}$ = 3·4) (S 109). Methylisobutylketone has also been recommended as a suitable solvent (D 28).
Mn (II)	Only 15% of manganese can be extracted with chloroform at pH 4·5–9·5 if 0·05 M HCup is present. At pH < 3 manganese is practically not extracted (S 109). By using a 1:1 mixture of isoamyl alcohol and benzene the extraction becomes more complete (F 27).
Mo (VI)	Quantitative extraction of molybdenum (VI) with chloroform takes place from 0·005 M HCup solutions of pH 0–1·5. Molybdenum is practically not extracted at pH higher than 7 (S 109). With isoamyl alcohol as solvent the extraction of molybdenum (VI) is complete even from 3 M sulphuric acid if 0·1% HCup is present (A 34).
Nb (V)	More than 90% of niobium can be extracted with chloroform from 2% ammonium tartrate at pH 0–5 which is also about 3% in HCup (A 15). Ethyl acetate, carbon tetrachloride, benzene, or cyclohexanone can also be used as suitable solvents (T 40).
Ni (II)	Nickel is only partially extracted (~ 50%) with chloroform from 0·05 M HCup solution at pH 9–12 (S 109). By using a 1:1 mixture of isoamyl alcohol and benzene almost quantitative extraction of nickel cupferrate takes place at pH 6–8 (F 27).
Pa (V)	More than 90% of protactinium can be extracted as cupferrate with amyl alcohol from 0·1–6 M hydrochloric acid. Protactinium can be back extracted from the organic phase into 1 M citric acid (M 8, M 9).
Pb (II)	Quantitative extraction of lead with chloroform in the presence of 0·05 M HCup occurs at pH 3–9 (log K = −1·53, $pH_{1/2}$ = 2·06) (S 109). A 1:1 mixture of isoamyl alcohol with benzene can also be used as the organic solvent (F 27).
Pm (III)	Promethium cupferrate can be extracted from an acetate buffer with chloroform (K 35, K 36).

TABLE 18 (*continued*)

Metal	Optimum conditions for extraction
Pu (IV)	Plutonium (IV) forms with HCup at pH 0·3–2 a precipitate extractable into chloroform (H 17); $\log K = 7\cdot0$ (M 83).
Sb (III)	White antimony (III) cupferrate is quantitatively extracted in the presence of an excess of HCup (0·005 M solution) in the pH region 0–12 when chloroform is used as solvent (S 109). HCup extraction can be used for the isolation of antimony (III) from arsenic (III) which cannot itself be extracted as a cupferrate (F 33).
Sb (V)	Antimony (V) is not precipitated and extracted as cupferrate (A 48, F 33).
Sc (III)	About 95% of scandium can be isolated by a single extraction in the pH range 3–12 when 0·005 M reagent solution is present. With chloroform as solvent $\log K = 3\cdot32$, $pH_{1/2} = 0\cdot2$ (S 109).
Sn (II)	Stannous cupferrate is practically completely precipitated from diluted mineral acids. This precipitate is soluble in benzene or chloroform (A 48, F 33).
Sn (IV)	White stannic cupferrate, which is completely precipitated in dilute acid solutions, can be extracted by chloroform or ethyl acetate (A 48, F 33).
Ta (V)	Tantalum (V) cupferrate can be extracted with isoamyl alcohol at pH ~ 0 when 0·5% tartaric acid is present. At pH > 3 tantalum (V) is practically not extracted (A 15).
Th (IV)	Thorium is quantitatively extracted by 0·005 M HCup in chloroform at pH 2·5–8·5 ($\log p_N = 2\cdot79$, $\log K = 4\cdot4$, $pH_{1/2} = 1\cdot25$) (D 28). When using methylisobutylketone or n-butyl acetate as solvents the extraction of thorium takes place from more acidic solutions ($\log K = 6\cdot0$ and 5·6 for methylisobutylketone and n-butyl acetate respectively) (D 28, H 5).
Ti (IV)	Quantitative extraction of titanium (IV) cupferrate (0·005 M HCup was present) with chloroform takes place at pH 0–4 (S 109). Isoamyl alcohol (A 15) and 4-methyl-2-pentanone (C 11) have also been recommended as suitable solvents. In slightly acid medium EDTA can be used as a masking agent for many metals (C 11). The complex in chloroform absorbs at 375 mμ (S 109).
Tl (III)	About 50% of thallium (III) is extracted by chloroform in the presence of 0·005 M HCup ($\log K \sim 3\cdot0$) (S 109).
U (IV)	Uranium (IV) can be extracted as cupferrate with diethylether from acid solutions ($\log K = 8\cdot0$) (K 48) or ethyl acetate (S 92, W 25).
U (VI)	Uranium (VI) forms a cupferrate that is rather soluble in water (K 48). When using 0·01 M HCup in chloroform, less than 30% of uranium (VI) is extracted at pH 3·5–6. With less concentrated solutions of HCup uranium (VI) is practically not extracted at pH < 3 (S 109).

TABLE 18 (*continued*)

Metal	Optimum conditions for extraction
V (IV)	Vanadium (IV) is quantitatively extracted from 0·5 M hydrochloric acid if the concentration of the reagent in ethyl acetate is higher than 9×10^{-2} M (S 92).
V (V)	Vanadium (V) cupferrate can be quantitatively extracted with chloroform at pH 0–2·5 in the presence of 0·005 M HCup solution. At pH > 9 vanadium is practically not extracted (B 56, S 109). The chelate absorbs at 505 mμ (W 25). Extraction with HCup has been used for the isolation and determination of vanadium in rocks and meteorites (K 23).
W (VI)	In the presence of 0·005 M HCup, less than 25% of tungsten (VI) can be extracted with chloroform at pH 0–3. At pH > 4 extraction of tungsten practically does not occur (S 109). In the presence of a higher reagent concentration the extraction becomes more effective (S 109).
Y (III)	At pH > 5 more than 75% of yttrium can be extracted as cupferrate with chloroform when 0·005 M HCup solution is present (S 109). Extraction with cupferron has been used for the separation of yttrium from fission products (K 35, K 36).
Zn (II)	Zinc can only be partially extracted as cupferrate into chloroform. Maximum extractability (about 82%) in the presence of 0·05 M HCup takes place at pH 9–10·5 (S 109). The extraction of zinc cupferrate becomes more quantitative when a 1:1 mixture of isoamyl alcohol and benzene is used (F 27).
Zr (IV)	Quantitative extraction of zirconium with 0·005 M HCup in chloroform occurs at pH 0–3 (E 7, S 109). The extraction of previously precipitated zirconium cupferrate is not suitable because of the slow separation of the organic and aqueous phases (E 7). Extraction of zirconium by HCup has been used for the separation of this element from fission products (K 36) and from tungsten, which can be masked by oxalic acid (P 48).

5.6.2. *Ammonium salt of N-nitrosonaphthylhydroxylamine (neocupferron)*

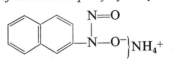

The ammonium salt of *N*-nitrosonaphthylhydroxylamine, called neocupferron, has been prepared and shown to behave similarly to cupferron (W 7). Up to now it has not been extensively applied to extraction studies. A point of interest is the extractability of neodymium by this reagent (B 47).

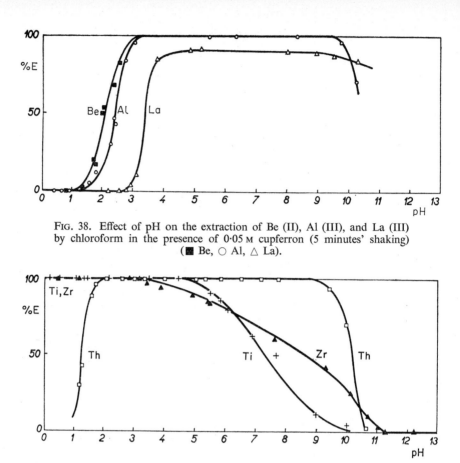

FIG. 38. Effect of pH on the extraction of Be (II), Al (III), and La (III) by chloroform in the presence of 0·05 M cupferron (5 minutes' shaking) (■ Be, ○ Al, △ La).

FIG. 39. Effect of pH on the extraction of Ti (IV), Zr (IV), and Th (IV) by chloroform in the presence of 0·005 M cupferron (5 minutes' shaking) (+ Ti, ▲ Zr, □ Th).

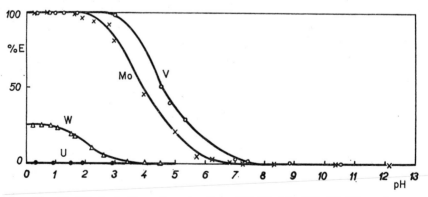

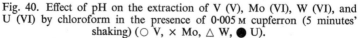

Fig. 40. Effect of pH on the extraction of V (V), Mo (VI), W (VI), and U (VI) by chloroform in the presence of 0·005 M cupferron (5 minutes' shaking) (○ V, × Mo, △ W, ● U).

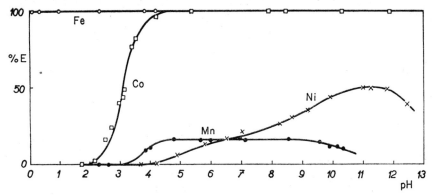

FIG. 41. Effect of pH on the extraction of Mn (II), Fe (III), Co (II), and Ni (II) by chloroform in the presence of 0·05 M cupferron (5 minutes' shaking) (● Mn, ○ Fe, □ Co, × Ni).

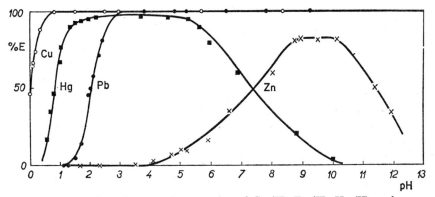

FIG. 42. Effect of pH on the extraction of Cu (II), Zn (II), Hg (II), and Pb (II) by chloroform in the presence of 0·05 M cupferron (5 minutes' shaking) (○ Cu, × Zn, ▣ Hg, ● Pb).

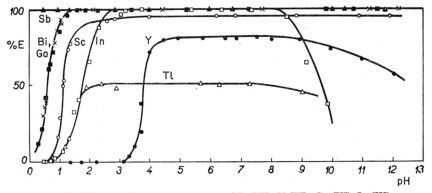

FIG. 43. Effect of pH on the extraction of Sc (III), Y (III), Ga (III), In (III), Tl (III), B. (III), and Sb (III) by chloroform in the presence of 0·005 M cupferron (5 minutes' shaking) (○ Sc, ● Y, × Ga, □ In, △ Tl, ■ Bi, ▲ Sb).

5.7. HYDROXAMIC ACIDS

Organic reagents with grouping

form extractable chelates with many metals among which vanadium complexes are of chief interest analytically. The most important reagent of this group is *N*-benzoyl-*N*-phenylhydroxylamine.

5.7.1. *Benzhydroxamic acid*

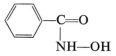

The reagent forms with uranium (VI) a soluble complex that is extractable into 1-hexanol (M 47). When using 1-octanol as solvent vanadium (V) is extracted at pH 1·1–4·7. The absorbancy of the vanadium chelate at 450 mμ has been used for the determination of this element in plant materials (J 15). 1-Hexanol has been used as solvent for the colorimetric determination of vanadium in uranium materials (K 78) and in steels and oils (W 31).

5.7.2. *Salicylhydroxamic acid*

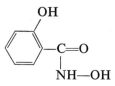

The reagent forms with vanadium (V) a blue to intense violet substance that can be quantitatively extracted with organic solvents like ethyl acetate, butyl acetate, butyl alcohol, etc. (B 58); this permits its direct determination in the presence of all other elements except iron. The optimum pH for extraction lies between 3·0 and 3·5; the maximum absorbancy is at 470–480 mμ (B 59). This method has been used for the determination of vanadium in steel (B 59).

The extraction of titanium as a complex with salicylhydroxamic acid into acetylacetone has been recommended for the determination of titanium in pure aluminium. The complex absorbs at 375 mμ ($\varepsilon = 4860$) (A 26).

5.7.3. *Anthranilohydroxamic acid (2-aminobenzhydroxamic acid)*

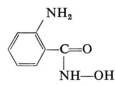

This reagent forms an orange-red complex with iron (II) and with iron, (III) which can be extracted with isobutyl alcohol in the pH range 4–7; its maximum absorbancy is at 450 mμ (D 22).

The red manganese (II) complex can only be extracted at pH > 9; its maximum absorbancy is at 490–500 mμ (D 22).

5.7.4. *Quinaldinohydroxamic acid*

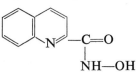

The reagent gives a red precipitate with iron (II) and iron (III) which can be quantitatively extracted with isobutyl alcohol at pH 3–9. The complex absorbs at 450 mμ (D 21).

In the pH range 3·0–4·0 the reagent forms a dirty purple precipitate with vanadium (V) which can readily be extracted with higher alcohols. The coloured complex has its maximum absorbancy at 440–450 mμ (D 21).

5.7.5. *N-Benzoyl-N-phenylhydroxylamine*

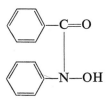

N-Benzoyl-*N*-phenylhydroxylamine (M.Wt. 213·22, M.p. 121–122°C) is difficultly soluble in water (0·002 M), but it dissolves freely in chloroform (0·74 M), benzene, ethyl acetate, and other solvents. The partition coefficient of the reagent between chloroform and the aqueous phase equals 214 at 25°C, $\mu = 0·1$ (D 37).

In aqueous solution *N*-benzoyl-*N*-phenylhydroxylamine is a weak acid ($pK_{HA} = 8·15$, 25°C, $\mu = 0·1$) (D 37).

The reagent is stable towards heat, light, and air. It is destroyed by alkali and by concentrated nitric acid (but not by sulphuric acid and hydro-chloric acid up to 8 N).

N-Benzoyl-N-phenylhydroxylamine forms water-insoluble chelates with many metals which, with the exception of those of antimony, mercury, zinc, and cadmium, are readily soluble and extractable into chloroform or isoamyl alcohol.

Titanium (IV), vanadium (V), niobium (V), cerium (IV), uranium (VI), molybdenum (VI), cobalt (II), nickel (II), iron (II) and (III), and copper (II) give coloured chelates so that spectrophotometric methods can be used for the determination of these elements. The reagent itself does not absorb at above 370 mμ.

The principal study of the extraction potentialities of N-benzoyl-N-phenyl-hydroxylamine was carried out by Dyrssen (D 37) and a review of the use of this reagent in chemical analysis has recently been given by Alimarin (A 30).

A survey of extraction data for the metals investigated is given in Table 19.

5.7.6. N-2-Thenoyl-N-phenylhydroxylamine

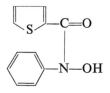

The reagent forms intense violet chelates with vanadium (V) which can be extracted with chloroform from 2·8–5·0 M hydrochloric acid. By measuring the absorbancy at 530 mμ ($\varepsilon = 5750$) the amount of vanadium present may be determined. The reagent itself does not absorb at this wavelength but iron (II) and (III), molybdenum, titanium, and zirconium interfere (T 20).

N-2-Thenoyl-N-p-tolylhydroxylamine gives analogous reactions (T 20).

5.7.7. N-Cinnamoyl-N-phenylhydroxylamine

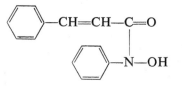

The reagent consists of pale green crystals (M.p. 162–163°C) which are stable to heat, light, and air. It reacts with vanadium (V) in 2·7–7·5 M hydrochloric acid to give a violet complex which can be extracted with chloroform. The complex absorbs at 540 mμ (P 56).

TABLE 19. A SURVEY OF EXTRACTION DATA FOR METALS

Metal	Optimum conditions for extraction
Al (III)	Aluminium forms with the reagent a white precipitate which can be extracted at pH $\sim$ 3 with chloroform (C 56).
Be (II)	The complex of beryllium with the reagent can be extracted with chloroform at pH $\sim$ 5 (C 56).
Bi (III)	Bismuth can be precipitated with the reagent at pH $\sim$ 3. The precipitate can be extracted with chloroform (C 56).
Cd (II)	Cadmium forms a sparingly soluble precipitate with the reagent at pH $\sim$ 4 which is extractable into chloroform (C 56).
Ce (III)	At pH $\sim$ 6 the reagent forms a white precipitate with cerium (III) which can be extracted with chloroform (C 56).
Ce (IV)	In 3 N acids an orange precipitate is formed between cerium (IV) and the reagent, which is extractable with chloroform (C 56).
Cr (III)	Chromium (III) forms at pH $\sim$ 4 a yellow precipitate extractable into chloroform (C 56).
Cu (II)	A green-yellow precipitate of copper with the reagent can be extracted into chloroform in the pH range 3–11 (C 21, C 56).
Fe (II)	Iron (II) forms a red extractable precipitate at pH $\sim$ 5 (C 56).
Fe (III)	Iron (III) can be separated from aluminium and other metals by extracting a violet complex of iron (III) with the reagent from 0·5 M hydrochloric acid into chloroform. The complex absorbs at 440 mμ (ε = 4450) (C 56, Z 6).
Ga (III)	A white gallium (III) precipitate with the reagent can be extracted with chloroform at pH $\sim$ 3. The solubility of the chelate in organic solvents is very low (C 56).
Hf (IV)	More than 90% of hafnium is extracted with chloroform from 3 M hydrochloric acid in the presence of excess of the reagent (C 56).
Hg (I) Hg (II)	Mercury (I) and mercury (II) form a yellow-green precipitate with the reagent which can only be extracted with chloroform with difficulty (C 56).
In (III)	Indium (III) gives a white precipitate which can be extracted with chloroform at pH = 3 (C 56).
La (III)	About 99% of lanthanum is extracted at pH $\sim$ 6·6 with 0·10 M reagent solution in chloroform (log K = −14·4) (D 37).
Mn (II)	A light yellow precipitate of manganese (II) with the reagent is formed at pH = 6. The complex can be extracted by chloroform (C 56).

TABLE 19 (*continued*)

Metal	Optimum conditions for extraction
Mo (VI)	At pH $\sim$ 3 a light yellow precipitate is formed which is extractable into chloroform (C 56).
Nb (V)	More than 90% of niobium (V) can be extracted from 6–12 M sulphuric acid by a 1% solution of the reagent in chloroform (15 minutes' shaking was used). If tartrate is present (pH 4–6), niobium (V) can be separated from tantalum (V) by using a 1% solution of the reagent in chloroform (A 25, A 28).
Nd (III)	A white neodymium (III) precipitate can be extracted with chloroform at pH > 6 (C 56).
Ni (II)	More than 98% of nickel can be extracted as a complex with the reagent into chloroform at pH $\sim$ 5 (C 21, C 56).
Pb (II)	More than 96% of lead can be isolated as a complex with the reagent by a single extraction with chloroform at pH 7–10.
Pd (II)	A rose-coloured palladium precipitate can be extracted with chloroform at pH $\sim$ 3 (C 56).
Pr (III)	A complex between praseodymium and the reagent can be extracted by chloroform at pH > 6 (C 56).
Sb (III) Sb (V)	Antimony (III) and antimony (V) form colourless, sparingly soluble precipitates at pH $\sim$ 1 and in 3 N acid respectively which are extractable into chloroform (C 56).
Sc (III)	In the pH range 4–6 scandium is quantitatively extracted by a 0·5% solution of the reagent in isoamyl alcohol (A 22). Chloroform is also suitable as a solvent (C 56).
Sn (II) Sn (IV)	Tin (IV) is probably reduced by the reagent to the divalent state and the colourless precipitate can then be extracted from 3 M acid into chloroform (C 56, R 38).
Ta (V)	Tantalum (V) is only partially extracted from 5–14 M sulphuric acid by a 1% solution of the reagent in chloroform; but once extracted the tantalum chelate is not destroyed even by shaking with 0·01–12 M sulphuric acid (A 28). Only a very small amount of tantalum can be extracted at higher pH (A 25).
Th (IV)	Quantitative extraction of thorium ($\log p_N = 3\cdot45$) by a 0·10 M solution of the reagent in chloroform takes place at pH 3–9 ($\log K = -0\cdot68$) (D 37). By using a 3% solution of the reagent in isoamyl alcohol, thorium is completely extracted in the pH range 3·5–7 ($pH_{1/2} = 2\cdot6$). At pH < 5·5 thorium can easily be separated from rare earths (A 23).
Ti (IV)	A yellow titanium complex can be separated from aluminium and other metals by extraction from 0·5 M acid with chloroform. The complex absorbs at 345 mμ ($\varepsilon = 5300$) (A 22, C 56).

TABLE 19 (*continued*)

Metal	Optimum conditions for extraction
Tl (III)	Tervalent thallium is precipitated by the reagent and the precipitate formed can be extracted by chloroform at pH $\sim$ 4 (C 56).
U (VI)	At pH $>$ 3·5 more than 90% of uranium is extracted by a 0·10 M solution of the reagent in chloroform (log $K = -3\cdot14$) (D 37).
V (V)	Vanadium (V) can be extracted from 2·8–4·3 M hydrochloric acid by a 0·1% solution of the reagent in chloroform. The purple-red complex absorbs at 510–530 mμ ($\varepsilon = 4500$) (R 39, P 55, P 57). This method has been used for the determination of vanadium in steels, chrome ores (R 39), or in titanium (Z 5).
W (VI)	At pH $\sim$ 3 tungsten forms a light yellow complex extractable with chloroform (C 56).
Y (III)	At pH $\sim$ 6 a colourless precipitate is formed which can be extracted into chloroform (C 56).
Zn (II)	A sparingly soluble white precipitate of zinc with the reagent is extractable into chloroform (C 56).
Zr (IV)	Zirconium forms a precipitate with the reagent which can be extracted with chloroform or isoamyl alcohol (Z 7).

5.8. 1-(2-PYRIDYLAZO)-2-NAPHTHOL AND RELATED COMPOUNDS

1-(2-Pyridylazo)-2-naphthol and related compounds fall in the group of polydentate organic reagents which contain a hydrogen atom replaceable by the equivalent of a metal and nitrogen atoms suitably located to form chelate rings.

The most important reagent of this group is 1-(2-pyridylazo)-2-naphthol itself.

5.8.1. 1-(2-Pyridylazo)-2-naphthol

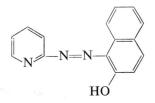

1-(2-Pyridylazo)-2-naphthol (PAN) is an orange-red amorphous solid, nearly insoluble in water, but soluble in alkali (in which it forms a soluble alkali salt) and in a variety of organic solvents to which it imparts a yellow colour. The maximum absorbancy of the reagent in organic solvents is at about 470 mμ and at wavelengths above 560 mμ the reagent is effectively transparent.

The dissociation constants of PAN, $pK_{HA} = 12\cdot3$, $pK_{H_2A} < 2$, have only been determined in aqueous dioxan (50 per cent v/v) (C 48).

The reagent is very stable even in the presence of oxidizing agents. For analytical purposes a $0\cdot1$ per cent solution of the reagent in ethanol or methanol is normally used.

With many metals PAN forms intensively coloured complexes which can be extracted into chloroform, amyl alcohol, benzene, carbon tetrachloride, or diethyl ether. Most of these are reddish coloured; only palladium and cobalt form greenish-coloured chelates (S 55–58), so that direct spectro-photometric determination is possible.

The conditions of extraction and determination of various metals are summarized in Table 20.

5.8.2. 1-(2-Thiazolylazo)-2-naphthol

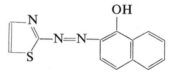

The potentialities of 1-(2-thiazolyl)-2-naphthol have been studied by Kawase (K 19, K 20). With copper, zinc, and cerium (III) the reagent was found to give chelates soluble in water, but the chelate complexes of other elements were insoluble. Almost all these chelates, including those of copper and cobalt, can be extracted by solvents such as chloroform or isoamyl alcohol.

Chelate complexes of palladium (II) and cobalt (III) with the reagent are green, the others are red or violet.

5.8.3. Erio OS (I)

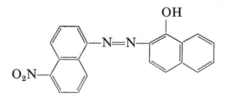

TABLE 20. EXTRACTION DATA AND DETERMINATION OF VARIOUS METALS

Metal	Optimum conditions for extraction
Bi (III)	Bismuth forms with PAN a pink complex soluble in amyl alcohol but only partially soluble in carbon tetrachloride (C 9).
Cd (II)	In the presence of 0·005% PAN cadmium (II) can be extracted with chloroform as a red complex at pH 7–10 (B 54, D 14). The complex absorbs strongly at 550–560 mμ ($\varepsilon = 49,000$–$51,000$) (B 54, S 58). Extraction with PAN has been used for the determination of cadmium in nickel (B 54).
Ce	The pink complex of cerium and PAN can be extracted with amyl alcohol (C 9).
Co (II)	Cobalt (II) can be extracted at pH 4–7 with chloroform in the presence of the excess of the reagent (0·005% PAN solution) (B 54).
Co (III)	A green cobalt (III) complex with PAN can be extracted with chloroform at pH 3–6 giving a solution which exhibits absorption maxima at 590 mμ ($\varepsilon = 25,000$) and at 640 mμ ($\varepsilon = 20,000$). The above method was used for the determination of cobalt in thorium oxide (G 16).
Cu (II)	A complex of copper with PAN can be extracted with chloroform at pH 4–10 (B 54). Maximum absorbancy of the complex lies at 550 mμ ($\varepsilon = 45,000$) (B 54). Amyl alcohol has also been recommended as a suitable solvent (C 9).
Eu (III)	A red complex of europium and PAN can be extracted into amyl alcohol (C 9).
Fe (III)	The optimum pH value for the extraction of the complex of iron (III) with PAN by chloroform or benzene lies between 4 and 7 when 0·005–0·010% PAN solution is present (B 54). The complex has its maximum absorbancy at 775 mμ ($\varepsilon = 16,000$); at this wavelength many other PAN complexes do not absorb (S 57, S 58). The method has been used for the determination of iron in minerals (S 58).
Ga (III)	In the presence of 0·005–0·010% PAN solution gallium can be extracted with chloroform at pH 6–7·5. The complex absorbs strongly at 560 mμ (S 58).
Hg (II)	A red mercury (II) chelate with PAN can be extracted in the presence of the excess of the reagent with chloroform at pH 6–7·5. The complex absorbs strongly at 560 mμ (S 58).
In (III)	At pH 5·3–6·7 indium can be extracted with chloroform as its complex with PAN (G 53, S 57, S 58). Very different values for the molar extinction coefficient at 560 mμ have been published, viz. $\varepsilon = 36,000$ (G 54) and $\varepsilon = 19,000$ (S 57).
Mn (II)	A wine-red chelate of manganese and PAN can be extracted with chloroform in the presence of 0·005% PAN solution at pH 7–10. The chelate absorbs strongly at 550 mμ ($\varepsilon = 40,000$) (B 54).

TABLE 19 (*continued*)

Metal	Optimum conditions for extraction
Mn (II) (*cont.*)	When using diethyl ether as the organic solvent pH 9 to 10 has been recommended as optimal for the extraction (S 58).
Ni (II)	On being heated at 80°C with PAN at pH 4–10 nickel (II) reacts to form a complex extractable into chloroform or benzene (D 14, D 15, S 54, S 59). The maximum absorbancy of the red complex lies at 575 mμ ($\varepsilon = 50{,}900$).
Pb (II)	The red complex of lead with PAN can be extracted with amyl alcohol or chloroform (C 9, S 58).
Pd (II)	A green palladium complex with PAN can be extracted at pH 3–7 with chloroform; excess of the reagent must be present (B 54). At pH 3–4 rhodium, platinum, gold, silver, and mercury do not interfere (B 99). The maximum absorbancy of the complex lies at 675–678 mμ ($\varepsilon = 14{,}000$–$16{,}000$) (D 14, B 99). This method has been used for the determination of palladium in titanium alloys (EDTA and citrate were used as masking agents) (D 14, S 16).
Sc (III)	The red scandium chelate can be extracted with amyl alcohol (C 9).
Sn (II)	A chelate of tin (II) with the reagent can be extracted into amyl alcohol (C 9).
Th (IV)	A yellow thorium chelate with PAN can be extracted into amyl alcohol (C 9).
U (VI)	A red chelate of uranium (VI) with the reagent can be extracted with chloroform at pH 5–10 (0·005% PAN solution was present). The complex absorbs at 560 mμ (B 54, S 55). By using *o*-dichlorobenzene as solvent, uranium can be selectively determined by measuring the absorbancy at 570 mμ ($\varepsilon = 23{,}000$). EDTA and cyanide are suitable masking agents (C 10, C 13). The method has been used for the determination of uranium in calcium fluoride (C 13).
V (V)	A blue chelate of PAN and vanadium is formed in the pH range 3·5–4·5 (W 3). No chelation occurs below pH 1·5 or above pH 7·5. When extracted into chloroform the maximum absorbancy of the complex is at 615 mμ ($\varepsilon = 16{,}900$). A procedure using PAN has been used for the determination of vanadium in ferrous alloys and in organic materials (S 111).
Y (III)	A red yttrium chelate with PAN can be extracted at pH 8·5–11 by using diethyl ether as solvent. The absorbancy at 560 mμ can be used for its colorimetric determination (S 58).
Zn (II)	At pH 4·5–8 zinc can be extracted with chloroform in the presence of 0·005% reagent solution (B 54). The complex absorbs strongly at 550–560 mμ. Extraction with PAN has been used for the determination of zinc in nickel (B 53, B 54).

Erio OS (I) forms extractable chelates with several divalent metals and also with gallium and indium (F 18).

5.8.4. 2-(2-Pyridylazo)-4-methylphenol

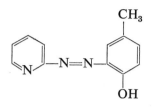

The reagent forms rose to blue chelates with copper, nickel, cobalt, indium, zinc, cadmium, lead, and uranium. Most of these are soluble in water but can also be extracted with organic solvents (N 3).

5.8.5. 2-Pyridylazoresorcinol

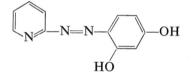

This reagent has been used for the solvent extraction of uranium (VI) from neutral medium. Polar solvents such as amyl alcohol, ethyl acetate, or n-butyl alcohol are more efficient than nonpolar solvents. The uranium chelate absorbs at 540 mμ (B 104).

5.8.6. 1-(2',4'-Dihydroxyphenylazo)-5-chloro-2-hydroxybenzene-3-sulphonic acid

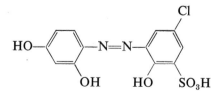

In slightly acid media the reagent forms with molydenum a complex extractable by polar solvents such as isoamyl alcohol, butyl alcohol, or methylethylketone (B 110). The chelate absorbs at 510 mμ. The uranium chelate is not extracted by chloroform, carbon tetrachloride, or benzene (B 110).

5.8.7. *2-(2-Hydroxy-5-methoxyphenylazo)-4-methylthiazole*

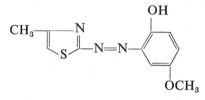

The reagent forms with zinc a blue complex extractable into isoamyl alcohol with maximum absorbancy at 612 mμ (Y 2, Y 3).

5.9. 8-MERCAPTOQUINOLINE AND ITS DERIVATIVES

8-Mercaptoquinolines have an hydrogen atom replaceable by a metal and a heterocyclic nitrogen which completes a five-membered chelate ring.

The most important reagent of this type is 8-mercaptoquinoline itself.

5.9.1. *8-Mercaptoquinoline* (*thiooxine*)

8-Mercaptoquinoline† (HTOx), briefly called thiooxine, is an intensively blue liquid which is transformed into a solid, black-coloured dihydrate on exposure to the air. At 58–59°C the molecules of water are removed and the dihydrate is again transformed into liquid thiooxine (K 85).

HTOx is slightly soluble in cold water (0·1 g per 100 ml), but readily soluble in ethyl alcohol (12·5 g per 100 ml), acetone, mineral acids (with formation of mercaptoquinolinium ions) and alkali (with formation of mercapto-quinolinate ions) (K 85).

In the solid state and also in aqueous solutions thiooxine is quickly oxidized by atmospheric oxygen to a disulphide. For analytical purposes it is prefer-able to use the hydrochloric salt of thiooxine, which is more stable (K 85).

Generally speaking, thiooxine gives precipitates with those metals that form insoluble sulphides. Chelate complexes are usually formed, e.g. $Zn(TOx)_2$, but in some cases cationic complexes, e.g. $[H_2TOx]_2[Zn(CNS)-]$, are produced.

† The synthesis of thiooxine has been described by Bankovskij *et al.* (B 20).

Thiooxinates of copper (II), zinc (II), mercury (II), thallium (I), tin (II), lead (II), arsenic (III) and arsenic (V), antomony (III), bismuth (III), vanadium (V), molybdenum (VI), iron (III), cobalt (II), and palladium (II) are readily soluble in organic solvents. The thiooxinates of gold (III), cadmium (II), and tungsten (VI) are less soluble. Thiooxinates of silver (I) and mercury (I) are only soluble in pyridine. Bromoform, chloroform, benzene, bromo-benzene, and toluene have usually been used as solvents (K 85).

Many of these chelates give strongly coloured solutions and therefore a direct photometric method can be used for the determination of many metals. Most intensively coloured are the red thiooxinates of manganese (II), iron (III), and copper (II); less strongly absorbing is the green thiooxinate of molybdenum (VI).

The extractability of metal thiooxinates decreases in the following order: rhenium (VII), gold (III), silver (I), mercury (II), palladium (II), platinum (II), ruthenium, osmium (III), molybdenum (VI), copper (II), tungsten (VI), cadmium (II), indium (III), zinc (II), iron (III), iridium (III), vanadium (IV), cobalt (II), nickel (II), arsenic (III), antimony (III), tin (II), bismuth (III), lead (II), manganese (II), and thallium (I) (B 31).

When HTOx is used in the analysis strong masking agents are: concen-trated hydrochloric acid (for iron, molybdenum, mercury, silver, bismuth, tin, and cobalt), thiourea (for copper, silver, gold, platinum, mercury, ruthenium, and osmium), sodium fluoride (for iron and tin) and potassium cyanide in alkaline solution (for iron, silver, gold, platinum, ruthenium, osmium, iridium, palladium, nickel, and cobalt).

A survey of extraction data for various thiooxinates which have been systematically studied by Bankovskij *et al.* (B 20–37) are given in Table 21. Extraction curves are shown in Figs. 44 and 45.

5.9.2. *Derivatives of 8-mercaptoquinoline*

A study of the extraction of metal chelates with halogen derivatives of thiooxine has been carried out by Bankovskij and Lobanova (B 26, B 29). These authors found that the complexes of 3- and 5-halogenated derivatives are more soluble than those of 8-mercaptoquinoline itself. Halogenation in the sixth position results in a considerable decrease in the solubility of metal chelates in organic solvents (B 29).

6-Chloro-8-mercaptoquinoline has been used for the extraction of copper (B 26), rhenium (B 32), and vanadium (B 33).

8-Methylmercaptoquinoline forms chelates that are less soluble in organic solvents than those of 8-mercaptoquinoline (B 34).

A 0·2 per cent solution of 8,8'-diquinolyl disulphide in chloroform can quantitatively extract copper from aqueous solutions of pH 2·3–13 when ascorbic acid is present. The molar extinction coefficient of the complex in the organic phase is 9500 at 432 mμ (B 25).

TABLE 21. A SURVEY OF EXTRACTION DATA FOR VARIOUS THIOOXINATES

Metal	Optimum conditions for extraction*
Bi (III)	At pH 3·5–11 bismuth forms a precipitate with HTOx which is quantitatively extracted into chloroform (K 85).
Co (II)	The thiooxinate of cobalt (II) can be quantitatively extracted into chloroform from aqueous solutions of pH 3·5–11 (K 85).
Cu (II)	Copper (II) is reduced by the reagent to copper (I) which gives with HTOx a compound of type CuA(HA). Complete extraction of this complex by chloroform takes place in the pH range 0–14. The molar extinction coefficient of the complex at 431 mμ is 7530 (B 23).
Fe (III)	Iron thiooxinate can be quantitatively extracted with chloroform at pH 3–11. The complex absorbs at 444 mμ ($\varepsilon = 7000$) (K 85).
Ga (III)	Quantitative extraction of the gallium complex by toluene in the presence of thiourea as masking agent takes place at pH 6·5–10. The molar extinction coefficient at 397 mμ is 8400 (B 36).
In (III)	Indium thiooxinate is quantitatively extracted by toluene at pH 4–13. For selective isolation potassium cyanide can be used as a masking agent. At 407 mμ the molar extinction coefficient is 11,100 (B 36).
Ir (III)	Tervalent iridium reacts with HTOx only on heating. In the presence of a tenfold excess of HTOx (200 μg or Ir was present) quantitative extraction of iridium was obtained at pH 7·6–9. The complex absorbs at 485 mμ ($\varepsilon = 9950$) (B 37).
Ir (IV)	Iridium (IV) is reduced by HTOx to the tervalent state (B 37).
Mn (II)	At pH > 7 manganese is quantitatively extracted as thiooxinate by chloroform, toluene, xylene, benzene, or chlorobenzene. Manganese thiooxinate is less stable in chloroform than in other solvents ($\varepsilon \sim 7000$ at 413 mμ). Many interfering metals can be masked by cyanide (B 27).
Mo (VI)	Molybdenum (VI) thiooxinate is quantitatively extracted by chloroform at pH 2–5. When using toluene as the organic solvent, complete extraction takes place from 2·3 M hydrochloric acid up to pH 5 (A 9, B 28). In the presence of thiourea (1% solution in 2·3 M hydrochloric acid) many interfering metals are masked. The molybdenum (VI) chelate absorbs strongly at 420 mμ ($\varepsilon = 8600$) (B 28). HTOx has been used for the determination of molybdenum in alloys (G 23) and for the indirect determination of calcium in biological materials after a preliminary precipitation of calcium as its molybdate and subsequent determination of molybdenum spectrophotometrically (B 24).
Os (VI) Os (IV)	Osmium (VI) and osmium (IV) are reduced by HTOx to the tervalent state which reacts on being boiled with the reagent to give a violet-blue complex. In the presence of a tenfold excess of HTOx osmium is quantitatively extracted at pH 4–7·5. The complex absorbs strongly at 558 mμ ($\varepsilon = 11,200$) (B 37).
Pb (II)	The thiooxinate of lead can be quantitatively extracted with chloroform at pH 2·5–11 (K 85).

TABLE 21 (*continued*)

Metal	Optimum conditions for extraction†
Pd (II)	Palladium thiooxinate is completely extracted by chloroform from 6 M hydrochloric acid as well as from 1 M sodium hydroxide. The complex absorbs strongly at 485 mμ (ε = 7750) (B 22, B 37).
Pt (II)	Platinum (II) reacts very slowly with HTOx at room temperatures: the reaction can be accelerated by boiling. At pH 3·5–5·0 about 93% of platinum ($\sim$ 200 μg) can be extracted with the stoicheiometric amount of HTOx. If a 50-fold excess of the reagent is used, quantitative extraction takes place from pH 2·5 to 5·0. Solutions of the violet palladium thiooxinate in chloroform absorb at 567 mμ (ε = 7600) (B 37).
Pt (IV)	Tetravalent platinum is reduced by excess of HTOx to the divalent state (B 37).
Re (VII)	In the presence of an excess of HTOx, rhenium thiooxinate is quantitatively extracted from 5·0–11·7 M hydrochloric acid. The complex absorbs at 438 mμ (ε = 8470). The extraction of rhenium from concentrated hydrochloric acid is very selective (B 30).
Rh (III)	Rhodium (III) reacts incompletely with HTOx at room temperatures. After being heated for 10 minutes in the presence of a tenfold excess of 0·01 M HTOx, rhodium can be quantitatively extracted with chloroform at pH 5–6. By using a 100-fold excess of the reagent the extraction becomes quantitative in the pH range 4·8–7·6. The yellow complex absorbs strongly at 465 mμ (ε = 11,600) (B 37).
Ru (VII)	Ruthenium (VII) is reduced by excess of HTOx on heating in concentrated hydrochloric acid to give a violet-brown precipitate which can be quantitatively extracted by chloroform at pH 5–5·7. The complex absorbs at 555 mμ (ε = 7300) (B 37).
Sb (III)	Antimony thiooxinate is quantitatively extracted by chloroform from solutions of pH between 2·5 and 11 (K 85).
Tl (I)	Quantitative extraction of thallium (I) by chloroform in the presence of 0·004 M HTOx was observed at pH 10–12 (B 13, B 35). When using ethyl acetate, methylethylketone, isobutyl alcohol, or carbon tetrachloride as solvent only 80–90% of thallium is found to be extracted (B 13).
V (V)	Vanadium (V) is reduced by HTOx to vanadyl ions which form a green complex with HTOx extractable at pH 4 into chloroform (ε = 7400 at 412 mμ) or into toluene. Potassium cyanide can be used as a masking agent (B 21).
Zn (II)	Quantitative extraction of zinc thiooxinate by chloroform takes place at pH 1–11 (K 85).

† The extraction procedure was generally carried out as follows: a few ml. of a 1–4% solution of HTOx in ethanol were added to 50 ml of the solution for analysis and the thiooxinate formed was then extracted by a suitable solvent.

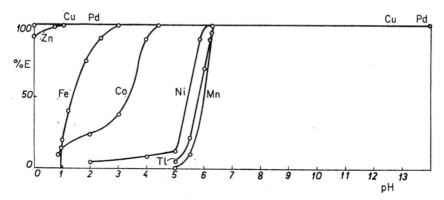

Fig. 44. Extraction of Cu (II), Pd (II), Zn (II), Fe (III), Co (II), Ni (II), Tl (I), and Mn (II) by chloroform as 8-mercaptoquinolinates.

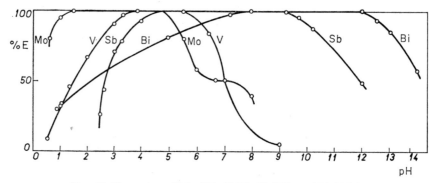

Fig. 45. Extraction of Mo (VI), V (V), Sb (III), and Bi (III) by chloroform as 8-mercaptoquinolinates.

5.10. DIPHENYLTHIOCARBAZONE (DITHIZONE) AND ITS DERIVATIVES

The reactive group of dithizone can be present in two forms: enol and keto.

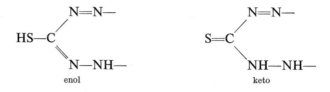

Many heavy metals can replace either one or both hydrogen atoms or dithizone, thus forming two different complexes, viz. primary (monobasic or "keto") and secondary (dibasic or "enol").

The fact that the sulphur-methylated derivative of dithizone (e.g. *S*-methyl-dithizone) does not react with heavy metals (I 17) shows that the probable structure of the primary dithizonates is as follows (I 17, S 14, I 48):

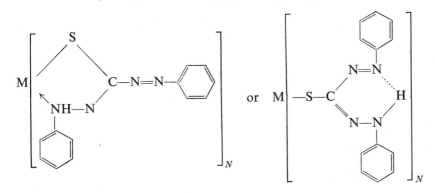

The structure of the secondary dithizonates can be expressed by the following structures:

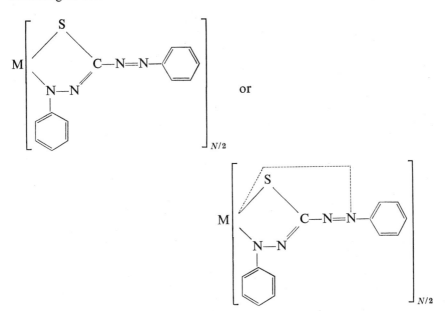

The primary dithizonates have a much greater importance than the secondary ones. Only some metals form secondary dithizonates and these are less stable and less soluble in organic solvents than primary dithizonates. The primary dithizonates are preferentially formed in acidic solutions and the secondary in alkaline media or with a deficiency of dithizone. The secondary

dithizonates can be transformed into the primary by treatment with acids
or by dithizone.

5.10.1. *Diphenylthiocarbazone (dithizone)*

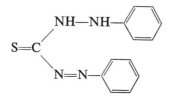

Diphenylthiocarbazone (M.Wt. 256·3), familiarly called dithizone, H_2Dz,
forms a violet-black crystalline powder practically insoluble in water and in
mineral acids (about 50 mg of dithizone dissolves in 1 litre, see Appendix).
In basic solutions, dithizone dissolves with a yellow colour to give completely
dissociated alkali metal dithizonates. On neutralization dithizone is again
precipitated.

Dithizone is only slightly soluble in hydrocarbons, but dissolves readily in
chloroform (6·8 × 10⁻² M) and less so in carbon tetrachloride (2·5 × 10⁻³ M)
(K 60). The latter two solvents are used almost exclusively for the prepara-
tion of dithizone solutions for analytical purposes. Dilute solutions of the
reagent in chloroform and carbon tetrachloride are green, but more concentrated ones are dichloric. In strongly polar solvents, such as nitrobenzene,
dithizone is yellow.

In aqueous solution dithizone behaves as a monobasic acid

$$H_2Dz \rightleftharpoons H^+ + HDz^-$$

with a dissociation constant K_{HA} of 2·8 × 10⁻⁵ (G 6) or 3·2 × 10⁻⁵ (I 14).
The second hydrogen cation is not removed below pH 12 (G 6).

The partition coefficient of dithizone between organic solvents and an
aqueous phase is very high (1·1 × 10⁴ for carbon tetrachloride (S 13) and
2 × 10⁵ for chloroform), and therefore it is expected that the partition coefficients of uncharged metal dithizonates will also be very high.

Dithizone is oxidized under weak oxidizing conditions to diphenylcarbodiazone. This oxidation product is sometimes present in commercial dithizone and purification of the reagent is based on the insolubility of the
diphenylcarbodiazone in aqueous ammonia. If a 0·01 per cent solution
of dithizone in carbon tetrachloride is shaken with dilute (1 : 100) metal-free
ammonia† until only a faint yellow colour remains in the organic phase, the
product may be used without further purification (S 14).

---

† Metal-free ammonia can be prepared by isopiestic distillation of concentrated ammonia
in the presence of EDTA and KCNS. Cf. I 50.

Dithizone may be purified by the following procedure: 0·5 g of dithizone is dissolved in 50 ml of chloroform and the solution is shaken in a separatory funnel with four successive portions of pure 1:100 ammonia each 50 to 75 ml in volume. The combined aqueous phase is filtered to remove droplets of chloroform and is then made slightly acid by hydrochloric acid or by sulphuric dioxide. The latter is preferable because of its reducing properties and because heavy metals are not introduced. The precipitated dithizone is extracted with several 15 to 20 ml portions of chloroform. These extracts are washed several times with water and evaporated in a beaker on a steam bath at 50°C to remove chloroform. The product may be dried in a desiccator and should be stored in the dark (S 14).

The simpler and more rapid purification procedure is based on recrystallization from chloroform. An almost saturated filtered solution of dithizone in chloroform is evaporated at about 40°C in a stream of filtered air until half the dithizone has crystallized out. The precipitate is collected on a sintered-glass filter crucible, washed with a few small portions of carbon tetrachloride and air dried (S 14).

Solutions of dithizone decompose rapidly if exposed to strong light and subjected to relatively high temperatures. Strong oxidizing agents destroy dithizone and they must therefore be removed before an extraction procedure by the use of hydroxylamine, hydrazine, or ascorbic acid. Manganese (II) destroys dithizone by induced oxidation—its interference can be removed also by adding hydrazine or other reducing agents.

Dithizone was introduced by H. Fischer (F 2) as a versatile organic reagent in 1925 and in conjunction with Miss Leopoldi he explored its use for the solvent extraction and quantitative determination of a group of heavy metals of considerable industrial and especially toxicological importance (F 2–15).

Dithizone is known to react with 20 metals: manganese (II), iron (II), cobalt (II), nickel (II), copper (I) and (II), silver (I), gold (III), palladium (II), platinum (II), zinc (II), cadmium (II), mercury (I) and (II), gallium (III), indium (III), thallium (I), tin (II), lead (II), bismuth (III), tellurium (IV), and polonium (IV). From the extraction constant it is evident that the order of extractability of metal dithizonates is as follows: palladium (II), gold (III), mercury (II), silver (I), copper (II), bismuth (III), platinum (II), indium (III), zinc (II), cadmium (II), cobalt (II), lead (II), nickel (II), tin (II), and thallium (I) (I 48).

Thus the extraction from dilute mineral acid solution (0·1–0·5 M) would permit the separation of silver, mercury, copper, palladium, and gold from the other metals ($c_{HA} \sim 10^{-4}$ M). Bismuth requires a slightly acid medium; zinc, cadmium, lead, and nickel require a neutral or mildly alkaline medium for their extraction. Although dithizone reacts with many metals, the extraction may be made more selective by the use of various masking agents (I 48).

TABLE 22. MASKING AGENTS USED IN DITHIZONE EXTRACTION

Conditions	Metal reacting
Basic solution containing cyanide	Pb, Bi, Sn, Tl (In)
Dilute acid solution containing thiocyanate	Hg, Au, Cu
Dilute acid solutions containing thiocyanate and cyanide	Hg, Cu
Dilute acid solutions containing bromide or iodide	Pd, Au, Cu
Dilute acid solutions containing EDTA	Hg, Ag
Slightly acid solutions (pH 4–5) containing thiosulphate and cyanide	Sn, Zn
Slightly alkaline solutions containing diethanolaminedithiocarbamate	Zn
Strongly alkaline solutions containing tartrate or citrate	Cd, Cu, Ag, Co, Ni, Tl

All metal dithizonates and dithizone itself absorb strongly in the visible region so that absorptiometric determinations can be carried out. In general, determinations with dithizone can be effected by a monocolour, a bicolour ("mixed colour"), or a reversion procedure (I 4, S 14). Extractive titration can sometimes be used as well.

In the monocolour method the aqueous phase, after being adjusted to the appropriate conditions, is shaken with successive portions of a solution of dithizone in an immiscible organic solvent until the green colour of the reagent solution remains unchanged. The combined extracts are then shaken with a dilute solution of ammonia to remove the excess of dithizone (see Fig. 9). This step involves a source of error; if the alkalinity of the wash solution is not high enough, an appreciable amount of dithizone may be left in the organic phase; if the alkalinity is too high, some of the metal dithizonate may be decomposed. Good results can be obtained only if the standard comparison solutions are prepared under identical conditions (S 14).

In the bicolour (mixed colour) method (G 45, S 14), the excess of dithizone remains in the organic phase with the metal dithizonate. The amount of the metal present is determined with the aid of a calibration curve from the absorption of light by the metal dithizonate and from the absorption by the excess of dithizone remaining after the reaction is completed. In Fig. 46 it can be seen that a minimum in the absorption curve of dithizone is at about 510 mμ and many dithizonates (e.g. lead dithizonate in Fig. 46) absorb strongly close to this wavelength. On the other hand, most metal dithizonates do not absorb light above 600 mμ, whereas the strongest absorption of dithizone solutions in carbon tetrachloride or chloroform is at approximately 620 mμ.

Another possibility consists in measuring the absorbancy at two suitable wavelengths, namely one at which dithizone absorbs strongly and the metal dithizonate as little as possible, and a second at which the reverse is true. The concentration of metal is then calculated from these absorbancies and the extinction coefficients of dithizone and the metal dithizonate at the two wavelengths. At 620 mμ the molar extinction coefficient of dithizone in carbon tetrachloride is 3·63 × 10⁴, and at 450 mμ it is 2·14 × 10⁴ (W 6); with chloroform as solvent the extinction coefficients are 4·00 × 10⁴ and 1·6 × 10⁴ at 605 mμ and 445 mμ respectively (I 48). The advantage of this method lies in the possibility of using solutions of dithizone whose concentrations are not exactly known.

Irving *et al.* (I 4, I 6, I 7, B 113) proposed a procedure for the determination of metals based on the principle of reversion, i.e. on the increase in the

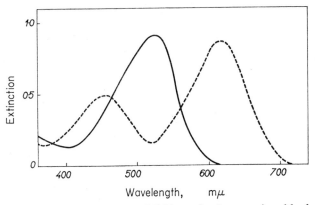

Fig. 46. Absorption curves of dithizone (broken curve) and lead dithizonate (full curve) in carbon tetrachloride.

absorbancy due to dithizone (at approximately 620 mμ) produced by quantitative back-extraction of the metal in question into the aqueous phase and the concomitant liberation of an equivalent amount of dithizone. Mineral acids can be used as reversion reagents for bismuth and lead, iodide for silver and mercury, and 3,3-dimercaptopropanol is a general reversion agent for dithizonates over the wide pH range.

After isolation of metals in the form of their dithizonates polarographic (see, for example, F 31, S 123), spectrographic (G 25, P 43) and other methods can also be used for their determination. For the determination of submicrogram amounts of various metals, substoicheiometric determination by isotopic dilution has been recommended (R 32, R 33, S 103, S 149).

Dithizone can also be used for the purification of many materials (see, for example, I 48, D 13).

Dithizone extractions have been reviewed by Fischer (F 9, F 12, F 14, F 17, F 25) and by Wichmann (W 23). An excellent book on dithizone and its application in micro- and trace-analysis, was recently published by Iwantscheff (I 48).

The conditions for the isolation and determination of metals in the form of their dithizonates are reviewed in Table 23.

TABLE 23. A SURVEY OF CONDITIONS FOR THE ISOLATION AND DETERMINATION
OF METALS

Metal	Optimum conditions for extraction
Ag (I)	Silver can be quantitatively extracted from 4 M sulphuric acid up to pH 7 with an excess of dithizone solution in carbon tetrachloride (25–50 μM) (F 10, K 60). In the acid medium a yellow primary dithizonate is formed (solubility $> 2 \times 10^{-3}$ M); in neutral or basic medium the secondary silver dithizone is formed, which is red-violet and virtually insoluble in carbon tetrachloride ($< 10^{-6}$ M) or in other organic solvents. Once formed, primary silver dithizonate is not appreciably converted into secondary even when the carbon tetrachloride solution is shaken with 5% sodium hydroxide solution.
	The extraction constant of primary silver dithizonate has been determined by some authors and is rather high. Log $K = 7 \cdot 16$ (K 60), $7 \cdot 6$ (T 37), $8 \cdot 94$ (P 38), $6 \cdot 5$ (D 24).
	The extraction of silver in highly acid solution is rather selective. Other metals extracted at such acidity are palladium, gold, and mercury. Copper can be extracted to a greater or less extent depending on its concentration. Mercury can be separated from traces of silver by extraction with 0·01% H₂Dz in carbon tetrachloride from a solution 0·02 M in hydrochloric acid and containing 10% sodium chloride. Silver can then be extracted by raising the pH to 5 (I 48). Another method depends on the back-extraction of silver from the combined mercury and silver dithizonates with 5% sodium chloride in 0·015 M hydrochloric acid or with 1% potassium thiocyanate in 0·1 M sulphuric acid (I 48).
	Palladium can be removed by a preliminary extraction with dimethylglyoxime; copper and many other metals can be masked at pH 4–5 (acetate or citrate buffer) by 0·001–0·50 M EDTA solutions (C 55, K 16, S 145).
	Chloride, bromide, iodide, and cyanide interfere strongly. This fact has been used for the indirect determination of traces of chloride (I 47, S 142), bromide and iodide (K 42) and cyanide (M 57).
	Also chloroform (log $K = 5 \cdot 8$–$6 \cdot 0$) (D 24, K 60), chlorobenzene (log $K = 6 \cdot 5$) (D 24), bromobenzene (log $K = 6 \cdot 5$) (D 24), benzene (log $K = 6 \cdot 3$) (D 24, K 16), toluene (log $K = 6 \cdot 2$) (D 24) and dichloromethane (log $K = 6 \cdot 0$) (D 24) are suitable organic solvents for silver dithizonate.
	Solutions of silver dithizonate in carbon tetrachloride absorb strongly at 426 mμ ($\varepsilon = 30,500$) (I 27). This dithizonate rapidly decomposes when exposed to light; if kept in the dark, it is fairly stable. For the determination of traces of silver extractive titration can be used as well as monocolour or mixed colour methods (F 10, E 14). From the extraction constants for silver dithizonate and copper dithizonate it follows that silver can displace copper quantitatively from its dithizonate and can be determined thus (M 67).
	The dithizone method has been used for the determination of silver in copper (C 55, F 10, M 73), zinc (C 55, F 10), lead (C 55, J 16), metallic bismuth (S 79), high purity gold (the gold was separated by a preliminary extraction with ethyl acetate) (M 71), in various alloys (K 16), in galena ores (B 83), and in water (F 10, K 79).
Au (III)	Gold (III) reacts with dithizone in dilute mineral acids (e.g. 0·5 M sulphuric acid) to give a primary complex which has a yellow-brown colour in carbon tetrachloride. Its solubility in this solvent is about 10^{-5} M. In an alkaline medium secondary dithizonate is formed which is insoluble in water and

TABLE 23 (*continued*)

Metal	Optimum conditions for extraction
Au (III) (*cont.*)	difficultly soluble in organic solvents (F 9, F 12). Once formed, the primary gold dithizonate is not transformed into secondary even when shaken with dilute ammonia so that the monocolour method can be used for the determination of gold (E 13). In acid media only silver, mercury, palladium, and large amounts of copper interfere. The first two elements may be masked by chloride, bromide or iodide (I 48, S 79, Y 14); palladium can be removed by a preliminary extraction with dimethylglyoxime (Y 14). In chloroform gold dithizonate absorbs strongly at 450 mμ ($\varepsilon = 2\cdot4 \times 10^4$) (E 13). For the determination of gold in bismuth (S 79) or in ores (E 13, S 79, T 31, Y 14) direct extractive titration has been recommended as well as monocolour methods.
Bi (III)	Bismuth (III) can be quantitatively extracted as primary dithizonate by excess of dithizone (25–50 μM solutions in carbon tetrachloride) at pH 3–10. The extraction constant has been determined by several workers. Log $K = 10\cdot76$ (P 38); $9\cdot75$ (aqueous phase, ammonium acetate) (K 60); $9\cdot54$ ($0\cdot1$ M potassium cyanide) (K 60); and $9\cdot98$ (aqueous phase $0\cdot2$ M perchlorate) (B 111). Using 25 μM reagent solution in chloroform, quantitative extraction takes place at pH 5–11. Log $K = 5\cdot2$–$5\cdot3$ (K 60); $8\cdot7$ (B 111). Benzene (log $K = 9\cdot75$), toluene (log $K = 9\cdot60$) or isoamyl acetate (log $K = 9\cdot23$) can also be used as suitable solvents (B 111). The solubility of bismuth dithizonate in carbon tetrachloride or in chloroform is rather low ($\sim 1\cdot2 \times 10^{-5}$ M) (I 48). In the presence of cyanide, the extraction of bismuth becomes rather selective for only lead (II), thallium (I) and tin (II) also react with dithizone under these conditions (F 9, H 3, O 9). Tin and thallium do not react in the stannic or thallic state, and lead can be separated from bismuth on the basis of the very different values of extraction constants for the dithizonates of bismuth and lead respectively. According to Fischer and Leopoldi (F 15, Y 12) extraction from aqueous solution at pH ~ 3 using 25–50 μM dithizone solution in carbon tetrachloride brings all the bismuth into the organic phase and leaves all the lead in the aqueous phase. An alternative method consists in shaking the organic extract, containing lead and bismuth dithizonate, with a buffer having such a pH that lead is back-extracted into the aqueous phase while bismuth is left in the organic phase. For carbon tetrachloride and chloroform solutions buffers of pH $2\cdot5$ and $3\cdot5$ respectively have been recommended (I 48, H 39). Alleged masking of lead by the magnesium complex with EDTA at pH 10 (B 41) could not be verified by the present author. Solutions of bismuth dithizonate in carbon tetrachloride absorb strongly at 490 mμ ($\varepsilon = 80,000$) (I 48). This complex is destroyed by shaking with diluted ammonia and therefore for the determination of bismuth only extractive titration or the mixed colour method can be used (I 48). The dithizone method has been used for the determination of traces of bismuth in copper (Y 5), in high purity lead (after a preliminary extraction of bismuth as cupferrate) (I 40), in high purity tellurium (I 41) or in biological materials (L 10, H 36, H 39).

TABLE 23 (*continued*)

Metal	Optimum conditions for extraction
Cd (II)	Quantitative extraction of cadmium by 25 μM dithizone solution in carbon tetrachloride takes place at pH 6·5–14 (D 11, K 46, I 48). Log $K = 2·14$ (B 2); 1·6 (K 60). With chloroform as solvent quantitative extraction of cadmium dithizonate occurs in the pH region from 7 to 14; log $K = 0·5$ (K 60, S 29). The solubility of cadmium dithizonate in chloroform (1·3 × 10⁻⁴ M) is much higher than its solubility in carbon tetrachloride (1·4 × 10⁻⁵ M) (I 48). From the extraction constants of metal dithizonates it is evident that many metals will accompany cadmium in the extraction procedure. Cadmium shows little tendency to form cadmate ions and at high concentrations of sodium hydroxide and in the presence of tartrate or citrate it can be separated from amphoteric metals such as zinc and lead; furthermore, bismuth and indium do not interfere under these conditions. Mercury, silver, copper, and other metals reacting in mineral acid medium may be pre-extracted with dithizone under these conditions (I 48). Nickel and cobalt can be masked by cyanide in strongly alkaline medium (S 5). A preliminary extraction of nickel as dimethylglyoximate has also been recommended (P 31, S 70). The red-violet cadmium dithizonate absorbs strongly at 520 mμ in carbon tetrachloride and in chloroform ($\varepsilon = 8·8 \times 10^4$ and 8·56 × 10⁴ for the two solvents respectively) (I 48). Monocolour or mixed colour methods have been used for the determination of traces of cadmium in zinc (F 5, F 13), metallic uranium (I 42, M 94, S 2), metallic bismuth (S 79), chromium (M 124), aluminium salts (T 42), nickel-plating baths (S 49), tungsten (G 20), in silicate rocks (S 9, S 93), sea water (M 126) and in biological materials (C 20, S 70).
Co (II)	Quantitative extraction of cobalt (II) by 25 μM dithizone solution in carbon tetrachloride takes place at pH 5·5–8·5 (E 17, K 60). Log $K = 1·6$ (K 60); 0·10 (P 38). With chloroform as organic solvent quantitative extraction of cobalt was obtained at pH 8 (K 60); log $K = -1·5$ (K 60). The solubility of the cobalt complex in carbon tetrachloride and chloroform corresponds to 1·6 × 10⁻⁴ M and 1·4 × 10⁻³ M solutions respectively (I 48). Cobalt dithizonate absorbs strongly at 542 mμ ($\varepsilon = 5·92 \times 10^4$) when dissolved in carbon tetrachloride (I 48). Although the dithizone method for the determination of cobalt is not selective it has been used for determination of this metal in silicate rocks (S 93), in soil extracts (H 26), and in biological materials (G 4, S 21).
Cu (I)	Copper (I) is quantitatively extracted by the excess of a 50 μM solution of H₂Dz in carbon tetrachloride from 1 M sulphuric acid up to pH 10 (F 16). In acid solutions the brown primary dithizonate is formed; the secondary dithizonate, formed in basic solutions, is practically insoluble in carbon tetrachloride (I 48).
Cu (II)	Quantitative extraction of copper (II) by 50 μM H₂Dz in carbon tetrachloride takes place at pH 1–4. Log $K = 10·53$ (G 6, K 60); 9·56 (P 38). Under these conditions primary copper dithizonate is formed. At pH higher than 7 copper can be quantitatively extracted as a secondary dithizonate. The

TABLE 23 (*continued*)

Metal	Optimum conditions for extraction
Cu (II) (*cont.*)	solubility of both complexes in carbon tetrachloride, as well as in chloroform, is of order 10^{-3} M (I 48).
	Chloroform can also be used as a suitable solvent for copper dithizonate; $\log K = 6 \cdot 5$ (K 60).
	As is evident from the high extraction constant of copper dithizonate, copper can be separated in diluted acid from zinc, cadmium, lead, and other metals whose dithizonate have low extraction constants. Only mercury, silver, gold, palladium and large amounts of bismuth interfere.
	The first two elements (and bismuth also) can be masked at pH ~ 1 by a $0 \cdot 1$ M solution of bromide, or more effectively by $0 \cdot 1$ M iodide (I 48). Palladium can be removed by a preliminary extraction with dimethylglyoxime. Another method for the separation of copper from mercury, silver, and bismuth consists in shaking the organic extract of metal dithizonates with $0 \cdot 01$ M hydrochloric acid containing 2% potassium iodide (B 51, M 103). Only copper dithizonate remains in the organic phase whereas the other dithizonates are destroyed.
	Large amounts of ferric ions can oxidize dithizone and therefore the preliminary extraction of ferric chloride from concentrated hydrochloric acid with diethyl ether can be recommended.
	Primary copper dithizonate in carbon tetrachloride absorbs at 550 mμ ($\varepsilon = 4 \cdot 52 \times 10^4$) (I 48).
	For the determination of traces of copper, extractive titration can be used as well as the mixed colour method (A 43, I 48, S 17). The monocolour method cannot readily be applied to the determination of copper because on washing the organic extract with dilute ammonia to remove the excess of dithizone, transformation into secondary dithizonate occurs. The dithizone method has been applied to the determination of copper in iron and steel (E 8, S 14), high purity aluminium (F 12), metallic uranium (M 97), metallic nickel (Y 7), nickel-plating baths (B 89), soil extracts (H 26), mineral oils (A 43), sugar syrups (K 69), and in biological materials (R 4, S 17).
Fe (II)	Iron (II) reacts with H_2Dz in carbon tetrachloride in the pH range from 7 to 9 to form a violet-red primary dithizonate (D 1, I 48). This chelate absorbs strongly at 520 mμ, but it has no analytical uses on account of the narrow pH range for complete extraction (I 48). In more alkaline media ferrous iron is oxidized by atmospheric oxygen to ferric iron which does not react with dithizone.
Fe (III)	Iron (III) does not form a complex with dithizone, but in large amounts of ferric iron may oxidize dithizone and must be reduced by hydroxylamine (I 48).
Ga (III)	At pH $4 \cdot 5$–$6 \cdot 0$ about 90% of trace amounts of gallium can be extracted by 10^{-3} M H_2Dz in chloroform ($\log K = -1 \cdot 3$) (P 36).
Hg (I)	Mercurous ions react with dithizone in acid solution forming orange-yellow primary dithizonate $Hg_2(HDz)_2$. In alkaline solution a violet dibasic dithizonate is formed which is nearly insoluble in water and organic solvents. This chelate has been used for analytical purposes (I 48).

TABLE 23 (*continued*)

Metal	Optimum conditions for extraction
Hg (II)	Mercury (II) can be quantitatively extracted by the excess of a 25–50 μM solution of dithizone in carbon tetrachloride as a primary dithizonate from 6 M sulphuric acid up to pH 4. This complex, once formed, is not destroyed even by shaking with 2 M sodium hydroxide (A 42, I 48, W 33). The solubility of primary mercury (II) dithizonate corresponds to a $1·3 \times 10^{-3}$ M solution (I 48). At pH 4–14 mercury can be quantitatively extracted as the violet dibasic dithizonate which is only slightly soluble in carbon tetrachloride ($6·6 \times 10^{-5}$) (I 48). The extraction constant of primary mercury dithizonate from carbon tetrachloride is very high (log $K = 26·75$–$26·79$) (B 86, K 13, P 38). Chloroform, xylene, and other solvents have been proposed as suitable organic solvents (I 48, Y 1). Only silver, palladium, gold, platinum, and large amounts of copper are extracted simultaneously with mercury from 1 N sulphuric acid. Chloroform solutions are preferable for the isolation of copper in acid medium. In addition the masking of copper by cobalticyanide (B 42, B 43) or by EDTA in slightly acid medium (A 50, F 26, V 9, Y 1) can be recommended. Silver can be masked by chloride (e.g. by 0·1 M hydrochloric acid) or alternatively silver dithizonate can be destroyed and the silver can be back-extracted into a mixture of equal parts of 20% sodium chloride and 0·03 M hydrochloric acid (F 26). Palladium can be removed by preliminary extraction with a solution of dimethylglyoxime in chloroform. Mercury can be back-extracted from the organic phase by shaking with 6% iodide at pH $\sim$ 4 or with 1·5% sodium thiosulphate solution (F 26). The separation of mercury dithizonate from other metal dithizonates on an alumina column has been proposed (A 42). Solutions of the primary mercury dithizonate in carbon tetrachloride absorb strongly at 485 mμ ($\varepsilon = 71·2 \times 10^3$), and the secondary at 515 mμ ($\varepsilon = 23·6 \times 10^3$) (I 48). Solutions of the mercuric complex in organic solvents are markedly sensitive to light and the orange colour changes to greenish-orange. Since the reaction is reversible the original colour is restored in the dark and also by shaking the organic extract with acid. Photochemical decomposition is also prevented if acetic acid is added to the aqueous solution of mercury. Some of the acetic acid is extracted into the organic phase and inhibits the decomposition of mercury dithizonate (R 8). For the determination of mercury by dithizone, extractive titration can be used as well as monocolour, mixed colour or reversion procedures (F 11, G 38, I 48). For highly selective determination of submicroamounts of mercury isotopic dilution analysis was recommended (R 32). The dithizone method has been used for the determination of traces of mercury in copper (I 48, M 62), zinc (I 48), silver (I 48), sodium hydroxide (K 25), coal (V 10), organic mercury fungicides (K 6), organic compounds (E 2), food products (H 34), urine (G 38, M 61), and other biological materials (A 2, A 38, C 16, K 68) and in antifouling compositions (B 42, B 43).
In (III)	Indium (III) can be quantitatively extracted by excess of dithizone at pH 5–6·3 when using carbon tetrachloride (log $K = 4·84$) (M 39, P 37) and at

TABLE 23 (*continued*)

Metal	Optimum conditions for extraction
In (III) (*cont.*)	8·2–9·5 when using chloroform (log $K = 0·6$) (S 31). The solubility of the red primary indium dithizonate in carbon tetrachloride and in chloroform corresponds to $7·8 \times 10^{-4}$ M and $1·1 \times 10^{-3}$ M solutions respectively (I 48).
	Chlorobenzene (log $K = 3·0$), bromobenzene (log $K = 3·0$), or toluene (log $K = 3·3$) can also be used as a suitable organic solvent (S 31).
	Mercury, silver, palladium, gold, and copper can be separated from indium by a preliminary extraction with dithizone at pH 1–2 (K 47). Other metals can be masked by 1% cyanide at pH ~ 8. Only bismuth, lead, tin (II), and thallium (I) will interfere (I 48). Sodium thiosulphate at pH 5–6 masks bismuth and lead (A 45).
	Solutions of indium dithizonate in carbon tetrachloride absorb at 510 mμ ($\varepsilon = 8·7 \times 10^4$) (A 45). For the determination of indium extractive titration can be used as well as the mixed colour method. A substoicheiometric determination using activation analysis has been recommended (R 37).
	The dithizone method has been used for the determination of indium in uranium and thorium metals and their salts (A 45) and in zinc (C 39).
Mn (II)	Manganese (II) can be extracted at about pH 10 by solutions of dithizone in chloroform as primary dithizonate. The complex has a violet colour in the organic phase and it is quickly destroyed by atmospheric oxidation. This dithizonate has no analytical uses (I 48).
Ni (II)	Nickel (II) can be quantitatively extracted with the excess of a 25 μM solution of dithizone in carbon tetrachloride at pH 6–9; log $K = -0·63$ (P 38), $-1·19$ (K 60). When using chloroform as solvent the extraction occurs in more alkaline regions, viz. pH 8–11 (log $K = -2·93$) (K 60, I 48).
	All metals extractable by dithizone may interfere and for a selective determination of nickel a preliminary extraction with a solution of dimethylglyoxime in chloroform is necessary (S 52, Y 13). Silver, mercury, palladium, gold, copper, and bismuth can be removed by extraction with dithizone at pH < 3.
	The brown-violet nickel dithizonate absorbs strongly at 665 mμ ($\varepsilon = 19,200$) in carbon tetrachloride, and at 670 mμ ($\varepsilon = 20,000$) when chloroform is the organic solvent. The solubility of the nickel complex in either solvent is approximately 10^{-3} M (I 48). For determinations of nickel, extractive titration can be used as well as monocolour and mixed colour methods (I 48, Y 13). The dithizone method has been used for the determination of nickel in metallic uranium (M 95) and in silicate rocks (S 93).
Pb (II)	Lead can be quantitatively extracted from slightly basic solutions by a small excess of dithizone (25–50 μM solutions) in either carbon tetrachloride or chloroform. With the former solvent the optimum pH range has been reported to be 8·0–10 (I 48, M 125), log $K = 0·44$ (K 60)† and with the latter as approximately 8·5–11·5 (B 60, G 50, I 48, S 84), log $K = -0·9$ (O 4, K 60).
	Benzene and other solvents can also be used as organic solvents (K 15).
	The solubility of primary lead-dithizonate in carbon tetrachloride ($1·3 \times 10^{-5}$ M) and in chloroform ($1·4 \times 10^{-4}$ M) is rather low (I 48). In the presence

TABLE 23 (*continued*)

Metal	Optimum conditions for extraction
Pb (II) (*cont.*)	of tartrate or citrate (~ 0.1 M solutions) to prevent precipitation of foreign metal hydroxides and of cyanide as masking agent (0.2–10% solution) only bismuth, thallium (I), tin (II), and indium are simultaneously extracted with lead (C 31, I 48, N 22).

The separation of lead from bismuth can easily be achieved because the extraction constants of the two dithizonates are sufficiently different. Bismuth can be quantitatively removed by a preliminary extraction with a 10^{-3} to 10^{-4} M solution of dithizone at pH ~ 2 for carbon tetrachloride and pH ~ 3 for chloroform as the organic solvent (I 48, H 35). Another method consists in extracting both lead and bismuth as dithizonates from alkaline cyanide solutions into carbon tetrachloride and then shaking them with diluted (0.01 M) mineral acid. Lead (and also thallium (I) and tin (II) if present) passes into the aqueous phase whereas bismuth remains quantitatively in the organic phase. By using chloroform as solvent, lead can be back-extracted into a phthalate buffer pH ~ 3.4 (B 18, I 48).

The interference of thallium (I) and tin (II) can be overcome by preliminary oxidation. Sulphur dioxide oxidizes tin (II) and reduces iron (III), which can otherwise oxidize dithizone. Lead can also be separated from thallium (I) by extraction at pH ~ 6 or 7.5 by using 50 μM solution of dithizone in carbon tetrachloride and chloroform respectively (I 48).

Small amounts of indium do not interfere at pH 9; larger amounts may be removed by a preliminary extraction from hydrobromic acid with diethyl ether (I 48).

The red solutions of lead (II) dithizonate in carbon tetrachloride and in chloroform absorb strongly at 520 mμ ($\varepsilon = 6.88$–7.24×10^4) (C 46, W 6) and at 518 mμ ($\varepsilon = 6.36 \times 10^4$) (I 48) respectively.

Lead dithizonate is partially destroyed on being shaken with dilute ammonia and therefore extractive titration (W 27) and mixed colour methods are preferable to the monocolour method (F 5). The reversion method has also been used for the determination of lead (I 18).

The dithizone method is undoubtedly the best for the determination of traces of lead (C 14, M 40, R 11). It has been used for the determination of lead in copper (S 75), tin and tin base alloys (M 64, O 14), nickel (Y 7), indium (V 16), uranium (S 3), manganese (G 27), chromium (M 124), high purity tellurium (I 41, K 21) and telluric acid (V 13), steel (B 87, Y 11, Y 12), antimony sulphide (N 22), monazites (P 50), rocks (B 46, S 7, S 14, S 93, S 127) and igneous materials (M 41), pharmaceutical chemicals (B 17, S 24), gasolines and naphthas (G 41), sugar (G 39) and other foodstuffs (L 15, L 16), human tissues and excreta (H 35, M 2, T 32), various biological and organic materials (C 14, C 17, B 16, G 1, I 18, K 67, W 21, W 27, W 29), natural waters (A 6, M 56), and in air (S 85).

| Pd (II) | Palladium can be quantitatively extracted by a small excess of dithizone even from very acid solutions when using carbon tetrachloride as the organic solvent. In acid solutions a green-brown primary dithizonate is formed whose solubility corresponds to a 4.5×10^{-4} M solution, whereas in neutral media a red-violet secondary dithizonate is formed which is practically insoluble in organic solvents. Once formed, the primary dithizonate is very stable. It is not destroyed even by shaking with 6 M sulphuric acid or 2 M sodium hydroxide (I 48, S 14). |

TABLE 23 (*continued*)

Metal	Optimum conditions for extraction
Pd (II) (*cont.*)	At pH < 0 only silver, mercury, and gold can interfere; silver can be back-extracted from the organic phase with 0·5 M hydrochloric acid. Palladium can be separated from mercury, gold, and large amounts of copper by a preliminary extraction with dimethylglyoxime (Y 14). In carbon tetrachloride the palladium dithizonate absorbs strongly at 620 mμ. For the determination of palladium, extractive titration can be used as well as monocolour and mixed colour methods (I 48, Y 14).
Po	About 95% of polonium can be extracted at pH 0–5 by a 400 μM solution of dithizone in chloroform, and at pH 0·6–9 when using carbon tetrachloride as solvent (B 81). Cyanide and citrate do not interfere (K 39). The complex extracted has probably the composition $PoO(HDz)_2$ (B 12, I 43). Dithizone extraction has been used for the separation of polonium (RaF) from bismuth (RaE) and lead (RaD). When the organic extract containing polonium and bismuth dithizonates is shaken with 0·3–0·5 M hydrochloric acid, bismuth passes into the aqueous phase whereas polonium remains unaffected in the organic phase (B 81). This method has also been used for the isolation of ^{210}Po (RaF) and ^{218}Po (RaA) from spring water (I 44).
Pt (II)	Platinum (II) can be readily extracted from 1–10·5 N sulphuric acid with a 0·01% solution of dithizone in benzene. Interfering elements can be removed by washing the organic extract with hydrochloric acid or by a preliminary extraction with a saturated solution of dithizone in benzene before the reduction of platinum (IV) with stannous chloride. The excess of dithizone can be washed out completely by diluted aqueous ammonia containing sodium sulphite and absorbancy at 490 mμ ($\varepsilon = 26,000$) or at 720 mμ ($\varepsilon = 27,000$) is then available for the determination of platinum by the monocolour method (K 17). Extraction titration can also be used for the determination of traces of platinum (Y 14). The dithizone method has been used for the determination of platinum in high purity gold (the gold was first removed by repeated extractions with isopropyl ether from hydrobromic acid) (M 72).
Sn (II)	Divalent tin reacts with dithizone at pH 5–9 to form a red complex extractable into carbon tetrachloride (log $K = -2$) (P 38). Tin (II) dithizonate is not stable for the divalent tin is oxidized with atmospheric oxygen to the tetravalent state which does not react with dithizone; it has therefore no practical uses (I 48).
Te (IV)	More than 95% of carrier-free tellurium (^{129m}Te) can be extracted by a $1·8 \times 10^{-3}$ M solution of dithizone in carbon tetrachloride from 0·1–1·0 M mineral acid solutions. At higher pH values the extraction of tellurium decreases (M 1). The complex has its maximum absorbancy at 430 mμ (M 1).
Tl (I)	In alkaline solution thallium (I) forms a primary dithizonate which can be extracted into carbon tetrachloride (log $K = -3·5$) (P 37) or into chloroform (I 48). Only about 50% of thallium was found to be extracted from 1 M sodium hydroxide if carbon tetrachloride was used as organic solvent. By using chloroform as solvent about 80% of thallium can be isolated by single extraction at pH 11–14·5 in the presence of the excess of dithizone. At pH < 7 thallium is back-extracted into the aqueous phase.

TABLE 23 (*continued*)

Metal	Optimum conditions for extraction
Tl (I) (*contd.*)	Only lead, bismuth, and stannous tin accompany thallium during dithizone extraction in the presence of cyanide as masking agent. However, bismuth and indium do not interfere at pH > 12 and lead at pH > 13. A preliminary extraction of thallium as $HTlCl_4$ with diethyl ether greatly increases the selectivity of the method (I 48). The red solutions of thallium dithizonate in chloroform absorb strongly at 505 mμ ($\varepsilon = 3{\cdot}36 \times 10^4$) (I 48). The dithizone method has been used for the isolation of thallium from many elements (O 8) and for the determination of this element in various ores (S 74).
V (V)	At pH $\sim$ 4 metavanadate forms a complex with dithizone which is soluble in water and in butanol (B 67).
Zn (II)	Quantitative extraction of zinc with an excess of a 25 μM solution of dithizone in carbon tetrachloride takes place at pH 6–9·5 (log $K = 2{\cdot}0$–$2{\cdot}3$) (I 13, K 60). With the same concentration of dithizone in chloroform the extraction is complete in more alkaline regions at pH 7–10 (I 48, H 25). Log $K = 0{\cdot}64$ (K 60); $1{\cdot}0$ (I 13). The solubility of zinc dithizonate in carbon tetrachloride or in chloroform is relatively high ($> 10^{-3}$ M) (I 48). Since many other metals react with dithizone under the same conditions it is necessary to use masking agents to prevent their interference. Sodium diethyldithiocarbamate which has been extensively applied for the determination of zinc in biological materials (S 14) is not a suitable masking agent as it reduces the colour intensity of zinc dithizonate by forming colourless zinc diethyldithiocarbamate. Thiosulphate at pH 4–5·5 largely prevents the extraction of copper, mercury, silver, gold, bismuth, lead, and cadmium (B 44, F 22); cobalt can be masked by dimethylglyoxime (J 14). The ideal masking agent for a highly selective determination of zinc is diethanolaminedithiocarbamate, bis-(2-hydroxyethyl)-dithiocarbamate (K 11, K 13, M 29, S 48, S 103, Z 2). Solutions of zinc dithizonate in carbon tetrachloride and chloroform have their absorption maxima at 535 mμ ($\varepsilon = 96,000$) (C 46) and at 530 mμ ($\varepsilon = 88,000$) (I 48) respectively. The determination of zinc can be carried out by extractive titration as well as by mixed colour methods (I 48, K 61). The substoicheiometric method using isotopic dilution has been recommended as a highly selective and sensitive determination of zinc (S 103). The dithizone method has been used for the determination of traces of zinc in cadmium (B 11, M 26), nickel (F 1, Y 10), uranium (M 96), antimony (H 2), steels (B 88, M 14), germanium dioxide (Z 2), silicate rocks (S 93), meteorites (N 20), natural waters (A 3), soil extracts (H 26), foodstuffs (F 22), in tissues (B 38), urine (K 1), in plant and other biological materials (C 49, J 14, B 39, R 4).

* The value of log $K = -3{\cdot}5$ reported in V 18 seems to be too low.

5.10.2. *Di-(o-tolyl)thiocarbazone (o,o-dimethyldithizone)*

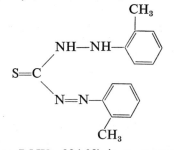

o,o-Dimethyldithizone (M.Wt. 284·38) is more weakly acidic than dithizone itself. The reagent may have some advantages in the determination of copper, mercury, and silver. The reagent absorbs at 460 mμ and 628 mμ whereas the copper, mercury, and silver chelates have their absorption maxima at 538 mμ, 486 mμ, and 476 mμ respectively (T 7). Mercury and silver can be extracted at pH $\sim$ 1; copper can be quantitatively extracted at pH 2–4·5. Zinc, cadmium, lead, and bismuth in a citrate medium do not react with the reagent up to pH 6·3 (T 7).

5.10.3. *Di-(p-tolyl)thiocarbazone (p,p-dimethyldithizone)*

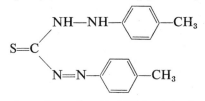

The absorption maxima of *p,p*-dimethyldithizonates in carbon tetrachloride lie at longer wavelengths than those of unsubstituted dithizonates and the extraction coefficients are a little larger (T 6). The stabilities of these complexes are lower than those of dithizonates (B 112, T 6).

5.10.4. *Di-(o-diphenyl)thiocarbazone*

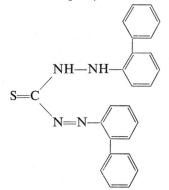

The absorption spectra of the reagent (M.Wt. 408·53) and its metal complexes in carbon tetrachloride show the same shape as those of dithizone but, except for bismuth, the absorption peaks appear at longer wavelengths (T 14).

Silver and mercury ($\log K = 25\cdot13$) are quantitatively extracted at pH $> 0\cdot4$, copper ($\log K = 9\cdot91$) at pH $> 1\cdot9$. Lead, zinc, and bismuth could not be extracted quantitatively from an acetate medium (pH $\sim 5\cdot5$) or from phosphate buffers (pH < 8), but cadmium could be quantitatively extracted from phosphate buffers at pH < 7 (T 14).

5.10.5. Di-(p-diphenyl)thiocarbazone

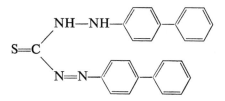

This reagent has been used for the extraction of the following metals: silver, bismuth, cadmium, copper, mercury, lead, and zinc (T 14).

5.10.6. Di-(p-chlorophenyl)thiocarbazone (p,p-dichlorodithizone)

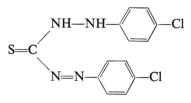

A $1\cdot1 \times 10^{-4}$ M solution of the reagent (M.Wt. 408·53) in carbon tetrachloride has been used for the extraction of bismuth ($\log K = 11\cdot25$; $\text{pH}_{1/2} = 0\cdot8$) (B 112).

5.10.7. Di-(o-bromophenyl)thiocarbazone (o,o-dibromodithizone)

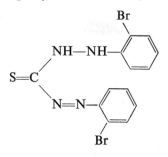

The absorption spectra of the reagent (M.Wt. 414·15) show the same shape as those of dithizone and its complexes, but the absorption peaks are shifted to the longer wavelengths (I 17, T 13). The reagent forms extractable complexes with mercury (II) (log $K = 26·30$, maximum absorbancy at 485 mμ), with silver (548 mμ), with copper (log $K = 7·06$, maximum absorbancy at 545 mμ), with lead (518 mμ), with cadmium (532 mμ), and with zinc (538 mμ) (T 13).

5.10.8. *Di-(p-bromophenyl)thiocarbazone (p,p-dibromodithizone)*

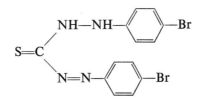

Extractable complexes are formed with mercury (log $K = 26·91$, maximum absorbancy 502 mμ) (T 13), with bismuth (log $K = 11·1$, maximum absorbancy at 500 mμ) (B 112), with copper (log $K = 9·0$, maximum absorbancy at 565 mμ) (T 13), with lead (542 mμ), and with zinc (552 mμ).

5.10.9. *Di-(p-iodophenyl)thiocarbazone (p,p-diiododithizone)*

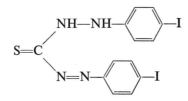

The reagent (M.Wt. 511·16) has been used for the extraction of micro amounts of bismuth. When using a $1·1 \times 10^{-4}$ M solution of the reagent in carbon tetrachloride, log $K = 9·75$ and pH$_{1/2} = 0·9$. The complex absorbs at 505 mμ (B 112).

5.10.10. *Di-(β-naphthyl)thiocarbazone*

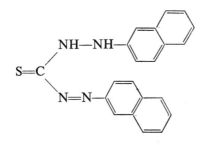

Di-(β-naphthyl)thiocarbazone (M.Wt. 356·40) is similar in its properties to dithizone, but it is a weaker acid (log K_{HA} + log p_{HA} = 12·74 when tetrachloride was used as organic solvent) (G 47).† It reacts with the same metals as dithizone, giving strongly coloured complexes soluble in carbon tetrachloride or chloroform.

Pure di-(β-naphthyl)thiocarbazone is not obtainable in good yield. The

TABLE 24. EXTRACTION DATA BY USING DI-(β-NAPHTHYL)THIOCARBAZONE

Metal	Optimum conditions for extraction
Bi (III)	Bismuth (III) can be extracted at pH $\sim$ 2 by using a 1·1 × 10^{-4} M solution of the reagent in carbon tetrachloride. Log K = 6·75; pH$_{1/2}$ = 1·58 (B 112); log K = 8·9 (G 48, G 49). The complex absorbs at 520–530 mμ with ε = 170,000 (B 108, G 47, G 49).
Cd (II)	Cadmium can be extracted from strongly basic solutions containing tartrate with a solution of the reagent in carbon tetrachloride or chloroform (log K = 1·6) (G 49). Under these conditions zinc, lead, and bismuth are left in the aqueous phase.
Co (II)	Complete extraction of cobalt by a solution of the reagent in chloroform takes place at pH 9·8 (citrate buffer).
Cu (II)	With a 200% excess of reagent, the extraction of copper begins at pH > 1 but it is only complete at pH 9–10 (M 33).
Hg (II)	Mercury (II) can be extracted from dilute mineral acids with a solution of the reagent in chloroform. The chief advantage is said to lie in the stability of the mercury chelate when exposed to light (M 37). The method has been used for the determination of mercury in urine (M 37).
Ni (II)	Nickel (II) can be extracted at pH 6·9–10·2 with a solution of the reagent in carbon tetrachloride (log K = 0·2) (G 49). The complex absorbs at 533 mμ (ε = 93,000) (G 47, G 48).
Pb (II)	Lead can be completely extracted from an ammoniacal buffer of pH = 9·8 by a solution of the reagent in chloroform. This method has been used for the determination of lead in biological materials (V 14).
Zn (II)	Zinc can be quantitatively extracted at pH 8–10 by an excess of the reagent dissolved in chloroform (M 33). When the chloroform extract is shaken with 2 M hydrochloric acid, zinc is brought into the aqueous phase whereas cobalt and copper remain in the organic phase. Carbon tetrachloride is also a suitable solvent (log K = 4·5) (G 48, G 49). The zinc chelate absorbs strongly at 533 mμ (ε = 170,000) (G 49). Di-(β-naphthyl)thiocarbazone has been used for the determination of zinc in biological materials (C 15).

† Thus the organic reagent cannot be stripped from the organic phase into diluted ammonia and the monocolour method cannot therefore be used (C 45).

commercial product is of low purity and even after purification it may contain little more than one-half of its weight of the active reagent (C 45, H 40, S 14).

Suprunovich (S 141) was the first to use this reagent in analytical chemistry and he claimed that its sensitivity for lead was greater than that of dithizone. No significant difference has been found in the determination of lead and bismuth and the same is likely true for other metals (S 14). Compared with dithizone and its metal complexes, the absorption maxima of di-(β-naphthyl)-thiocarbazone and its metal chelates lie at longer wavelengths. The reagent has no absorption maximum at about 450 mμ.

The greatest advantage of this reagent lies in the possibility of using it for the purification of alkaline solutions.

Extraction data obtained by the use of di-(β-naphthyl)thiocarbazone are summarized in Table 24.

5.10.11. *Di-(α-naphthyl)thiocarbazone*

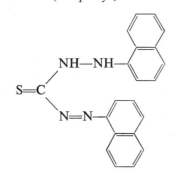

The reagent was synthesized and its fundamental properties investigated by Takei (T 8–12). It shows only one absorption maximum at 681 mμ and there is no absorption peak in the neighbourhood of 450 mμ. Compared with those of dithizone, the absorption maxima of solutions of metal complexes of di-(α-naphthyl)thiocarbazone are all shifted to longer wavelengths.

Extraction data for metal di-(α-naphthyl)thizonates are summarized in Table 25.

5.11. DITHIOCARBAMATES

Carbon disulphide reacts with primary or secondary amines in the presence of sodium hydroxyde to form a dithiocarbamate according to the equation:

$$R_2NH + CS_2 + NaOH \rightarrow R_2N-C\overset{\displaystyle S}{\underset{\displaystyle SNa}{\diagdown}} + H_2O$$

TABLE 25. A SURVEY OF EXTRACTION DATA FOR METAL DI-(α-NAPHTHYL)THIZONATES

Metal	Optimum conditions for extraction
Ag (I)	The silver chelate with the reagent is practically insoluble in organic solvents (T 11).
Bi (III)	Bismuth is only partially extracted at pH 4–8 by solutions of the reagent in organic solvents (T 9–10).
Cd (II)	The cadmium chelate is practically insoluble in organic solvents (T 11).
Cu (II)	Copper (II) can be quantitatively extracted by a solution of the reagent in carbon tetrachloride in the pH region 1·3–5·5 ($\log K = 8·31$). The complex absorbs at 560 mμ ($\varepsilon = 66{,}300$) (T 10–12).
Hg (II)	Quantitative extraction of mercury by a solution of the reagent in carbon tetrachloride occurs at pH 0·5–5 ($\log K = 22·14$) (T 11). The molar extinction coefficient of the complex at 525 mμ is 51,500 (T 10–12).
Pb (II)	Lead is only partially extracted at pH 4–8. The chelate absorbs at 555 mμ (T 11).
Zn (II)	Zinc is only partially extracted at pH 4–8 with a solution of the reagent (T 11).

Dithiocarbamates react with metals which form insoluble sulphides to give insoluble precipitates of the type:

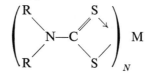

which are soluble in and extractable by a variety of organic solvents.

A review of the analytical uses of dithiocarbamates was recently given by Podtzaynova (P 42).

The most important reagents of this group are sodium diethyldithiocarbamate and diethylammonium diethyldithiocarbamate.

5.11.1. *Sodium diethyldithiocarbamate (cupral)*

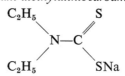

Sodium diethyldithiocarbamate NaDDC (M.Wt. 171·25) is a white crystalline compound. It is soluble in water (35 g per 100 ml) and much less soluble in organic solvents (M 22). In the form of diethyldithiocarbamic acid, however, it is readily soluble and extractable by organic solvents such as chloroform.

The dissociation constant of diethyldithiocarbamic acid is $4·5 \times 10^{-4}$ at

$0°C$ (pK_{HA} = 3·35) (B 76); its partition coefficient between an organic and an aqueous phase equals 343 for carbon tetrachloride ($\log p_{HA}$ = 2·39) and 2360 ($\log p_{HA}$ = 3·37) for chloroform respectively (B 76). From these values it is evident that at a pH lower than 4 more than 99 per cent of the reagent will be in the carbon tetrachloride phase, whereas at a pH higher than 8 the reagent will exist almost entirely in the aqueous phase (B 72).

Diethyldithiocarbamic acid is very unstable even in weakly acidic medium and it is therefore of limited value in acid solutions (M 32). The rate of decomposition is directly proportional to the hydrogen ion concentration. The half-lives of the acid at room temperature are as follows (B 72):

TABLE 26

pH	4·0	5·0	6·0	7·0	9·0
Half-life in minutes	0·5	4·9	51	498	5040

If the acid is dissolved in an organic solvent, its stability is much higher.

Sodium diethyldithiocarbamate reacts with a greater number of elements than dithizone and this fact, together with the limited pH range of existence of its complexes, makes it less useful for the separation or determination of various metals. However, by using EDTA and other masking agents the separations become more selective, as will be evident from Table 27.

Some of the metal diethylcarbamates are coloured and direct absorbtiometric determination is therefore possible. The colour and wavelengths of maximum absorption in chloroform are as follows: bismuth—yellow (370 mμ), cobalt—green (650 mμ), copper—brown (440 mμ), iron (II) and (III)—brown (515 mμ), nickel—yellow-green (395 mμ), and uranium (VI)—red-brown (390 mμ). The reagent itself practically does not absorb at wavelengths higher than 400 mμ (B 72).

By using exchange reactions the following stability order of metal diethyldithiocarbamates was found: mercury (II), palladium (II), silver (I), copper (II), thallium (III), nickel (II), bismuth (III), lead (II), cadmium (II), thallium (I), zinc (II), indium (III), antimony (III), iron (III), tellurium (IV), and manganese (B 76, E 3, E 5).

Thus for instance copper can completely displace thallium (I), nickel (II), bismuth (III), lead (II), cadmium (II), zinc (II), antimony (III), tellurium (IV), and manganese from their dithiocarbamates and thus an indirect absorptiometric determination of these metals is possible (S 38–40).

Other methods, e.g. spectrographic (P 43), flame photometric (S 20), etc., can also be used for the determination of various metals after their extraction as dithiocarbamates (M 20).

A systematic study of the extractability of diethyldithiocarbamates with carbon tetrachloride was carried out by Bode (B 73–75). A summary of extraction data for metal diethyldithiocarbamates is given in Table 27.

TABLE 27. A SURVEY OF EXTRACTION DATA FOR METAL DIETHYLDITHIOCARBAMATES

Metal	Optimum conditions for extraction
Ag (I)	Silver (I) can be completely extracted with carbon tetrachloride in the presence of 0·01–0·03 M NaDDC in the pH region from 4 to 11 (B 75). EDTA ($\sim$ 0·006 M solution) does not interfere. Cyanide ($\sim$ 0·03 M solution) completely masked silver at a pH higher than 8 (B 73). Silver (I) completely displaces copper from its complex with diethyldithiocarbamate and this fact can be used for the indirect determination of silver in copper (K 73).
Al (III)	Aluminium is not extracted into organic solvents in the presence of NaDDC at any pH value (B 73, B 75).
As (III)	Arsenic (III) can be completely extracted at pH 5–6 with carbon tetrachloride in the presence of 0·01–0·03 M reagent solution. In these conditions EDTA ($\sim$ 0·006 M solution) does not interfere. Arsenic is practically not extracted above pH 8 (B 73). Chloroform can also be used for the isolation of arsenic as its diethyldithiocarbamate (N 6). The HDDC method was used for the isolation of arsenic from high purity germanium (G 27, S 1).
Au (III)	Gold (III) can only be incompletely extracted with carbon tetrachloride as its diethyldithiocarbamate. EDTA ($\sim$ 0·006 M solution) does not interfere, but cyanide ($\sim$ 0·03 M solution) at higher pH masks gold completely (B 73). The complex in the carbon tetrachloride phase absorbs in the region 300–800 mμ with absorption peaks at 410 mμ ($\varepsilon = 1970$) and at 474 mμ ($\varepsilon = 1850$) (B 75).
Ba (II)	Barium (II) is not extracted into organic solvents containing NaDDC (B 73).
Bi (III)	Bismuth is quantitatively extracted at pH 4–11 with carbon tetrachloride containing 0·01–0·03 M NaDDC. At pH > 11 in the presence of EDTA ($\sim$ 0·006 M) and cyanide ($\sim$ 0·03 M) the extraction of bismuth is very selective (B 73, I 40). Only thallium (III) is extracted under these conditions (B 73). Selective extraction of bismuth can also be achieved using chloroform as solvent. The last traces of lead and cadmium can be removed from organic phase by stripping with 0·2 M hydrochloric acid (N 8). Bismuth diethyldithiocarbamate has its maximum absorbancy at 366–370 mμ ($\varepsilon = 8620$) (C 8, B 75). However, a measurement of the absorbancy at 400 mμ, although less sensitive, is specific for the bismuth complex (C 8). An indirect determination of bismuth through an exchange reaction with copper has been recommended (S 40). HDDC was used for the determination of bismuth in high purity gold and silver (M 73), in vanadium and niobium (N 8), and in alloys (C 8).
Ca (II)	Calcium is not extracted as a diethyldithiocarbamate with carbon tetrachloride (B 75).
Cd (II)	Quantitative extraction of cadmium with carbon tetrachloride in the presence of 0·01–0·03 M NaDDC takes place at pH 5–11. EDTA ($\sim$ 0·006 M) and KCN (0·03 M) do not interfere at pH 4–6 and at 7–11 respectively (B 73).

TABLE 27 (*continued*)

Metal	Optimum conditions for extraction
Cd (II) (*cont.*)	The solubility of the cadmium complex in carbon tetrachloride is low (2 mg in 25 ml). By using chloroform as solvent the solubility is increased to 2·0 g per 100 ml (M 22). Cadmium can be back-extracted from the organic phase with 1 M hydrochloric acid; mercury, copper and many other metals remain in the extract (L 9, U 11).
Co (III)	Cobalt (III) diethyldithiocarbamate can be quantitatively extracted by carbon tetrachloride at pH 4–11 if 0·01–0·03 M reagent solution is present. EDTA (0·006 M) and KCN ($\sim$ 0·03 M) completely mask cobalt at pH > 8 (B 73). Once formed the cobalt (III) is very stable; the interfering metals co-extracted as dithiocarbamates can be decomposed by stripping the organic extract with diluted acids or with an excess of a mercury salt (P 52). Solutions of cobalt (III) diethyldithiocarbamate in carbon tetrachloride absorb at 300–800 mμ. The maximum absorbancy lies at 367 mμ (ε = 15,700) and at 650 mμ (ε = 549) (B 75). The solubility of this complex was found to be 0·4 g per 100 ml (M 22). Chloroform (solubility 7·5 g per 100 ml) (M 22, L 1) or ethyl acetate (P 52, P 53) can also be used as suitable solvents. Extraction by HDDC was used for the determination of cobalt in nickel (P 53), steels (P 52), rocks (S 118) and in blood serum (P 44).
Cr (III)	Chromium (III) is not extracted as a diethyldithiocarbamate with carbon tetrachloride (B 75).
Cu (II)	Copper (II) can be quantitatively extracted with carbon tetrachloride in the presence of 0·01–0·03 M NaDDC at pH 4–11. EDTA ($\sim$ 0·006 M) can be used as a suitable masking agent for many metals (B 73, C 25, J 5, J 10, F 30, S 37, S 38). Cyanide interferes strongly (B 73). Copper (II) diethyldithiocarbamate in carbon tetrachloride (solubility 0·2 g per 100 ml) (M 22) absorbs from 300 to 800 mμ. The absorption maximum lies at 436 mμ (ε = 13,000) (B 75). At this wavelength only bismuth, thallium (III), gold (III), and large amounts of palladium, platinum, and osmium interfere. By measuring the absorbancy at 600 mμ only gold can interfere in the determination of copper. Chloroform (solubility 3·3 g per 100 ml), xylene, isoamyl acetate and other solvents can also be used for the extraction of the copper complex (L 1, M 22, M 127). The HDDC method has been used for the determination of copper in nickel (K 72, R 10), nickel and cobalt solutions (K 4, P 42), cadmium (G 43, K 44, M 27, P 42), zinc (G 43, K 44), tin (I 1), titanium and zirconium (W 35), tantalum (H 20), selenium (S 128), high purity chromium (Y 4), high purity antimony (P 58), high purity tellurium (M 127), and other metals (P 45). This method has also been used for the determination of copper in alloys (M 59), ores (P 42), sodium hydroxide (J 10), alkali metals of high purity (B 66), water (J 9, N 2, S 147), soils (C 6), plants (F 20) and other biological materials (K 38).
Fe (III)	Iron (III) diethyldithiocarbamate can be quantitatively extracted with carbon tetrachloride (solubility 1·0 g per 100 ml) (M 22) at pH 4–11 if excess of

TABLE 27 (*continued*)

Metal	Optimum conditions for extraction
Fe (III) (*cont.*)	the reagent is present (0·01–0·03 M). EDTA and KCN interfere (B 73). Chloroform (solubility 5·8 g per 100 ml), ethyl acetate, and other solvents have also been recommended for extraction procedures (L 1, M 22, U 11).
Ga (III)	A gallium chelate with the reagent can be quantitatively extracted with ethyl acetate at pH 1·5–5. At higher pH values gallium is not extracted (B 105, T 43). Only partial extraction of a gallium complex takes place at pH < 5 with carbon tetrachloride as solvent (B 75).
Hg (II)	Mercury (II) is quantitatively extracted at pH 4–11 with carbon tetrachloride in the presence of 0·01–0·03 M NaDDC. EDTA (~ 0·006 M) does not interfere and thus can be used as a masking agent for many metals (B 75). The mercury complex absorbs strongly in the ultraviolet region (H 9), but the indirect determination of mercury, based on an exchange reaction with copper diethyldithiocarbamate in the organic phase, has been recommended (S 39).
In (III)	Indium (III) reacts at pH 4–10 with NaDDC when present in excess (0·01–0·03 M) to give a precipitate which is completely extracted into carbon tetrachloride. KCN does not interfere and thus can be used as a suitable masking agent (B 73). By using ethyl acetate as the solvent, quantitative extraction takes place at pH 3–10 (B 105, T 43).
Ir (IV)	Solutions of Na_2IrCl_6 react very slowly with NaDDC; only after 4 days is a precipitate formed which can be extracted into carbon tetrachloride. KCN interferes strongly (B 75).
La (III)	Lanthanum (III) cannot be extracted as a diethyldithiocarbamate into carbon tetrachloride (B 75).
Mg (II)	Magnesium is not extracted by carbon tetrachloride in the presence of NaDDC (B 75).
Mn (II)	At pH 6–9 manganese is oxidized by atmospheric oxygen and in the presence of NaDDC (0·01–0·03 M) it can be quantitatively extracted by carbon tetrachloride (B 73, D 12). EDTA completely masks the extraction of manganese, but KCN does not interfere at pH 7–9 (B 73). Many interfering ions can be removed by preliminary extraction as thiocyanates (S 86). Chloroform can also be used as the organic solvent (S 86). Manganese (III)-diethyldithiocarbamate has its maximum absorbancy at 355 mμ ($\varepsilon = 9520$) and at 505 mμ ($\varepsilon = 3710$). The HDDC method has been used for the determination of manganese in steel (M 55, S 86).
Mo (VI)	Molybdenum (VI) can be extracted as its diethyldithiocarbamate from slightly acid medium by ethyl acetate (T 43). At a higher pH molybdenum is not extracted even when using chloroform as the solvent (T 43, B 75).
Nb (V)	Only incomplete extraction of niobium (V) as diethyldithiocarbamate was observed at pH < 6 when tartrates were present (B 73).
Ni (II)	Complete extraction of nickel with carbon tetrachloride in the presence of 0·01–0·03 M NaDDC (solubility 0·1 g per 100 ml) takes place in the pH

TABLE 27 (*continued*)

Metal	Optimum conditions for extraction
Ni (II) (*cont.*)	range 5–11. EDTA and KCN interfere strongly at any pH value (B 73). Many interfering metals can be removed by ion-exchange methods (C 34). Chloroform (solubility 2·8 g per 100 ml) (M 22), ethyl acetate, isoamyl alcohol, or chlorobenzene can replace carbon tetrachloride as the organic solvent (L 1, E 4). The maximum absorbancy of nickel diethyldithiocarbamate in carbon tetrachloride lies at 326 mμ ($\varepsilon = 34{,}200$) (B 73) and in isoamyl alcohol at 325 mμ ($\varepsilon = 37{,}000$) (C 34). The HDDC method has been used for the determination of nickel in food after preliminary extraction with dimethylglyoxime (A 12), and in human blood (C 34).
Os (IV)	Osmium (IV) is only incompletely extracted by diethyldithiocarbamate in carbon tetrachloride. KCN completely masks the extraction, but EDTA does not interfere (K 75).
Pb (II)	Lead is quantitatively extracted with carbon tetrachloride in the presence of excess of the reagent (0·01–0·03 M) at pH 4–11 (solubility 0·2 g per 100 ml) (M 22). EDTA interferes at higher pH values, but cyanide can be used as suitable masking agent for many metals. In the presence of cyanide ($\sim 0{\cdot}03$ M) only bismuth, thallium (III), and cadmium can be extracted at pH $>$ 8 (B 73). Chloroform (solubility 6·6 g per 100 ml) (M 22), ethyl acetate and a pentanol–toluene mixture have also been recommended for extraction of the lead complex (G 1, G 2, L 1, N 8). Lead diethyldithiocarbamate in organic solvents does not absorb in the visible region, but it can be completely exchanged with copper and determined indirectly as copper diethyldithiocarbamate (S 40, T 26). The method has been used for the isolation and/or determination of lead in thallium (B 94), vanadium and niobium (N 8), selenium (S 128), zirconium and its alloys (W 36), aluminium, copper, and iron (T 26), metallurgical products (K 41), and organic materials (G 2).
Pd (II)	Quantitative extraction of palladium with carbon tetrachloride containing 0·01–0·03 M reagent ensues at pH 4–11. EDTA (0·006 M) does not interfere, but cyanide (0·03 M) completely masks palladium at pH $>$ 8 (B 73).
Po	The diethyldithiocarbamate of polonium, which is formed in acidic solution (pH 1–6), is partially extracted with chloroform, carbon tetrachloride, or amyl alcohol (I 45, K 39).
Pt (IV)	At pH 4–11 only partial extraction of a platinum chelate with the reagent takes place using carbon tetrachloride. EDTA does not interfere, but cyanide completely masks platinum (B 75).
Pu (IV)	A purple-brown complex of plutonium and NaDDC is extractable with amyl acetate or amyl alcohol at pH $\sim$ 3 (H 17).

TABLE 27 (*continued*)

Metal	Optimum conditions for extraction
Re (VII)	Rhenium (VII) is not extracted with carbon tetrachloride in the presence of NaDDC (B 75).
Rh (III)	Rhodium (III) reacts with NaDDC very slowly—even after a day of contact the reaction is not complete. The rhodium complex absorbs at 300–580 mμ (B 75).
Ru (III)	The reaction of ruthenium and NaDDC is also very slow—it is not complete even after a day. When extracted into carbon tetrachloride the ruthenium complex absorbs from 300 to 800 mμ (B 75).
Sb (III)	Quantitative extraction of antimony with carbon tetrachloride in the presence of excess of NaDDC (0·01–0·03 M solution) takes place at pH 4–9·5 (B 73). The solubility of the complex in this solvent is 4·4 g per 100 ml (M 22). In the presence of EDTA ($\sim$ 0·006 M) and KCN ($\sim$ 0·03 M) at pH 8–9·5 only bismuth, tellurium, and thallium are extracted simultaneously with antimony (B 73). The molar extinction coefficient at 350 mμ equals 3370 (B 75).
Sc (III)	Scandium (III) is not extracted in the presence of NaDDC with carbon tetrachloride (B 75).
Se (IV)	Selenium (IV) is completely extracted with carbon tetrachloride in the presence of 0·01–0·03 M NaDDC at pH 4–6·2. At pH 7·5 selenium is practically not extracted. EDTA does not interfere (B 75).
Sn (IV)	Tetravalent tin can be extracted quantitatively with carbon tetrachloride as its complex with NaDDC (solubility 0·1 g per 100 ml) (M 22) from a solution of pH 4 to 6·2. At pH higher than 7·5 tin is practically not extracted even if 0·01–0·03 NaDDC is present. EDTA, citrate, tartrate and phosphate do not interfere (B 73). Chloroform can also be used as a solvent for the extraction of tin diethyldithiocarbamate (solubility 17·0 g per 100 ml) (M 22). The complex absorbs at 300–500 mμ (B 73, B 75).
Sr (II)	Strontium is not extracted with carbon tetrachloride in the presence of NaDDC (B 75).
Ta (V)	Tantalum is not extracted with carbon tetrachloride in the presence of NaDDC (B 75).
Te (IV)	Quantitative extraction of tellurium with carbon tetrachloride in the presence of 0·01–0·03 M reagent solution takes place at pH 4–8·8. At pH > 10 tellurium is practically not extracted (B 73). In the presence of EDTA (0·006 M) or KCN (0·03 M) at pH 8·5–8·8 only bismuth, antimony (III), and thallium (III) are extracted into the organic phase along with tellurium (B 73, P 4). The complex absorbs at 300 to 530 mμ. The maximum of absorbancy lies at 428 mμ (ε = 3160) (B 74, B 75). The HDDC method has been used for the separation of tellurium (IV) from tellurium (VI) (I 3) and for the determination of tellurium in selenium (B 74).

TABLE 27 (*continued*)

Metal	Optimum conditions for extraction
Ti (IV) Th (IV)	Titanium and thorium are not extracted by solutions of NaDDC in carbon tetrachloride (B 75).
Tl (I)	Thallium (I) can be quantitatively extracted with carbon tetrachloride at pH 5–13 in the presence of 0·01–0·03 M NaDDC. EDTA (0·006 M) does not interfere at pH 5–7, cyanide (0·03 M) at pH > 8 (B 73, B 75). In the presence of cyanide at pH ~ 11 only bismuth, cadmium, and lead are co-extracted (B 77). An indirect determination of thallium (I) as thallium (I) diethyldithiocarbamate is based on the quantitative exchange by copper (S 40).
Tl (III)	Quantitative extraction of thallium (III) with carbon tetrachloride or with chloroform takes place at pH 4–11 if 0·01–0·05 M reagent solution is present (B 73, I 40). Cyanide does not interfere (B 73). The thallium (III) complex absorbs at 300–550 mμ. The molar extinction coefficient at 426 mμ is 1330 (B 75).
U (VI)	Uranium (VI) diethyldithiocarbamate is soluble in water and it cannot be extracted into carbon tetrachloride. By using benzene (F 28, F 29), chloroform (L 1), methylisobutylketone (H 14) and other solvents, the uranium (VI) chelate can easily be extracted. The uranium chelate absorbs at 300 to 620 mμ. For its spectrophotometric determination the absorbancy is generally measured at 400 mμ (B 75). The HDDC method was used for separating uranium from various metals (P 59) and for separating ^{233}U from irradiated thorium (H 14).
V (V)	Vanadium (V) is quantitatively extracted in the presence of 0·01–0·03 M NaDDC by carbon tetrachloride at pH 3–6 (B 73, B 75). By using ethyl acetate or chloroform as the solvent quantitative extraction takes place at pH ~ 3 (K 63, T 43). At pH > 7 vanadium is practically not extracted. The vanadium chelate absorbs at 300 to 580 mμ. For the determination of vanadium in, for example, plant materials (J 13) measurement of the absorbancy at 400 mμ ($\varepsilon = 3790$) is generally used (B 75).
W (VI)	Tungsten (VI) diethyldithiocarbamate is not extracted at pH > 5 by carbon tetrachloride (B 75). With ethyl acetate as the solvent the tungsten complex can be extracted at pH 1–3 (T 43).
Y (III)	Yttrium is not extracted as a diethyldithiocarbamate with carbon tetrachloride (B 75).
Zn (II)	At pH 4–11 the zinc chelate with the reagent can be quantitatively extracted with carbon tetrachloride (solubility 10·6 g per 100 ml) (M 22, B 75). Chloroform (M 22) and ethyl acetate (M 12) can also be used as organic solvents. HDDC extraction has been used for the isolation of radiozinc from fission products (M 12), from rubber products (K 74), and from biological materials (S 117).
Zr (IV)	Zirconium is not extracted by solutions of the reagent in carbon tetrachloride (B 75).

5.11.2. *Diethylammonium diethyldithiocarbamate*

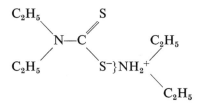

Diethylammonium diethyldithiocarbamate DDDC (M.Wt. 222·49) is less soluble in water, but dissolves readily in chloroform and carbon tetrachloride.

In acid solutions the reagent is quickly destroyed, but its solutions in organic solvents are rather stable (B 77). Bode and Neumann (B 77) determined values of $\log p_{HA} + pK_{HA}$ from the reagent when using carbon tetrachloride and chloroform as solvents: 5·5 and 6·5 for both solvents respectively. From these values it is evident that at any pH lower than 4, DDDC is present almost entirely in the organic phase and at a pH higher than 8 the reagent is transferred practically completely into the aqueous phase.

DDDC forms extractable diethyldithiocarbamates with the same metals as sodium diethyldithiocarbamate but its greatest advantage lies in the possibility of extracting metals even from very acid medium.

A systematic study of the extraction of many metals by a 0·04 per cent solution of the reagent in carbon tetrachloride has recently been carried out by Bode and Neumann (B 77).

Extraction data for many metals are summarized in Table 28.

5.11.3. *Dibenzyldithiocarbamic acid*

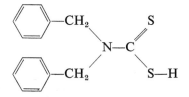

Dibenzyldithiocarbamic acid, which is itself unstable, can generally be used in the form of its potassium salt, its zinc chelate, or as dibenzyl-ammonium dibenzyldithiocarbamate. The potassium salt is generally used in aqueous solutions; the dibenzylammonium salt and the zinc chelate of the reagent are used in organic solvents such as carbon tetrachloride.

The reagent has been used for the isolation and determination of copper in phosphates (K 50), in oils and fats (A 1), and in malt beverages (S 119). When dissolved in an organic solvent copper dibenzyldithiocarbamate absorbs at 435 mμ (A 1).

TABLE 28. A SURVEY OF EXTRACTION DATA FOR METALS

Metal	Optimum conditions for extraction
Ag (I)	Silver can be quantitatively extracted with a 0·04% solution of DDDC in carbon tetrachloride within a wide pH region (from 10 N sulphuric acid or from 3 M hydrochloric acid to pH 12) (B 77).
As (III)	Quantitative extraction of arsenic (III) with 0·04 % solution of the reagent in carbon tetrachloride takes place from 5 N sulphuric or hydrochloric acid up to pH 5 (B 77). By using 1% DDDC in chloroform quantitative extraction of arsenic can be achieved even from 10 N sulphuric acid (W 38). Extraction with DDDC has been used for the isolation of traces of arsenic in germanium or silicon (L 19).
As (V)	Arsenic (V) is not extracted by solutions of the reagent in organic solvents (B 77).
Au (III)	Gold (III) is only partially extracted at pH 1–12 when using 0·04% solution of the reagent in carbon tetrachloride (B 77).
Bi (III)	Bismuth can be quantitatively extracted within a wide pH region (from 10 N sulphuric or 3 M hydrochloric acid to pH 12) by a 0·04% solution of DDDC in carbon tetrachloride (B 77). The extraction of bismuth from 5–6 M hydrochloric acid with a 1% solution of DDDC in chloroform can be used for its separation from lead (S 126, T 29).
Cd (II)	Cadmium is completely extracted at pH 1–12 when using a 0·04% solution of DDDC in carbon tetrachloride (B 77).
Co (II)	Complete extraction of cobalt (II) by a 0·04% solution of the reagent in carbon tetrachloride ensues at pH 2·5–12 ($pH_{1/2} = 1·5$). The complex absorbs at 650 mμ (B 77).
Cr (III)	Chromium (III) is not extracted by a solution of the reagent in carbon tetrachloride (B 77).
Cr (VI)	Quantitative extraction of chromium (VI) can only be achieved by using a 0·25% solution of the reagent in carbon tetrachloride at pH $\sim$ 5 (B 77, L 1).
Cu (II)	Copper (II) can be quantitatively extracted in the range from 10 N sulphuric acid or 7·5 hydrochloric acid up to pH 12 with 0·04% DDDC in carbon tetrachloride (B 77). Potassium iodide serves as a suitable masking agent in acid solutions (A 7). Copper can be separated from bismuth, lead, and other metals by back-extraction of copper from the organic phase with cyanide; bismuth, lead, etc., remain in the extract (L 17). The copper chelate absorbs at 436 mμ (B 77). Extraction with DDDC has been used for the isolation and determination of copper in lead (a chloroform solution of the reagent was used) (L 17), nickel–iron alloys (C 35) and organic materials (W 37).
Fe (II) Fe (III)	Both iron (II) and (III) are quantitatively extracted at pH 2–10 by a 0·04% solution of the reagent in carbon tetrachloride ($pH_{1/2} \sim 2$) (B 77).

TABLE 28 (*continued*)

Metal	Optimum conditions for extraction
Ga (III)	Complete extraction of gallium (III) takes place at pH 4·5–5·5 when 0·04% solution of DDDC in carbon tetrachloride is used (pH$_{1/2}$ ∼ 3) (B 77).
Hg (II)	Mercury (II) is quantitatively extracted from 10 M sulphuric acid or 6 N hydrochloric acid up to pH 12 by a 0·04% solution of the reagent in carbon tetrachloride (B 77).
In (III)	Indium is completely extracted at pH 0–12 by a 0·04% solution of DDDC in carbon tetrachloride (B 77).
Mn (II)	Manganese (II) can be quantitatively extracted at pH 6–9 by a 0·04% solution of DDDC in carbon tetrachloride (pH$_{1/2}$ = 4) (B 77). The complex absorbs at 505 mμ (B 77). Solutions in chloroform can also be used for the extraction of the manganese chelate (C 33). Extraction by DDDC has been used for the determination of manganese in organic materials (W 37).
Mo (VI)	Quantitative extraction of molybdenum (VI) by a 0·04% solution of the reagent in a mixture of carbon tetrachloride and amyl alcohol (4:1) takes place in the range from 10 N sulphuric acid or 2 N hydrochloric acid up to pH 4·5 (B 77).
Nb (V)	Less than 6% of niobium (V) can be extracted by a 0·04% solution of the reagent in carbon tetrachloride. By using 0·4% DDDC in chloroform about 30–40% of niobium can be extracted in the pH range from 2 M hydrochloric acid to pH 3·5. The rate of formation of the niobium chelate is very slow (B 77).
Ni (II)	Nickel is quantitatively extracted from pH 2·5–10 by a 0·04% solution of the reagent in carbon tetrachloride (pH$_{1/2}$ = 1·0). The complex absorbs at 433 mμ (B 77).
Os (IV)	About 30–50% of osmium can be extracted after 5 minutes' shaking at pH 4·6–9 with a 0·04% solution of the reagent in carbon tetrachloride. No osmium is extracted at pH < 2 (B 77).
Pb (II)	Complete extraction of lead takes place at pH 0–12 when a 0·04% solution of DDDC in carbon tetrachloride is used (B 77). Chloroform is also a suitable solvent (H 16).
Pd (II)	Palladium (II) can be quantitatively extracted by a 0·04% solution of DDDC in carbon tetrachloride from 10 N sulphuric acid or hydrochloric acid up to pH 12 (B 77, T 30). Extraction by DDDC has been used for the isolation of palladium from foodstuffs (L 15).
Pt (II)	Divalent platinum can be extracted even from 10 N sulphuric or hydrochloric acids by a 0·04% solution of DDDC in carbon tetrachloride (B 77).
Pt (IV) Rh (III) Ru (III)	Platinum (IV), rhodium (III), and ruthenium (III) are not extracted by a 0·04% solution of the reagent in carbon tetrachloride at any pH investigated (B 77).

TABLE 28 (continued)

Metal	Optimum conditions for extraction
Sb (III)	Only incomplete extraction of antimony (III) takes place throughout the pH range from 10 N sulphuric acid or 5 N hydrochloric acid to pH 10 when using a 0·04% solution of DDDC in carbon tetrachloride (B 77). When a 1% solution in chloroform is used, antimony (III) can be extracted from 1–10 N sulphuric acid (W 38).
Sb (V)	Antimony (V) is not extracted by solutions of DDDC in carbon tetrachloride (B 77).
Se (IV)	Quantitative extraction of selenium takes place in the pH range from 5 M sulphuric or hydrochloric acid to pH 5·5 when using a 0·04% solution of the reagent in carbon tetrachloride. At pH 7·5 selenium is practically not extracted (B 77).
Sn (II)	Divalent tin can be quantitatively extracted from 1–10 N sulphuric acid by a 0·04% solution of the reagent in carbon tetrachloride or by 1% solution in chloroform (B 77, W 38). Extraction by DDDC has been used for the isolation of tin from antimony–tin alloys (L 21).
Sn (IV)	Tin (IV) is not extracted by solutions of DDDC in carbon tetrachloride (B 77).
Te (IV)	Quantitative extraction of tellurium (IV) by 0·04% DDDC in carbon tetrachloride takes place from pH 0 to 8·5 (B 77).
Tl (I)	Thallium (I) can be completely extracted by a 0·04% solution of DDDC in carbon tetrachloride at pH 3·5–12 ($pH_{1/2} = 2$) (B 77).
Tl (III)	By using a 0·04% solution of the reagent in carbon tetrachloride, complete extraction of thallium (III) can be achieved within a wide pH range, viz. from 5 M sulphuric or hydrochloric acid up to pH 12 (B 77).
U (VI)	Uranium (VI) can be quantitatively extracted by a 0·04% solution of DDDC in chloroform at pH 6·5–8. With carbon tetrachloride as solvent, uranium (VI) is practically not extracted (B 77).
V (V)	Vanadium (V) can be quantitatively extracted by a 0·04% solution of DDDC in carbon tetrachloride at pH 4·0–5·5 ($pH_{1/2} = 2–3$) (B 77).
W (VI)	Tungsten (VI) is not extracted by a 0·04% solution of the reagent in carbon tetrachloride. A few per cent of tungsten can be extracted by a 0·04% solution of DDDC in chloroform, but with a 0·4% solution in the same solvent about 70% of tungsten can be extracted from 0·1 M hydrochloric acid (B 77).
Zn (II)	Quantitative extraction of zinc by a 0·04% solution of DDDC in carbon tetrachloride takes place at pH 2·5–12 ($pH_{1/2} = 1·5$) (B 77).

Thallium (III) is extracted by zinc dibenzyldithiocarbamate in carbon tetra-chloride from 0·5 M sulphuric acid. The coloured thallium (III) chelate has its maximum absorbancy at 438 mμ. Copper and bismuth seriously inter-fere but they can be removed by a preliminary extraction with the same reagent after reducing the thallium with sodium sulphite. This method has been used for the determination of thallium in zinc, and zinc sulphate (H 8).

5.11.4. *Ammonium pyrrolidindithiocarbamate*

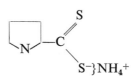

The extraction of metal pyrrolidindithiocarbamates into chloroform was investigated by Malissa and Gomišček (M 21). In the presence of a 0·2 per cent solution of the reagent, iron, cobalt, nickel, vanadium, copper, arsenic, antimony, tin, and lead are practically completely extracted at pH $\sim$ 1. Quantitative extraction of copper, antimony, and tin takes place even from 6 M hydrochloric acid (M 21).

The reagent has been used for determination of bismuth in steel, with EDTA and KCN as masking agents. The molar extinction coefficient of the bismuth complex in carbon tetrachloride at 360 mμ is 9860 (K 64–66).

Spectrographic analysis can also be used for the determination of traces of metals after a preliminary extraction as pyrrolidindithiocarbamates (K 49, W 26).

5.11.5. *Other dithiocarbamates*

Piperidindithiocarbamate has been used for the extraction of ruthenium after a preliminary extraction with hydroxylamine. About 97 per cent of ruthenium can be extracted with chloroform from a 0·1 M solution of the reagent at pH 1–11 (A 44).

5-Phenylpyrazoline-1-dithiocarbamate has been used for the isolation and determination of molybdenum in the presence of tungsten (B 103).

5.12. XANTHATES

Alcohols react with carbon disulphide in alkaline solutions to give xanthates

$$R—OH + KOH + CS_2 = R—O—CSSK + H_2O$$

Xanthates react with metals to give extractable chelates of the type:

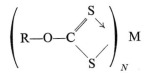

Ethyl-, isopropyl-, isoamyl-, and benzyl-xanthates have been used extensively as organic reagents (S 53), but ethyl xanthates have proved to be the most generally applicable.

5.12.1. *Potassium ethyl xanthate*

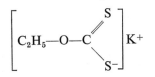

Potassium ethyl xanthate is a pale yellow, crystalline solid soluble in both water and alcohol. It can easily be prepared by reaction of alcohol with carbon disulphide in alkaline medium. The aqueous solution of the reagent is highly alkaline. The solid and its solutions should be stored in stoppered bottles protected from the light. The reagent is commonly used as a 0·1 per cent aqueous solution and should be prepared freshly every few days.

The extraction data for metal xanthates are summarized in Table 29.

5.12.2. *Potassium benzyl xanthate*

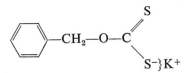

By using excess of the reagent, practically complete extraction of cobalt occurs at pH 0·85–5·2, and of zinc and cadmium at pH 1·9–5·2. In all cases chloroform was used as organic solvent (S 53).

5.13. DIALKYL- AND DIARYL-DITHIOPHOSPHORIC ACIDS

Dialkyl- and diaryl-dithiophosphoric acids react with many metals to give extractable chelates of the type:

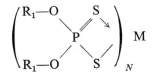

TABLE 29. A SURVEY OF EXTRACTION DATA FOR METAL XANTHATES

Metal	Optimum conditions for extraction
As (III)	Arsenic xanthate can be quantitatively extracted by carbon tetrachloride from 0·1–0·25 M sulphuric acid (D 16). Xanthate extraction has been used for the isolation of arsenic from natural waters, silicates, food, and biochemical materials (K 45, S 138).
Bi (III)	Bismuth forms a yellow precipitate with the reagent at pH $\sim$ 4 (P 39).
Co (II)	A dark green cobalt complex with the reagent can be extracted with carbon tetrachloride at pH 4–9 (P 39). Cyclohexanone is also a suitable solvent (K 80).
Cu (II)	The complex of copper with the reagent can be extracted by diethyl ether at pH 7–8·5 (M 99).
Fe (III)	Iron (III) forms a brown precipitate with the reagent extractable into chloroform (P 39, H 11).
Mo (VI)	In slightly acid medium molybdenum (VI) forms with the reagent a violet-red precipitate soluble in chloroform, amyl alcohol, and other solvents (B 39, G 7, H 9). Extraction with xanthates has been used for the isolation of molybdenum present in steel (M 23, M 24).
Ni (II)	At pH 4–7 nickel forms a yellow-brown precipitate extractable into chloroform (P 39, H 11).
Sb (III)	The antimony (III) complex with the reagent can be extracted from acid media into carbon tetrachloride (K 45).
U (VI)	Uranium (VI) forms with the reagent a coloured complex extractable with chloroform (H 9, H 11).
V	In slightly acid medium vanadium forms a yellow complex, extractable into chloroform or carbon tetrachloride (A 36, H 11).

The most extensively studied reagent of this group is diethyldithiophosphoric acid (B 102).

5.13.1. Diethyldithiophosphoric acid

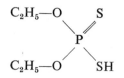

Diethyldithiophosphoric acid was first used for analytical purposes by Busev (B 96) in 1949. It is preferable to use the nickel complex of this acid for it is easily prepared and is readily soluble in water as well as in organic solvents (B 102).

With those elements that form sulphides of very low solubility the reagent gives precipitates which are insoluble in water but soluble in and extractable by various organic solvents. Diethyldithiophosphoric acid is more selective than diethyldithiocarbamate or xanthate for it does not react with vanadium (V), tungsten (VI), tin (VI), gallium (III), iron (II), zinc (II), or cobalt (II).

Extraction data for those diethyldithiophosphates that have so far been studied are summarized in Table 30.

5.14. DITHIOLS

The reagents with grouping

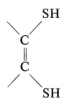

form extractable complexes with some metals; the complexes of molybdenum (VI) and tungsten (VI) are of great importance analytically.

5.14.1. *Toluene-3,4-dithiol*

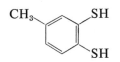

Toluene-3,4-dithiol (M.Wt. 156·25), commonly called "dithiol", is a low melting solid which changes to a colourless oil at 31°C. The reagent is extremely sparingly soluble in aqueous acid solutions, but in consequence of its acidic character ($pK_{HA} = 5.4$; G 13) it dissolves in basic solutions.

Toluene-3,4-dithiol is rapidly oxidized by the air to a disulphide in alkaline as well as in organic solutions; it is therefore necessary to store this reagent in sealed ampoules.

Zinc-dithiolate has recently been recommended as a suitable source of dithiol. This reagent is a stable, colourless compound from which dithiol is instantly liberated by the action of alkalis or acids.

The reagent is suitable for the determination of molybdenum, especially in the presence of tungsten. Although many heavy metals give complexes with

TABLE 30. A SURVEY OF EXTRACTION DATA FOR SOME DIETHYLDITHIOPHOSPHATES

Metal	Optimum conditions for extraction
Ag (I)	The white precipitate of silver (I) with the reagent can readily be extracted into carbon tetrachloride from acid as well as from slightly alkaline solutions (B 102).
As (III)	Arsenic (III) can be extracted as a diethyldithiophosphate with organic solvents from strongly acid as well as from slightly acid media (B 102).
Au (III)	Gold (III) is reduced by excess of the reagent to give a precipitate which is partially extracted into organic solvents (B 102).
Bi (III)	Bismuth forms with the reagent in acid solutions a yellow complex extractable into organic solvents (B 102).
Cd (II)	In slightly acid, neutral, or slightly alkaline media cadmium gives a white precipitate extractable into organic solvents (B 102).
Co (II)	The complex of cobalt with the reagent is only extractable with organic solvents to a small extent (B 102).
Cu (II)	Copper (II) reacts with diethyldithiophosphoric acid in acid as well as in slightly alkaline media to give a precipitate extractable into carbon tetrachloride. The complex absorbs at 420 mμ ($\varepsilon = 16{,}000$) (B 102). This method has been used for the isolation and determination of copper in alloys (B 97), nickel solutions (B 101), aluminium and indium (B 107), water, and biological materials (B 98).
Fe (III)	The iron (III) complex can be quantitatively extracted at pH 2–3. At a lower pH, iron (III) is reduced to the ferrous state which does not react with the reagent. The iron (III) complex absorbs at 600 mμ ($\varepsilon = 3300$). Reproducible results can only be obtained in the presence of 50% acetic acid (B 102).
Hg (II)	Mercury (II) can be quantitatively extracted as a diethyldithiophosphate over a wide pH range by carbon tetrachloride, chloroform, benzene, and other solvents. EDTA at pH ~ 9 does not interfere, but cyanide interferes strongly and must be absent (B 102).
In (III)	At pH 1–3 indium forms an extractable precipitate with the reagent (B 102).
Ir (III)	Iridium (IV) is reduced by excess of the reagent to the tervalent state, which is not quantitatively precipitated and extracted into organic solvents (B 102).
Mo (VI)	Molybdenum (VI) reacts with the reagent in acid media to give a red extractable complex. The colour of the organic phase is not permanent (B 102).
Ni (II)	Nickel diethyldithiophosphate is soluble in water as well as in organic solvents. Its quantitative isolation requires several repetitions of the extraction procedure. The complex absorbs at 330 mμ ($\varepsilon = 17{,}800$) (B 102).

TABLE 30 (*continued*)

Metal	Optimum conditions for extraction
Pb (II)	Lead diethyldithiophosphate is completely extracted by carbon tetrachloride from acid or neutral solutions. The complex absorbs at 295 mμ ($\varepsilon = 7700$) (B 102).
Pd (II)	The palladium complex can readily be extracted from acid media by various organic solvents (B 100, B 102).
Pt (II)	Platinum (II) diethyldithiophosphate is soluble in organic solvents (B 102).
Ru, Rh	On being heated with the reagent ruthenium and rhodium give a precipitate extractable by organic solvents. The rhodium complex absorbs at 465 mμ ($\varepsilon = 14,600$) (B 102).
Sb (III)	In the presence of excess of the reagent antimony (III) can be quantitatively extracted from acid solutions by various organic solvents (B 102).
Sn (II)	Divalent tin can be quantitatively extracted as diethyldithiophosphate from strongly acidic solutions (B 102).
Te (IV)	Tellurium (IV) can be extracted as a diethyldithiophosphate from a strongly acid medium (B 102).
Tl (I)	Thallium (I) forms a precipitate with the reagent that is readily soluble and extractable from slightly acid media by carbon tetrachloride and other solvents (B 102).

dithiol (C 27), the majority of these are said to be insoluble and not extractable into butyl acetate, the solvent generally used in the extraction procedures (S 14).

Extraction data for metal dithiolates are summarized in Table 31.

5.14.2. *Diacetyltoluene-3,4-dithiol (diacetyldithiol)*

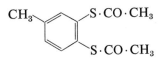

The reagent is a stable, colourless, crystalline compound, hydrolysed by alkalis to give dithiol, but stable to acids. A solution of the reagent in ethyl acetate or in ethyl cellosolve can be kept for a year without change (C 28).

Diacetyldithiol can replace dithiol in its reactions.

TABLE 31. A SURVEY OF EXTRACTION DATA FOR METAL DITHIOLATES

Metal	Optimum conditions for extraction
Mo (VI)	An acidic solution of molybdenum (VI) reacts only slowly at room temperature with an alkaline solution of the reagent which is precipitated under these conditions. Small amounts of iron (present as Fe^{2+} in the reducing environment) and a higher temperature accelerate the reaction between molybdenum and dithiol. In the absence of iron, equilibrium is reached at 75°C in 15–20 minutes. However, heating is not permissible when tungsten is present for its rate of reaction with dithiol is also increased (S 14). In the presence of 0·5–2·0 mg of iron, molybdenum reacts with the reagent even in relatively concentrated hydrochloric acid (3·7 M) or sulphuric acid (6–14 M) (A 34, S 14). At these acidities the corresponding tungsten (VI) complex is not formed. Citric acid has also been recommended as a masking agent for tungsten (J 7). Once formed, the molybdenum (VI) dithiolate can be extracted by carbon tetrachloride, benzene (solubility $2·3 \times 10^{-3}$ M) (S 14), butyl acetate, iso-amyl acetate, petroleum ether, etc. (C 26, B 14, P 41, A 34, A 39, S 116, S 122). Solutions of the molybdenum (VI) complex in an organic phase absorb strongly at 670–680 mμ; in benzene the molar extinction coefficient is 24,400 at 680 mμ (G 13). The dithiol method has been used for the determination of molybdenum in tungsten ores (J 7), tungsten compounds (B 114), soils and rocks (C 26, J 6, S 116), steels (W 8), tantalum, titanium, and zirconium (G 40, S 72, S 122), niobium (H 27), and in biological materials (A 34, O 3, P 41).
Se (IV)	After adding excess of the reagent selenium (IV) can be completely extracted from 6–8 N hydrochloric acid containing 5% of perchloric acid by a 1:1 mixture of carbon tetrachloride and ethylenedichloride (W 5).
Sn (II)	On being warmed in acid solutions, the reagent forms a magenta-red precipitate with stannous salts. Stannous dithiolate can be extracted with some organic solvents to give a low solution which can be used for its determination (S 14). Tin dithiolate is practically not extracted by petroleum ether because of its insolubility in this solvent (A 34).
Tc	The complex of technetium with dithiol can be extracted from 2·5 M hydrochloric acid with carbon tetrachloride. The molar extinction coefficient at 450 mμ is 15,000 (M 60).
W (VI)	Tungsten (VI) forms with the reagent a slightly soluble bluish-green complex which can be extracted into butyl acetate, petroleum ether, and other organic solvents (S 14, S 116, S 122). With petroleum ether as the extracting solvent the maximum extraction of tungsten takes place over the pH range 0·5–2·0 (A 34, J 6). Quantitative extraction of tungsten (VI) is not obtained unless phosphoric acid (0·3 ml of H_3PO_4, sp. gr. 1·7) is added; this probably accelerates the tungsten–dithiol reaction. Heating to 97°C has also been recommended to make the reaction quantitative (J 6). In the presence of strong reducing agents, tungsten can be extracted even from hot concentrated hydrochloric acid (B 14). The dithiol method has been used for the determination of tungsten (VI) in minerals (S 116), in silicate rocks (after a preliminary extraction with α-benzoinoxime) (J 6), and in biological materials (after a preliminary extraction with cupferron) (A 34).

5.15. MISCELLANEOUS REAGENTS

5.15.1. *Salicylic acid (o-hydroxybenzoic acid)*

Salicylic acid (M.Wt. 138·12) consists of white odourless crystals, melting at 157–159°C and subliming at 76°C.

Salicylic acid is slightly soluble in cold water but more soluble in chloroform, furfurol, and other solvents (see Appendix) (H 21). The dissociation constant of salicylic acid is $1·5 \times 10^{-3}$ ($pK_{HA} = 2·82$); its partition coefficient between organic and aqueous phases equals 3 and 320 for chloroform and methylisobutylketone respectively (H 30, H 31).

Salicylates of beryllium can be extracted by aliphatic alcohols (D 10) and vanadium salicylate is quantitatively extracted with diisobutylketone (C 40). By using isobutylmethylketone as solvent, salicylates of uranium (VI) and thorium (IV) can be practically completely extracted (H 32, H 33). A saturated solution of salicylic acid in furfurol has been recommended for the separation of zirconium from hafnium (C 37). Salicylates of copper (G 26), plutonium (H 17), scandium, and other metals (S 132) can also be extracted into organic solvents.

5.15.2. *Salicylidineamines*

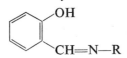

Salicylidineamines form chelate complexes with nickel that are readily soluble and extractable into organic solvents (T 24, T 25).

5.15.3. *Ethyl acetoacetate*

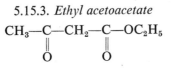

Ethylacetoacetate forms a chelate with iron (III) which can be extracted at pH 5·2–5·5 into chloroform. The complex absorbs at 450 mμ (K 71).

5.15.4. *Flavonol*

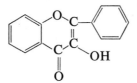

Flavonol forms a yellow complex with uranyl ions, which is easily soluble in tri-n-butylphosphate (K 7). At pH 6–7 uranium can be extracted by an 8.4×10^{-4} M solution of the reagent in a 1:1 mixture of tri-n-butylphosphate and n-hexane. The complex absorbs at 410 mμ ($\varepsilon = 28{,}700$) (K 7).

5.15.5. *Morin (3,5,7,2′,4′-pentahydroxyflavone)*

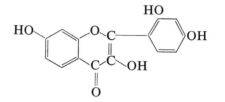

Morin (M.Wt. 238·26, M.p. 285°C) forms a pale-yellow crystalline solid, very sparingly soluble in water, but soluble in alcohol and alkalis.

The reagent reacts with a considerable number of metals to give lake-like chelates which can be extracted by butyl alcohol, amyl alcohol, or cyclo-hexanol. A few metals, particularly zirconium, and scandium and thorium to a lesser extent, react in mineral acid medium; other metals, including aluminium, beryllium, cerium (III), gallium, indium, iron (III) and titanium, react in weakly acidic medium (acetic acid–acetate buffer) (B 48).

5.15.6. *2-Hydroxy-1,4-naphthoquinone*

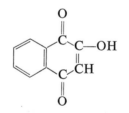

The properties (i.e. pK_{HA} and log p_{HA}) of the reagent and its application for extraction of thorium have been studied by Zozulya and Peshkova (Z 20).

5.15.7. *1,2,5,8-Tetrahydroxyanthraquinone (quinalizarin)*

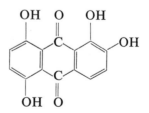

The reagent (M.Wt. 272·20) occurs as red, rhombic needles which possess a green metallic lustre. The compound is insoluble in water and only slightly soluble in ethyl alcohol and diethyl ether, but dissolves readily in alkaline solutions. The chelates of aluminium, iron, scandium, titanium, thorium, and to some extent also that of zirconium, can be extracted by ethyl acetate and by isoamyl alcohol (B 48, S 14).

5.15.8. 6,7-Dihydroxy-2,4-diphenylbenzopyrillium chloride

The reagent forms with molybdenum (VI) a chelate of the type

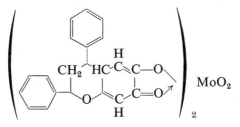

which can be extracted into chloroform. Maximum absorption is at 535 mμ ($\varepsilon = 50,400$). The method has been used for the determination of molybdenum in steels (B 109).

5.15.9. Diphenylcarbazide and diphenylcarbazone

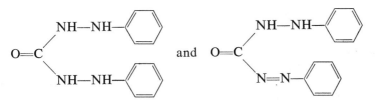

The initial reaction of diphenylcarbazide involves its oxidation to diphenyl-carbazone which is the active reagent in the reaction with mercury (maximum absorbancy of the chelate at 562 mμ) (S 46), copper (λ_{max} 545–550 mμ) (L 6, M 123, S 47) and chromium (VI) (λ_{max} 540 mμ) (S 14, S 15). The products can be extracted by benzene and other solvents (S 14).

5.15.10. Diphenylthiosemicarbazide

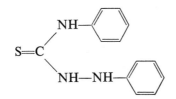

The reagent gives extractable precipitates with molybdenum, rhenium, osmium, ruthenium, platinum, palladium, and tungsten (G 9, G 10, H 13).

5.15.11. *Phenylthiourea*

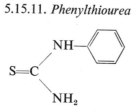

The reagent is a white crystalline solid which is slightly soluble in water and readily soluble in alcohol. In dilute hydrochloric acid it forms a complex with palladium which can be extracted into ethyl or amyl acetate (A 51).

Substituted thioureas (e.g. diphenylthiourea, *o,o*-ditolylthiourea or *p,p'*-ditolylthiourea) can be used as organic reagents to form extractable complexes with ruthenium, platinum, phodium, and palladium (G 10, S 112).

5.15.12. *2-Mercaptobenzthiazole*

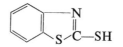

A white crystalline compound, melting at 179°C, 2-mercaptobenzthiazole is insoluble in water but soluble in alkalis, alcohol, and diethyl ether, and forms precipitates with bismuth, cadmium, cobalt, copper, gold, lead, mercury, nickel, thallium, and zinc (W 7). The copper precipitate can be quantitatively extracted at pH 2·6–4·2 into amyl acetate, and the nickel complex into chloroform (S 49).

5.15.13. *2-Mercapto-4,5-dimethylthiazole*

$$H_3C-C\text{---}CH$$
$$H_3C-C\diagdown_{S}\diagup\text{---}SH$$

The reagent forms an amber-red complex with rhodium (II) in 3–9 M hydrochloric acid which can be extracted into chloroform (R 40).

CHAPTER 6

SELECTIVE EXTRACTION PROCEDURES
FOR INDIVIDUAL METALS

IN THE following pages are given the most selective procedures for the isolation by liquid–liquid extraction of each of forty-eight metals in the form of their chelate complexes. In many cases these chelates are coloured, so that direct spectrophotometric determination of the metal in question is possible.

The reader is recommended to use these procedures in conjunction with the previous sections on the various extraction systems. Once a particular method has been selected, a study of the relevant section on the extraction system involved will provide a proper orientation to the overall characteristic features of the general procedure.

6.1. ACTINIUM

Thenoyltrifluoracetone method (H 4). The complex of actinium with HTTA is quantitatively extracted at pH ~ 5.5 with benzene. Actinium can be rather selectively back-extracted from the extract into dilute nitric acid at pH 4·0.

Procedure. Adjust the pH of the sample solution containing actinium to 5·5 and shake for 15 minutes with an equal volume of 0·25 M HTTA in benzene. Under these conditions many other metals are also extracted (e.g. lead, thallium (III), bismuth, polonium, thorium, etc.), but actinium can be separated from these metals by back-extraction into dilute nitric acid adjusted to pH 4·0. After removal of the aqueous phase, readjust its pH to 5·5, when actinium can again be extracted with the 0·25 M solution of HTTA in benzene.

6.2. ALUMINIUM

8-Hydroxyquinoline method (R 15). Aluminium can be completely extracted by 0·10 M HOx in chloroform in the pH range 4·5–11. This extraction is not selective, but many interfering metals can be removed by a preliminary extraction by 8-hydroxyquinaldine (HMOx).

Procedure. To 10 ml of the solution containing not more than 200 μg of aluminium add 0·5 M sodium acetate to bring the pH to 4·0. This solution is then equilibrated for 15 minutes with two portions of a 1 per cent solution of HMOx in chloroform. Add to the aqueous phase 1 ml of 0·2 M sodium potassium tartrate (to prevent the precipitation of aluminium hydroxide) and an ammonia–ammonium chloride buffer to bring the solution to pH 10. Extract the solution again with two successive portions of 1 per cent HMOx in chloroform (10 minutes' shaking) and then remove remaining traces of the reagent by extraction with 5 ml of chloroform. Aluminium that remains in the aqueous phase is then extracted

179

for 5 minutes with 10·0 ml of 0·10 M HOx in chloroform and the absorbancy of aluminium oxinate is measured at 390 mμ.

Only uranium (VI) and zirconium (IV) interfere. Uranium (VI) can be masked at pH 9·5–10 by a saturated solution of ammonium carbonate (A 40) and zirconium can be removed by a preliminary extraction with cupferron from 1 N sulphuric acid (E 7).

6.3. AMERICIUM

Thenoyltrifluoracetone method (M 15). Americium (III) can be extracted at pH 3·5 or higher by 0·2 M HTTA in benzene. Many interfering metals can be removed by a preliminary extraction with the same HTTA solution at pH < 2·5.

Procedure. Adjust the pH of the solution containing americium to 2·5 and extract interfering metals such as uranium (IV), neptunium (IV), plutonium (IV), zirconium (IV), thorium (IV), protactinium (V), iron (III), etc., by several portions of 0·2 M HTTA in benzene. After readjusting the pH of the solution to 3·5 americium can be extracted by three successive portions of equal volumes of 0·2 M HTTA in benzene.

6.4. ANTIMONY

Diethyldithiocarbamate method (B 75). Antimony (III) can be selectively isolated and determined as diethyldithiocarbamate in the presence of EDTA and KCN as masking agents.

Procedure. To a solution containing up to 300 μg of antimony (III) add 10 ml of 5 per cent EDTA and adjust the pH of the solution to 9·0. Next add 5 ml of 10 per cent KCN solution and readjust the pH to 9·2–9·5. After addition of 1 ml 0·2 per cent sodium diethyldithiocarbamate add 10·0 ml of carbon tetrachloride and shake the mixture for 1 minute.

The antimony (III) chelate absorbs strongly at 350 μm. Only bismuth, thallium (III), tellurium (IV), and large amounts of mercury (II), arsenic (III), selenium, and copper interfere. The first two elements can be removed as diethyldithiocarbaminates by a preliminary extraction at pH 11–12.

6.5. ARSENIC

Diethyldithiocarbamate method (W 37, W 38). Trivalent arsenic is extractable from mineral acid solutions by a chloroform solution of diethylammonium diethyldithiocarbamate. Many interfering metals can be removed by a preliminary extraction with the same reagent, provided arsenic is present in the non-extractable pentavalent state.

Procedure. To about 40 ml of solution containing arsenic in the pentavalent state and containing 4–8 ml of concentrated sulphuric acid add 1 ml of hydrogen peroxide and then extract interfering metals with two successive portions of a 1 per cent solution of the reagent in chloroform. Transfer the acid layer to a flask, add 1 ml of 30 per cent hydrogen peroxide and boil gently for 15 minutes. Add 1 ml of saturated bromine water and boil off the bromine. Remove the flask from the source of heat, allow it to stand for 15 minutes, cool, and add 1 ml of an iodide–ascorbic acid solution (15 g potassium iodide and 2·5 g ascorbic acid in 100 ml). Extract arsenic (III) together with antimony (III) and tin (II) by two successive portions of 10 ml of the 1 per cent reagent solution in chloroform. Finally shake the aqueous phase with 5 ml of chloroform and add this to the main extract. Antimony (III), if present, can be removed by a preliminary extraction with cupferron.

6.6. BERKELIUM

Thenoyltrifluoracetone method (M 15). About 80 per cent of berkelium (III) can be extracted at pH 3·4 by a 0·2 M solution of HTTA in toluene. The separation becomes more selective if the interfering metals are removed by a preliminary extraction with the same HTTA solution at pH = 2·0.

Procedure. Adjust the pH of solution to 2·0 and extract interfering metals with several portions of 0·2 M HTTA in toluene. After readjusting the pH of the solution to 3·4, berkelium can be extracted by 3–5 successive portions of 0·2 M HTTA in toluene.

6.7. BERYLLIUM

Acetylacetone method (A 8, S 67). A very selective method for the isolation and determination of beryllium is based on the extraction of beryllium acetylacetonate in the presence of EDTA as masking agent.

Procedure. To 50 ml of solution of pH 0·5–1·5 containing up to 50 μg of beryllium add 2·0 ml of 10 per cent EDTA and adjust the pH to about 6–7 by the addition of 0·1 M sodium hydroxide. Add 5 ml of 5 per cent aqueous acetylacetone and readjust the pH to 6–8. Allow the solution to stand 5 minutes and then extract it with three 10 ml portions of chloroform. Chloroform is preferable to carbon tetrachloride as it absorbs less light in the ultraviolet region and the solution of beryllium–acetylacetonate is more resistant to washing with aqueous alkali.
Before the spectrophotometric determination of the beryllium chelate at 295 mμ, the excess of the reagent (which also absorbs at this wavelength) must be removed by washing with 2–4 portions of 0·1 M sodium hydroxide (0·5–1 minute's shaking).

6.8. BISMUTH

(*a*) *Dithizone method.* Bismuth can be selectively extracted as a dithizonate from dilute ammonia containing potassium cyanide. Only lead, tin (II), and thallium (I) interfere. Bismuth can be separated from these metals by a preliminary extraction at pH 2·5 (L 10).

Procedure. Bismuth is extracted from the aqueous phase in the presence of 20 per cent acetic acid (the pH is adjusted to 2·5) with several portions of a 400 μM solution of dithizone in chloroform. Bismuth is transferred to the aqueous phase by shaking the combined organic extracts with 4 per cent sodium bromide in 0·04 M nitric acid. After adding potassium cyanide and readjusting the pH to 9·5 bismuth is selectively isolated by several portions of the same dithizone solution. Bismuth in the organic phase can be determined by a mixed colour method by measuring absorbancy at 490 and 620 mμ.

(*b*) *Diethyldithiocarbamate method.* Bismuth can be selectively isolated and determined after its extraction as diethyldithiocarbamate from aqueous solution of pH 11–12 containing tartrate, EDTA, and KCN as masking agents (C 8).

Procedure. To 10–20 ml of the solution containing bismuth, which may be 0·10 M in acid, add 10 ml or more of the masking mixture (50 g of EDTA and 50 g of KCN in 1 litre of 1·5 M aqueous ammonia (1 : 10)) and 1 ml of a 0·2 per cent aqueous solution of the sodium salt of diethyldithiocarbamic acid (cupral). Finally extract this solution with exactly 10·0 ml of carbon tetrachloride for 30 seconds and measure the absorbancy of the extract so obtained at 400 mμ.

6.9. CADMIUM

Dithizone method (C 20). Cadmium can be extracted from alkaline solution by a solution of dithizone in chloroform. After back-extraction of cadmium from the organic extract into diluted acid, cadmium can be separated from copper and mercury, which are also extracted from alkaline solutions. Small amounts of cobalt, which interfere, can be masked by dimethylglyoxime (S 70).

Procedure. To approximately 50 ml of a solution containing up to 50 μg Cd add 5 ml of 20 per cent sodium potassium tartrate solution and 1 ml of 20 per cent hydroxylamine hydrochloride solution. Make the solution alkaline and add 5 ml of 25 per cent potassium hydroxide solution (excess). Shake for 5 minutes with 5 ml of dithizone solution (20 mg per 1000 ml of chloroform). Separate the phases and add to the aqueous phase several successive 5 ml portions of dithizone and shake till the aqueous phase remains brown. Add 5 ml of dithizone solution (200 mg per 1000 ml of chloroform) to the combined chloroform extracts and wash with water to remove the entrained alkali. Remove the cadmium from the chloroform extract by shaking for at least 2 minutes with 50 ml of buffer of pH 2. All the cadmium will now be in the aqueous phase and should probably be shaken with a little dithizone solution to remove traces of metals such as copper and mercury. After adjusting the aqueous solution to pH 14 with sodium hydroxide, cadmium can again be extracted with dithizone solution and determined by a monocolour by the mixed colour method.

6.10. CALCIUM

8-Hydroxyquinoline method (U 6). A selective method for the isolation and determination of calcium is based on its extraction by a 2 per cent solution of oxine in chloroform in the presence of n-butylamine. Interfering ions are removed by a preliminary extraction with oxine at a lower pH.

Procedure. To 50 ml of solution at pH 2–3 add 3 ml of 30 per cent hydrogen peroxide and extract the aqueous phase with several portions of a 2 per cent solution of oxine in chloroform. Then add aqueous ammonia to bring the pH to 9–10 and again extract the aqueous phase with several 20 ml portions of 2 per cent oxine solution in chloroform. Magnesium, if present, may be removed by extraction with a 0·1 per cent solution of oxine in chloroform in the presence of n-butylamine at pH ~11. Calcium is then quantitatively extracted at pH 11·6 $\pm$ 0·2 with two 20 ml portions of 2 per cent oxine solution in chloroform in the presence of 2 per cent butylamine. Under these conditions about 5–10 per cent of any strontium and 1–3 per cent of any barium is co-extracted with the calcium. If excess of calcium and barium are present, the combined organic phase is stripped with 0·2 M hydrochloric acid. Calcium, strontium, and barium are thereby transferred into the aqueous phase, and after re-adjusting the pH to 11·6 calcium is again extracted with two portions of 2 per cent oxine solution in the presence of n-butylamine. By repeating these operations calcium can be separated from strontium and barium and then determined at 400 mμ.

6.11. CERIUM

8-Hydroxyquinoline method (W 20). A highly selective method for the determination of cerium (but not for its isolation) is based on the extraction of cerium oxinate, which absorbs strongly at 505 mμ. At this wavelength only the oxinates of iron (III), vanadium (V), and ruthenium (III) absorb. At higher pH values vanadium (V) is not extracted and the interference of iron (III) can be overcome by reduction and converting it into ferrocyanide.

Procedure. To 20 ml of the solution containing cerium add 2 ml of citric acid solution (500 g per litre), aqueous ammonia until the solution is just alkaline, and then 4 ml of potassium cyanide (400 g KCN and 15 g NaOH per litre). Heat to boiling, reduce with 1·0 ml of sodium dithionite solution and cool to room temperature. Add 2 or 3 drops of phenolphthalein indicator and then add citric acid until the red colour disappears followed by ammonia to restore a faint pink coloration. Add exactly 5 ml of concentrated ammonia (sp. gr. 0·88), transfer the solution to a separatory funnel and dilute to 50 ml with water. Shake the aqueous phase with two 5 ml portions of a 1–3 per cent solution of oxine in chloroform for 3 minutes. Filter the combined extracts and measure the absorbancy at 505 mμ.

6.12. CHROMIUM

Acetylacetone method (M 7). Hydrated chromium (III) is inert to chelate formation and solvent extraction at room temperature. This fact can be used for the selective separation of chromium from most other metals.

Procedure. Extract the solution containing chromium (III) with a 50 per cent solution (v/v) of acetylacetone in chloroform at pH 3–4 to remove other metals. Separate the aqueous phase which still contains all the chromium, adjust to pH 6, add 10 ml acetylacetone and heat under reflux for an hour to ensure that the formation of the chromium acetylacetonate proceeds to completion. Cool the solution to room temperature, acidify to between 1 and 3 N in sulphuric acid, and extract with a 50 per cent solution (v/v) of acetylacetone in chloroform. Back-washing the chloroform extract removes any remaining traces of iron and other metals. The red-violet extract can be used for the absorptiometric determination of chromium ($\varepsilon = 64\cdot3$ at 560 mμ).

6.13. COBALT

(*a*) *Acetylacetone method* (M 5). Cobalt (II) forms with acetylacetone in the presence of hydrogen peroxide a very stable cobalt (III) acetylacetonate. Interfering ions can be removed by a preliminary extraction with acetylacetone at pH < 4.

Procedure. Adjust the pH of the solution containing cobalt (II) to about 4 and extract with acetylacetone, with a 50 per cent solution (v/v) of acetylacetone in chloroform to remove metals which form extractable chelates with the reagent. Separate the aqueous phase, and add several millilitres of acetylacetone and 5 ml of 3 per cent hydrogen peroxide to form the extractable cobalt (III) complex. Adjust the solution to a pH of 8–9, heat to incipient boiling for 10 minutes, cool, and reacidify to pH 1. The cobalt is now quantitatively extracted with a 50 per cent solution (v/v) of acetylacetone in chloroform. The complex is intense green in colour.

(b) *Nitrosonaphthol method.* Both 1-nitroso-2-naphthol and 2-nitroso-1-naphthol yield strongly coloured cobaltic complexes which can be extracted by nonpolar solvents. Once formed, the cobalt (III) complex is very stable— it is not destroyed even on being shaken with relatively concentrated acids or alkalis. Under these conditions the excess of the reagent and most interfering metals are stripped into the aqueous phase (S 14).

Procedure. Treat the acidic sample solution, containing iron in ferric state, with 10 ml of 40 per cent sodium citrate solution; dilute to 50–75 ml and adjust the pH to 3–4. Cool to room temperature, add 10 ml of 3 per cent hydrogen peroxide and, after a short interval, 2 ml of 2-nitroso-1-naphthol solution (1 g of the reagent dissolved in 100 ml of glacial acetic acid).

Allow to stand for 30 minutes, transfer the solution to a separatory funnel and shake vigorously for some minutes with 25 ml of chloroform. Draw off the chloroform into a 50 ml volumetric flask and repeat the extraction twice with 10 ml portions of chloroform. Dilute the combined extracts to 50 ml with chloroform and transfer the solution to a clean separatory funnel.

Add 20 ml of 2 M hydrochloric acid and shake for 1 minute. Run the chloroform layer into another separatory funnel and shake with 20 ml of 2 M sodium hydroxide for 1 minute. Measure the absorbancy of the organic phase at 530 mμ.

6.14. COPPER

(a) *Dithizone method* (B 51, M 103). Copper can be extracted by dithizone from acidic solutions. Dithizonates of silver, mercury, and bismuth, which are co-extracted under these conditions, can be destroyed by shaking with potassium iodide solution.

Procedure. Extract the slightly acid solution (pH $\sim$ 2) that contains copper with portions of a 0·0015 per cent solution of dithizone in carbon tetrachloride until the organic phase after extraction remains green. Note the total volume used. Then shake the combined extracts with a 2 per cent solution of potassium iodide in 0·01 M hydrochloric acid to decompose the dithizonates of silver, mercury, and bismuth. Copper is thus left alone in the organic phase in which it can be determined by the mixed colour method. Only palladium (II) and gold (III) interfere.

(b) *Diethyldithiocarbamate method* (C 25, S 37). A selective method for the determination of copper (but not for its isolation) depends on measuring the absorbancy of copper diethyldithiocarbamate. EDTA is a suitable masking agent for many metals.

Procedure. To the solution for analysis add 5 ml of 40 per cent ammonium citrate, 10 ml of 10 per cent disodium ethylenediaminetetraacetate and two drops of 0·1 per cent cresol red indicator, followed by concentrated ammonia until the indicator shows its alkaline colour (pH $\sim$ 8·5). Dilute to about 50 ml and transfer the solution to a separatory funnel. Add 5 ml of 0·1 per cent sodium diethyldithiocarbamate and shake vigorously for 1–2 minutes with 10 ml of chloroform. Repeat the extraction twice more with 5 ml portions of chloroform. Dilute the combined extract to 25 ml with chloroform and measure the absorbancy at 435 mμ.

6.15. GALLIUM

8-Hydroxyquinoline method (S 106).   Gallium can be extracted from a slightly acid medium by 8-hydroxyquinoline in chloroform.

Procedure. Adjust the pH of solution for analysis to approximately 2 and extract gallium with two successive portions of 0·01 M solution of 8-hydroxyquinoline in chloroform. The gallium complex absorbs strongly at 385 mμ so that a direct absorptiometric determination of gallium in the organic phase is possible. Ferric iron can be reduced by hydroxylamine to the divalent state which does not react with 8-hydroxyquinoline in acid solutions. Elements accompanying gallium in this extraction are zirconium, vanadium (V), molybdenum (VI), palladium, copper (II), indium, and thallium (III).

6.16. GOLD

Dithizone method (E 13, Y 14).   Gold (III) can be selectively isolated and determined by dithizone extraction from 0·1–0·5 M sulphuric acid.   In acid solution only palladium, mercury (II), silver, and large amounts of copper interfere.   Palladium can be masked by thiocyanate; mercury and silver can be stripped from the organic phase into a 2 per cent solution of potassium iodide in 0·01 M sulphuric acid.   Platinum may be oxidized to the tetravalent state, in which it does not react with dithizone.

Procedure. To 50 ml of solution for analysis containing $AuCl_3$ add 5 ml of 1 N sulphuric acid and extract with successive portions of a 50 μM solution of dithizone in carbon tetrachloride until the organic phase remains green after extraction. Gold can be determined in the combined organic extracts by a mixed colour method or by a monocolour method after the excess of dithizone has been removed by stripping with aqueous ammonia (1 : 1000).

6.17. HAFNIUM

Thenoyltrifluoracetone method (H 41).   Milligram amounts of hafnium can be quantitatively extracted from 2 M perchloric acid by extraction with a 0·10 M solution of HTTA in benzene.   Zirconium (IV), uranium (IV), neptunium (IV), plutonium (IV), and protactinium (V) strongly interfere.

6.18. INDIUM

Dithizone method (A 45).   Indium can be extracted simultaneously with lead, bismuth, thallium (I), and tin (I) from an alkaline solution containing ammonium citrate and potassium cyanide using a solution of dithizone in chloroform.   Bismuth, if present, can be removed by dithizone extraction at pH < 3·5.   Lead can be masked at pH 5–6 by sodium thiosulphate.

Procedure. To 20 ml of the sample for analysis add 10 ml of 10 per cent ammonium citrate and adjust the pH with dilute nitric acid to 3·5–4·0. Then add 5 ml of a 0·02 per cent solution of dithizone in chloroform and shake for 1 minute. Repeat the extraction

2–3 times until the organic phase remains distinctly green. Discard the organic phase and wash the aqueous layer with chloroform. To the aqueous phase add 2 ml of 10 per cent potassium cyanide and 0·2 ml of hydroxylamine reagent. Adjust the pH to about 9 with a few drops of aqueous ammonia using universal indicator paper. Shake the solution for 2 minutes with 5 ml of the 0·02 per cent solution of dithizone in chloroform. Repeat the extraction 3–4 times. Collect all the organic phase in a 100 ml separatory funnel and shake with three portions of distilled water for 30 seconds. Add 20 ml of 1 per cent nitric acid to the organic phase and shake for 2 minutes to back-extract all the indium into the aqueous phase. Reject the chloroform phase and wash the remaining aqueous phase with carbon tetrachloride to remove all the chloroform.

Add to the acid solution 13 ml of 2 M sodium acetate and 2 ml of 20 per cent sodium thiosulphate. Adjust the pH of the solution to about 5·5 and shake for 2 minutes with 10 ml of a 0·002 per cent solution of dithizone in carbon tetrachloride. If necessary, repeat the extraction several times. Measure the optical density of the organic phase at 510 mμ and compare with the standard curve.

6.19. IRON

(a) *Acetylacetone method* (M 5). A very selective method for the determination of ferric iron (but not for its isolation) is based on measuring the absorbancy of ferric acetylacetonate at 440 mμ. Only large amounts of uranium can interfere.

Procedure. Adjust the pH of the solution containing up to a gram of iron (III) to the value 1·0 and shake for 3 minutes with 50 ml portions of a 50 per cent solution (v/v) of acetylacetone in chloroform. Approximately 96 per cent extraction can be obtained in a single pass. Repeat the extraction 2–3 times and measure the absorbancy at 440 mμ.

(b) *Thenoyltrifluoracetone method.* A very selective method for the isolation of iron (III) is based on its extraction from 10 M nitric acid with a 0·5 M solution of HTTA in xylene (M 91).

Procedure. To 3 ml of the sample for analysis add 10 ml of 10 M nitric acid and 1·3 ml of hydrogen peroxide (30–35 per cent). Mix well, add 15 ml of 0·5 M HTTA and extract for 5 minutes. With a single extraction more than 90 per cent of iron is removed. A second extraction with fresh solvent removes iron practically completely. Under these conditions only zirconium, hafnium, and partially also niobium (V) and protactinium are extracted. These elements can be removed from the organic phase by stripping with 0·25 M hydrofluoric—0·25 M hydrochloric acid.

6.20. LEAD

Dithizone method (S 14, S 84). From a slightly ammoniacal cyanide solution only lead, bismuth, thallium (I), indium (III), and tin (II) can be extracted with dithizone solution. Lead can be separated from bismuth by shaking the organic extract with dilute nitric acid. Bismuth remains in the organic phase.

Procedure: To the solution for analysis add 1 ml of 50 per cent ammonium citrate solution and then ammonia until slightly basic. For each 10 ml of solution add 10 ml of 10 per cent potassium cyanide. Thus prepared, the solution is shaken for 2–3 minutes with several ml of a 0·003 per cent solution of dithizone in carbon tetrachloride. Repeat the extraction procedure until the last portions of the dithizone are coloured pure orange (due to bismuth dithizonate if bismuth is present) or remain green (in the absence of bismuth and thallium). Shake the combined extracts which now contain all the lead with 5 ml of 1:100 nitric acid; separate the aqueous phase containing the lead, adjust its pH to 2·8–3·0 (yellow colour of thymol blue) and shake with small portions of a 0·006 per cent solution of dithizone in carbon tetrachloride until the last portion remains green. Lead, which remains in the aqueous phase, can then be determined by the usual dithizone methods.

6.21. MAGNESIUM

8-Hydroxyquinoline method (U 3). A selective method for the isolation and determination of magnesium is based on the extraction of magnesium oxinate in the presence of n-butylamine at pH 11·0. Interfering metals are removed by a preliminary extraction with oxine at a lower pH.

Procedure. To 20 ml of the solution containing 20–200 μg of magnesium add 5 ml of 1 M tartrate solution; when titanium, vanadium, and tungsten are present add in addition 1–3 ml of 30 per cent hydrogen peroxide solution. Dilute with water to 40 ml and add 1 M aqueous ammonia until the pH of the solution reaches about 9. Shake the aqueous phase with several portions of a 0·1 per cent solution of oxine in chloroform to remove interfering metals; the last portion of the organic phase must be colourless. To the aqueous phase add now 0·5–1·0 g of solid potassium cyanide, 1 ml of n-butylamine, and aqueous ammonia to reach pH 11·0 ± 0·5. Magnesium is then extracted with two 20 ml portions of a 0·1 per cent solution of oxine in chloroform and the absorbancy of the magnesium chelate is measured at 380 mμ. Small amounts of calcium, strontium, and barium do not interfere.

6.22. MANGANESE

8-Hydroxyquinaldine method (M 121). Manganese can be selectively determined by solvent extraction as a complex with 8-hydroxyquinaldine. The interfering metals are masked by cyanide or removed from the organic phase by washing with EDTA.

Procedure. Treat about 50 ml of the slightly acid solution containing 2–60 μg of manganese with 5 ml of 30 per cent ammonium citrate solution and add 3 ml of a 2 per cent solution of 8-hydroxyquinaldine. Adjust the pH to 11·4–12·4 with sodium hydroxide solution, add 1 ml of 5 per cent potassium cyanide and dilute to 100 ml. Transfer the solution to a separatory funnel, add exactly 10·0 ml of chloroform and shake vigorously for 1 minute. Transfer the chloroform extract to another separatory funnel containing about 10 ml of EDTA wash solution (0·1 per cent EDTA, adjusted to pH 11–12 before use). Although EDTA completely prevents the extraction of manganese, the complex once extracted is not affected by shaking with EDTA solution. After shaking for 1 minute, manganese is determined by measuring the absorbancy at 395 mμ and at 580 mμ (if it is necessary to make corrections for any iron present).

6.23. MERCURY

Dithizone method (F 26). Dithizone extraction of mercury from acid solutions is a very suitable method for the selective determination of traces of mercury. Silver can be masked by chloride, and large amounts of copper and other metals by EDTA. Only palladium (II), gold (III), and platinum (II) interfere.

Procedure. To determine mercury in the presence of copper and silver add an excess of 20 per cent sodium chloride solution to the sample solution and, ignoring the precipitate of silver chloride, extract with successive portions of a 0·0013 per cent solution of dithizone in carbon tetrachloride until the last portion remains green. Shake out the combined organic extracts twice with 3 ml portions of 6 M hydrochloric acid. Discard the organic phase and neutralize the acid with 6 M aqueous ammonia. Adjust the pH to 1·5–2·0; add 1 ml of 0·01 M disodium salt of EDTA for each 50 μg of copper present. Extract mercury with the 0·0013 per cent solution of dithizone, avoiding prolonged shaking. Mercury can then be determined by monocolour or mixed colour methods, or by the reversion procedure.

6.24. MOLYBDENUM

(*a*) *8-Hydroxyquinoline method* (E 1). A very selective method for the isolation and determination of molybdenum is based on the extraction of molybdenum (VI) oxinate from dilute sulphuric acid.

Procedure. To 50 ml of solution, containing less than 0·4 mg of molybdenum, add sulphuric acid to adjust the pH to 0·85. Transfer the solution to a separatory funnel, add 25 ml of a 4 per cent solution of oxine adjusted to pH 0·85 with sulphuric acid and 20·0 ml of chloroform. Shake for 2 minutes, transfer the organic phase containing all the molybdenum into another separatory funnel and wash with 50 ml of 4 per cent ammonium chloride solution (adjusted to pH 0·85 with hydrochloric acid). Filter the chloroform extract and measure the absorbancy at 385 mμ against pure chloroform as a reference. This procedure is made specific by the addition of fluoride to mask niobium, tantalum, and tungsten which interfere if present in large amounts.

(*b*) *Dithiol method* (W 8). This method is suitable for the determination of molybdenum in the presence of tungsten and other elements found in alloy steels.

Procedure. To 0·5 ml of a solution of steel (4 mg) in 12·7 M sulphuric acid and 2·5 M phosphoric acid add 0·5 ml of concentrated nitric acid and evaporate to fuming. Take up in 3 ml of 4 M hydrochloric acid (sp. gr. 1·075) and cool. Add 3 ml of a freshly prepared 1 per cent solution of toluene-3,4-dithiol in amyl acetate. Shake the mixture for 15 minutes and allow it to stand for 15 minutes. Remove the organic layer and wash it with 3 ml of concentrated hydrochloric acid to remove cloudiness. Measure the molybdenum spectrophotometrically at 607 mμ.

6.25. NEPTUNIUM

Thenoyltrifluoracetone method (M 87). Neptunium (IV) is quantitatively extracted from 1 M hydrochloric acid by a 0·5 M solution of HTTA in xylene. Under suitable reducing conditions a solution may contain neptunium (IV), plutonium (III), and uranium (VI), from which only neptunium is extracted by HTTA.

Procedure. Adjust the solution containing neptunium to the composition 1 M in hydrochloric acid, 1 M in hydroxylamine hydrochloride and 0·25 M in ferrous chloride. Mix well, heat to approximately 80°C and cool to room temperature before extracting with an equal volume of 0·5 M HTTA in xylene. Wash the organic phase with an equal volume of 1 M hydrochloric acid and strip the neptunium from the organic phase into 10 M nitric acid. The last traces of zirconium and protactinium are removed by extraction with a 0·5 M solution of HTTA in xylene. Neptunium remains quantitatively in the aqueous phase.

6.26. NICKEL

Dimethylglyoxime method (S 14). This is one of the most selective methods for the determination of traces of nickel, because only a few metals (palladium, copper) form chelate complexes extractable into chloroform.

Procedure. To 5–20 ml of the sample solution, containing 5–100 μg of nickel, add 5 ml of 10 per cent sodium citrate. Neutralize with concentrated ammonia, and add a few drops in excess (pH $\sim$ 7·5). Add 2 ml of 1 per cent reagent solution in ethanol (more if much copper and cobalt is present). Extract with three 2–3 ml portions of chloroform, shaking for half a minute each time. Shake the combined organic phase with 5 ml of 1:30 (0·5 M) ammonia. If much copper is present, repeat the washing with ammonia. Shake out the ammonia washes with 1–2 ml of chloroform and add the latter to the main chloroform extracts. Return the nickel from the organic phase into the aqueous phase by shaking the extract with two successive 5 ml portions of 0·5 M hydrochloric acid.

6.27. NIOBIUM

8-Hydroxyquinoline method (A 13, A 20). Niobium can be isolated and determined as oxinate by measuring the absorbancy at 380–385 mμ. Preliminary separation of niobium by the perchloric acid hydrolysis increases the selectivity of the method.

Procedure. To 5 ml of niobium solution in 2·5 per cent citric, oxalic, or tartaric acid add aqueous ammonia to adjust the pH to 9–9·4. Niobium is then extracted with two 5 ml portions of a 4 per cent solution of oxine in chloroform. Tantalum (V), molybdenum (VI), tungsten (VI), antimony, and tin are not extracted under these conditions.

6.28. PALLADIUM

(*a*) *Dimethylglyoxime method* (Y 14). Palladium dimethylglyoximate can be selectively extracted from acid solution with chloroform.

Procedure. To 50 ml of a solution containing palladium (II) in 1 M sulphuric acid add 2 ml of a 1 per cent aqueous solution of the sodium salt of dimethylglyoxime. Allow to stand for 10 minutes in a separatory funnel, shaking occasionally. Extract palladium with two successive portions (4–5 ml) of chloroform. In the presence of gold and palladium, addition of concentrated hydrochloric acid (about 1 ml) and concentrated nitric acid (about 0·5 ml) prevents these metals from interfering.

(*b*) *Nitrosonaphthol method* (C 7). Selective extraction of palladium as its 2-nitroso-1-naphtholate with toluene can be achieved using EDTA as masking agent.

Procedure. To 5 ml of a solution in a separatory funnel, containing 5–25 μg of palladium, add 2 drops of 3 N hydrochloric acid and 1 ml of 3 per cent disodium ethylenediamine-tetraacetate. Dilute to about 10 ml with water, add 0·1 ml of a 1 per cent solution of the reagent in ethanol, mix, and allow to stand for 10 minutes at room temperature. After the addition of 5 ml of toluene and 1 ml of (1:1) aqueous ammonia, shake vigorously and allow the layers to separate. The palladium complex in the organic phase absorbs at 550 mμ.

6.29. PLATINUM

Dithizone method (Y 14). Platinum (II) can be extracted by dithizone solution from acid medium. The interfering metals may be removed by a preliminary dithizone extraction if platinum is present in the tetravalent state.

Procedure. To 5 ml of the solution for analysis containing platinum in the tetravalent state add 15–20 ml of 2 M hydrochloric acid. Extract the interfering metals by successive portions of a 75 μM solution of dithizone until the organic extract remains unchanged. Discard the organic phase. To the aqueous phase which contains all the platinum add 0·3–0·5 ml of 35 per cent stannous chloride in 6 M hydrochloric acid and allow to stand for some minutes. Determine platinum (II) by extractive titration or by the mixed colour method after extraction with a 75 μM solution of dithizone in carbon tetrachloride.

6.30. PLUTONIUM

Thenoyltrifluoracetone method (M 88). A rapid and quantitative radio-chemical method for the separation of plutonium is based on the solvent extraction of plutonium (IV) with a 0·5 M solution of HTTA in xylene.

Procedure. Pipette 1 ml of the sample solution into a 10 ml beaker. Add 3 ml of 2 M nitric acid and 1 ml of 1 M hydroxylamine hydrochloride solution. Heat the solution to approximately 80°C. Then transfer the solution to a separatory funnel, add 2 ml of sodium nitrite and allow to stand until gas evolution ceases. The solution, which should be approximately 1 M in nitric acid, is then shaken for 10 minutes with an equal volume of a 0·5 M solution of HTTA in xylene. Wash the organic phase by shaking with an equal volume of 1 M nitric acid for 3 minutes. Strip the plutonium from the organic extract by equilibrating the latter with an equal volume of 10 M nitric acid for 2 minutes. Remove the last traces of zirconium and protactinium by a 5 minutes' extraction with 0·5 M HTTA in xylene. Plutonium remains quantitatively in the aqueous phase.

6.31. POLONIUM

Dithizone method (B 81). Polonium can be separated from bismuth (RaE), lead (RaD), and many other metals by dithizone extraction from diluted hydrochloric acid.

Procedure. Extract polonium with two successive portions of a 400 μM solution of dithizone in carbon tetrachloride. The aqueous phase must be approximately 0·1 M in hydrochloric acid. Wash the organic phase with 0·3–0·5 M hydrochloric acid to remove the last traces of bismuth from the organic phase. Polonium remains quantitatively in the organic phase.

6.32. PROTACTINIUM

Thenoyltrifluoracetone method (M 128, M 129). Protactinium can be selectively isolated by extraction with HTTA from relatively concentrated hydrochloric acid.

Procedure. Extract protactinium (V) from 2–6 M hydrochloric acid by a 0·5 M solution of HTTA in xylene. Repeat the extraction 2–3 times to achieve the quantitative isolation of protactinium.

6.33. RHENIUM

8-Mercaptoquinoline method (B 30). A very selective method for the isolation and determination of rhenium is based on the extraction of its complex with the reagent from 9–10 M hydrochloric acid.

Procedure. To 8 ml of solution for analysis containing rhenium (VII) add 37 ml of concentrated hydrochloric acid and 5 ml of 6 per cent 8-mercaptoquinoline hydrochloride in concentrated hydrochloric acid. Heat for 3 minutes on a water bath. Cool the solution to room temperature and extract the complex formed with exactly 10 ml of chloroform. Measure the absorbancy of the rhenium complex at 438 mμ.
Only arsenic (III) and palladium (II) interfere.

6.34. RUTHENIUM

8-Hydroxyquinoline method (J 3). Ruthenium (III)-oxinate absorbs strongly at 570 mμ. At this wavelength only oxinates of iron (III), vanadium (V), and cerium absorb, and therefore oxine extraction can be used for the rather selective determination of ruthenium.

Procedure. Adjust the solution containing ruthenium (III) to pH 6·4. Extract the ruthenium with an equal volume of a 5–15 per cent solution of oxine in chloroform. Repeat the extraction. After adding butyl cellosolve, extract the last traces of ruthenium with chloroform. Measure the absorbancy of the combined organic extracts at 570 mμ.

6.35. SCANDIUM

8-Hydroxyquinoline method (S 106). Scandium (III)-oxinate can be extracted from a slightly acid medium (pH 4–5) by a 0·10 M solution of oxine in chloroform. Potassium cyanide can be used as a masking agent. Many interfering ions can be removed by a preliminary oxine extraction at pH $\sim$ 2.

Procedure. Adjust the pH or solution for anlysis to pH $\sim$ 2 and extract interfering ions such as copper, iron (III), molybdenum (VI), gallium, indium, etc., by successive portions of a 0·10 M solution of oxine in chloroform until the organic phase remains colourless. Discard the organic extracts. Add to the aqueous phase 1 ml of 0·1 M potassium cyanide, adjust the pH of solution to 4–5, and extract scandium with an equal volume of 0·1 M oxine in chloroform. Repeat the extraction and measure the extinction of the combined organic phase at 380 mμ.

6.36. SELENIUM

Diethyldithiocarbamate method (B 73). Selenium diethyldithiocarbamate can be extracted by carbon tetrachloride. EDTA is a suitable masking agent for many metals.

Procedure. To a solution containing up to 100 mg of selenium (IV) add 10 ml of 5 per cent EDTA, adjust the pH to between 5 and 6, add 1 ml of a 0·2 per cent sodium diethyldithiocarbamate and 10 ml of carbon tetrachloride. Shake the mixture for 1 minute.

6.37. SILVER

Dithizone method (E 14, F 26). Silver can be selectively separated by a dithizone extraction from an aqueous solution containing EDTA. Interference from mercury can be removed by back-extraction of silver with a mixture of sodium chloride and hydrochloric acid.

Procedure. To 10 ml of the solution for analysis add 2 ml of 0·1 M disodium salt of EDTA and adjust the pH of 4–5 by the use of acetic acid and sodium acetate. Extract the silver with successive portions of 50 μM solution of dithizone in carbon tetrachloride until the colour of the organic phase remains unchanged. The combined organic extracts are shaken with 3 ml of a mixture of 20 per cent sodium chloride and 0·03 M hydrochloric acid. Silver is thus quantitatively transferred into the aqueous phase, whereas mercury remains in the extract. After dilution of the aqueous phase and readjusting the pH to approximately 5, extract silver with dithizone solution of the same concentration. Determine the content of silver by a monocolour or mixed colour method.

6.38. STRONTIUM

8-Hydroxyquinoline method (S 106). Strontium oxinate can be extracted with chloroform from alkaline solution (pH 11·5–12). Many interfering ions can be removed by a preliminary extraction as oxinates at lower pH values.

Procedure. Adjust the pH of the sample solution to approximately 9 and extract the interfering ions by successive portions of 0·1 M oxine solution in chloroform until the organic phase remains colourless. To the aqueous phase add 0·1 M sodium hydroxide to bring its pH to the value 11·5–12. Extract strontium with an equal volume of 0·5 M oxine in chloroform. Repeat the extraction and measure the extinction of the combined organic extracts at 400 mμ.

6.39. TELLURIUM

Diethyldithiocarbamate method (B 74, B 75). Tellurium can be selectively isolated as diethyldithiocarbamate by using tartrate, cyanide, and EDTA as masking agents. The interference of bismuth, antimony (III), thallium (III), and copper can be avoided by a preliminary extraction with cupferron.

Procedure. Adjust the pH of 20 ml of the solution for analysis, containing 10–150 μg of tellurium, to 1–2. Add a few ml of 2 per cent cupferron solution and extract the cupferrates formed with chloroform. Repeat this procedure until the cupferrates are precipitated. Remove the excess of cupferron by two successive extractions with chloroform. To the aqueous phase add 5 ml of a buffer containing EDTA (5 g of boric acid, 1 g EDTA, 1 g KH_2PO_4 in 100 ml; pH = 8·6), then the 50 mg of solid potassium cyanide, and adjust the pH to 8·5–8·8. After adding 1 ml of sodium diethyldithiocarbamate solution (0·5 g of the reagent in 100 ml) extract the resulting solution with three successive portions of carbon tetrachloride. The amount of tellurium can be determined by measuring the absorbancy at 428 mμ.

6.40. THALLIUM

(a) *Dithizone method* (I 48). Thallium (I) can be selectively determined as dithizonate after its extraction from a strongly alkaline medium. The interfering metals can easily be removed by a preliminary dithizone extraction at pH < 6.

Procedure. Adjust the pH of the sample solution to 5–6 and extract interfering ions with successive portions of a 100 μM solution of dithizone in chloroform until the organic phase remains unchanged. To the aqueous phase add 5 ml of 20 per cent sodium potassium tartrate, 10 ml of 2·5 M sodium hydroxide, and 5 ml of 10 per cent potassium cyanide. Extract thallium (I) with 2–3 portions of the 100 μM dithizone solution and measure the absorbancy at 505 mμ.

(b) *8-Hydroxyquinoline method* (M 113). Thallium (III) can be selectively determined by the differential method, based on the fact that only thallium (III)-oxinate can be removed from the organic phase with sodium sulphite.

Procedure. Add 3 ml of 1 per cent oxine solution to the analysed sample solution, containing thallium (III). Adjust the pH to about 5 and extract thallium (III) oxinate simultaneously with other metal oxinates with exactly 20 ml of chloroform. Divide the extract into two portions. One portion is washed with sodium sulphite at pH = 5 to remove thallium (III). The absorbancy of the other fraction is immediately measured at 400 mμ, using the washed one as a reference.

6.41. THORIUM

Thenoyltrifluoracetone method (H 4, M 43). Thorium can be extracted by HTTA in benzene from a slightly acid medium. Higher selectivity can be achieved by back-extraction of thorium into more concentrated acid solutions.

Procedure. Extract for 15 minutes tracer quantities of thorium from nitric acid solution of pH 1 by an equal volume of 0·25 M HTTA in benzene. Repeat the extraction, discard the aqueous phase and strip thorium from the combined extract with two successive portions of 1 M nitric acid. Metals such as zirconium, hafnium, plutonium (IV), neptunium (IV), protactinium (V), and iron (III) remain in the organic phase.

6.42. TIN

8-Hydroxyquinoline method (E 1). A selective method for the isolation and determination of tin (IV) is based on the extraction of its oxinate from acid solutions.

Procedure. To 50 ml of the sample solution in sulphuric acid at pH = 0·85 ± 0·10, containing less than 0·5 mg of tin (IV), add 5 ml of 20 per cent ammonium chloride and

25 ml of a 4 per cent solution of oxine in dilute sulphuric acid of pH = 0·85. Extract the tin for 2 minutes with exactly 20 ml of chloroform. Wash, and filter the organic phase, and measure the absorbancy of the tin (IV) oxinate at 385 mμ. Only molybdenum (VI), tungsten (VI), niobium (V), and vanadium (V) interfere. Molybdenum (VI) can be removed as oxinate by a preliminary chloroform extraction in the absence of halide at pH 0·85; tin (IV) is not extracted under these conditions.

6.43. TITANIUM

8-Hydroxyquinoline method (S 106). Titanium can be isolated and determined as its oxinate. EDTA and KCN are suitable masking agents.

Procedure. To 10 ml of the sample solution of titanium add 2 ml of 0·1 M disodium ethylenediaminetetraacetate and 2 ml of 0·1 M potassium cyanide. Adjust the pH with diluted sodium hydroxide to 8–9 and dilute to 20 ml with water. Extract titanium with 20 ml of 0·1 M oxine in chloroform by shaking for 5 minutes. Repeat the extraction twice more and measure the absorbancy of the combined chloroform extracts at 380 mμ.

6.44. TUNGSTEN

Dithiol method. Tungsten can be extracted as dithiolate from warm, strong hydrochloric acid in the presence of strong reducing agents. Molybdenum must be removed by a preliminary extraction as dithiolate from cold, less concentrated acid (B 14; see Section 6.24).

Procedure. To the fumed aliquot portion add 5 ml of hydrochloric acid (sp. gr. 1·06), warm gently until the salts are completely dissolved and cool to room temperature. Add 5 drops of a 10 per cent solution of hydroxylamine sulphate and 10 ml of a freshly prepared 1 per cent solution of toluene-3,4-dithiol in amyl alcohol. Allow to stand in a bath at 20–25°C for 15 minutes with periodic shaking. Transfer the solution into a separatory funnel, shake, and draw off the acid phase containing all the tungsten. Wash the amyl acetate layer with two consecutive 5 ml portions of hydrochloric acid (sp. gr. 1·06), and combine these acid washes with the original acid layer. Discard the amyl acetate layer which now contains the molybdenum. Evaporate the acidic tungsten solution carefully, add a few drops of concentrated nitric acid, and finally fume. Add 5 ml of a 10 per cent solution of stannous chloride in concentrated hydrochloric acid to the fumed liquid and heat on a steam bath for 4 minutes. Add 10 ml of a 1 per cent solution of toluene-3,4-dithiol and continue to heat for 10 minutes longer, shaking the flask periodically. Transfer to a separatory funnel and rinse three times with 2 ml portions of amyl acetate. Add 5 ml of concentrated hydrochloric acid to the organic layer, repeat the extraction and again discard the lower layer. The organic layer contains the red tungsten dithiolate.

6.45. URANIUM

Dibenzoylmethane method (S 107). A very selective method for the determination of uranium (VI) is based on the extraction of its complex with dibenzoylmethane in the presence of 1,2-diaminocyclohexanetetraacetic acid as masking agent.

Procedure. To 10 ml of the solution for analysis add 2 ml of 0·1 M 1,2-diaminocyclohexanetetraacetic acid (adjusted to pH 6–7 with sodium hydroxide), adjust the pH to 6–7, dilute to 20 ml, and extract uranium with two or three 20 ml portions of 0·2 M dibenzoylmethane in benzene. Measure the absorbancy of the uranium (VI) complex at 403 mμ.

Only beryllium is extracted under these conditions, but it does not interfere with the determination.

6.46. VANADIUM

8-Hydroxyquinoline method (S 106). Vanadium (V) can be selectively determined as vanadium (V)-oxinate. The interfering metals can be removed by a preliminary extraction at pH > 9.

Procedure. To the solution containing vanadium (V) add 2 ml of 0·1 M sodium tartrate and dilute sodium hydroxide to adjust the pH to 9–10. Dilute with distilled water to 20 ml and extract the interfering metals with several portions of 0·1 M oxine in chloroform until the organic phase remains colourless. Discard the organic phase; readjust its pH with dilute hydrochloric acid to 3–5 and extract vanadium with two 20 ml portions of 0·1 M oxine in chloroform. Measure the absorbancy of the vanadium (V) oxinate at 550 mμ. Molybdenum (VI), tungsten (VI), and zirconium (IV), which are extracted simultaneously with vanadium (V), do not interfere at this wavelength.

6.47. ZINC

Dithizone method (M 29, S 103). A highly selective method for the isolation and determination of zinc is based on the extraction of zinc dithizonate using diethanolaminedithiocarbamate as a masking agent.

Procedure. To 10 ml sample solution add 1 ml of the masking agent solution (this solution is prepared by mixing 6·0 g of ethanolamine in 120 ml absolute methanol with 3·5 g carbon disulphide; the resulting solution contains 7 per cent of diethanolaminedithiocarbamate and is stable for a week) and adjust the pH to 5·5–9·5 with sodium acetate and ammonia. Thus prepared, extract the solution with several portions of 0·01 per cent dithizone solution in carbon tetrachloride (ignoring the crystalline precipitate of the interfering ions with the masking agent) until the green colour of the dithizone solution remains unchanged. Zinc can be determined in the combined organic extract by monocolour as well as by mixed colour methods (see Section 5.10.1).
This method can be used for the determination of zinc even in the presence of 100–1000-fold excess of other metals that form extractable dithizonates.

6.48. ZIRCONIUM

Thenoyltrifluoracetone method (M 86). Zirconium can be extracted from acid solutions by HTTA dissolved in xylene or benzene. The selectivity of the separation may be increased by back-extraction of zirconium into dilute hydrofluoric acid.

Procedure. Extract zirconium (IV), dissolved in 2 M hydrochloric or nitric acid, with an equal volume of 0·5 M HTTA in xylene. Repeat the extraction. Discard the aqueous phase and back-extract zirconium from the combined organic extracts with dilute (0·25–0·50 M) hydrofluoric and nitric acid mixture.

APPENDIX

DISSOCIATION CONSTANTS K_{H_2A}, K_{HA}, PARTITION COEFFICIENTS p_{HA}, AND SOLUBILITY DATA OF ORGANIC REAGENTS THAT FORM EXTRACTABLE CHELATES

Organic reagent	pK_{H_2A}	pK_{HA}	$\log p_{HA}$ (solvent)	Solubility (Mol.) (solvent)	Remarks	Ref.
β-Diketones:						
Acetylacetone		8·94			25°C	S 25
		8·93			25°C	C 5, E 6
		8·95			20°C	R 41
		8·82	0·77 (C_6H_6)		25°C	R 45
			0·77 (hexone)			
			1·37 ($CHCl_3$)		30°C	V 6
		8·95			20°C, thermodynamic constant	I 49
		9·02	1·37 to 1·00 ($CHCl_3$)		0·0 to 1·9 M $HClO_4$	S 4
			0·52 to 0·15 (CCl_4)		0·0 to 1·9 M $HClO_4$	
			0·52 (CCl_4)	1·72 (0·1 M $NaClO_4$)	20°C, $\mu = 0·1$	R 24
			0·76 (C_6H_6)		20°C, $\mu = 0·1$	
			1·40 ($CHCl_3$)		20°C, $\mu = 0·1$	
		8·76	0·54 (C_6H_6)		25°C, $\mu = 1·0$	P 26
			1·21 ($CHCl_3$)		25°C, $\mu = 1·0$	
Benzoylacetone		8·70		$2·36 \times 10^{-3}$ (H_2O)	25°C	E 6
		8·74	2·82 (CCl_4)	1·9 (CCl_4)	20°C, $\mu = 0·1$	S 95
			3·14 (C_6H_6)	2·5 (C_6H_6)	20°C, $\mu = 0·1$	
			3·60 ($CHCl_3$)	3·9 ($CHCl_3$)	20°C, $\mu = 0·1$	
		8·24	2·79 (C_6H_6)	$2·10^{-3}$ (0·1 M $NaClO_4$)	20°C	P 25
					25°C, $\mu = 1·0$	

DISSOCIATION CONSTANTS K_{H_2A}, K_{HA}, PARTITION COEFFICIENTS p_{HA}, AND SOLUBILITY DATA OF ORGANIC REAGENTS THAT FORM EXTRACTABLE CHELATES (continued)

Organic reagent	pK_{H_2A}	pK_{HA}	$\log p_{HA}$ (solvent)	Solubility (Mol.) (solvent)	Remarks	Ref.
Benzoylacetone (cont.)		8·96	3·37 ($CHCl_3$)		25°C, $\mu = 1\cdot0$	Z 19
			3·14 (C_6H_6)		25°C, $\mu = 0\cdot1$	
			3·44 ($CHCl_3$)		25°C, $\mu = 0\cdot1$	
Dibenzoylmethane		9·35	4·51 (CCl_4)	1·3 (CCl_4)	20°C, $\mu = 0\cdot1$	M 122
			5·35 (C_6H_6)	1·8 (C_6H_6)	20°C, $\mu = 0\cdot1$	
			5·40 ($CHCl_3$)	2·4 ($CHCl_3$)	20°C, $\mu = 0\cdot1$	
				6×10^{-6} (0·1 M $NaClO_4$)	20°C	
Dipivaloylmethane		9·2	5·2 ($CHCl_3$)		30°C	S 32
Trifluoroacetylacetone		11·77			25°C, $\mu = 0\cdot01$	G 51
		6·3			25°C	R 7
Furoyltrifluoroacetone			0·18 (C_6H_6)		2 M $HClO_4$	L 7
Pyrroyltrifluoroacetone			0·87 (C_6H_6)		2 M $HClO_4$	L 7
Benzoyltrifluoroacetone		6·3	0·47 (C_6H_6)		2 M $HClO_4$	L 7
					25°C	R 7
Thenoyltrifluoroacetone		6·23	1·60 (C_6H_6)		25°C	R 7
			1·63 to 1·71 (C_6H_6)		[TTA] = 0·1 M; 25°C	K 40
			1·76 (C_6H_6)		[TTA] = 0·1 to 1·0 M	
					[TTA] = 1·7 M	
		6·38	1·69 to 2·65 (C_6H_6)		$\mu = 0\cdot6$ to 6·1	C 44
		6·53	2·12 (C_6H_6)		25°C, $\mu = 1\cdot0$	Z 1
			1·52 (xylene)			P 27
						D 9
Selenoylacetone		8·55	2·92 ($CHCl_3$)		25°C, $\mu = 0\cdot1$	Z 19
			3·00 (C_6H_6)		25°C, $\mu = 0\cdot1$	
Selenoyltrifluoroacetone		6·32	1·92 (C_6H_6)		25°C, $\mu = 1\cdot0$	P 27
Benzoylselenoylmethane		7·86	3·66 (C_6H_6)		25°C, $\mu = 1\cdot0$	M 44
			3·90 ($CHCl_3$)		25°C, $\mu = 1\cdot0$	
Furoylselenoylmethane		2·51	2·68 (C_6H_6)		25°C, $\mu = 1\cdot0$	

DISSOCIATION CONSTANTS K_{H_2A}, K_{HA}, PARTITION COEFFICIENTS p_{HA}, AND SOLUBILITY DATA OF ORGANIC REAGENTS THAT FORM EXTRACTABLE CHELATES (continued)

Organic reagent	pK_{H_2A}	pK_{HA}	$\log p_{HA}$ (solvent)	Solubility (Mol.) (solvent)	Remarks	Ref.
Furoylselenoylmethane (cont.)						
Thenoylselenoylmethane		2·53	3·10 (CHCl$_3$)		25°C, $\mu = 1\cdot0$	J 2, B 91
			2·75 (C$_6$H$_6$)		25°C, $\mu = 1\cdot0$	D 30, V 17
			3·17 (CHCl$_3$)		25°C, $\mu = 1\cdot0$	
Diselenoylmethane		2·50	3·15 (C$_6$H$_6$)		25°C, $\mu = 1\cdot0$	D 43
			3·17 (CHCl$_3$)		25°C, $\mu = 1\cdot0$	
Tropolone and its derivatives:						
Tropolone	0·03	7·00	1·70 (CHCl$_3$)		20°C	
		6·71			25°C, $\mu = 0\cdot1$	
					25°C, $\mu = 1\cdot0$	
β-Isopropyltropolone		7·04	3·37 (CHCl$_3$)		25°C, $\mu = 0\cdot1$	
γ-Isopropyltropolone		7·10	3·24 (CHCl$_3$)		25°C, $\mu = 0\cdot1$	
α-Isopropyltropolone		7·64			25°C, $\mu = 0\cdot1$	
8-Hydroxyquinoline and its derivatives:						
8-Hydroxyquinoline	4·8	10·4			18°C	F 21
	4·5	9·7			18°C	K 52
		10·38		6·12 × 10^{-3} (H$_2$O)	25°C	S 120
	5·09	9·82	2·81 (CHCl$_3$)	3·56 × 10^{-3} (H$_2$O)	18°C	L 2
				2·55 (CHCl$_3$)	18°C	
	4·81	9·71			20°C	P 34
	5·27	9·68		3·78 × 10^{-3} (H$_2$O)	20°C, 25°C	I 11
	5·017	9·813			thermodynamic const. $\mu = 0\cdot2$	N 5
	5·05	9·85	2·55 (CHCl$_3$)			B 80
	5·00	9·66	2·66 (CHCl$_3$)	2·63 M (CHCl$_3$)	25°C, $\mu = 0\cdot1$	M 80
			2·18 (hexone)	3·56 × 10^{-3} (H$_2$O)	25°C, $\mu = 0\cdot1$	D 26
	5·10	9·90			20°C	D 38
	5·33	9·60	2·6 (C$_6$H$_6$)	1·19 (C$_6$H$_6$)	18°C, $\mu = 0\cdot1$	B 70
						U 4

DISSOCIATION CONSTANTS K_{H_2A}, K_{HA}, PARTITION COEFFICIENTS p_{HA}, AND SOLUBILITY DATA OF ORGANIC REAGENTS THAT FORM EXTRACTABLE CHELATES (continued)

Organic reagent	pK_{H_2A}	pK_{HA}	log p_{HA} (solvent)	Solubility (Mol.) (solvent)	Remarks	Ref.
8-Hydroxyquinoline (cont.)	5·10	9·86	2·3 (CHCl$_3$)		25°C, butylcellosolve present	O 11
			2·65 (CHCl$_3$)			J 1
2-Methyl-8-hydroxyquinoline	5·55	10·3	3·4 (CHCl$_3$)	0·506 (CHCl$_3$)	$\mu = 0\cdot2$	P 34
	5·65	10·15			25°C, $\mu = 0\cdot1$	B 80
	5·77	10·04			25°C, $\mu = 0\cdot1$	D 38
5-Methyl-8-hydroxyquinoline	5·29	9·93	3·28 (CHCl$_3$)	0·190 (CHCl$_3$)	25°C, $\mu = 0\cdot1$	D 36
5-Acetyl-8-hydroxyquinoline	4·00	7·75	2·8 (CHCl$_3$)	0·0587 (CHCl$_3$)	25°C, $\mu = 0\cdot1$	
5,7-Dichloro-8-hydroxyquinoline	2·9	7·4	3·86 (CHCl$_3$)	0·0119 (hexanol)	25°C, $\mu = 0\cdot1$	
			3·14 (hexanol)		25°C, $\mu = 0\cdot1$	
5,7-Dibromo-8-hydroxyquinoline	2·6	7·3	4·15 (CHCl$_3$)	0·0302 (CHCl$_3$)	25°C, $\mu = 0\cdot1$	
			3·36 (hexanol)			
5,7-Diiodo-8-hydroxyquinoline	2·7	8·0	4·15 (CHCl$_3$)	0·0109 (CHCl$_3$)	25°C, $\mu = 0\cdot1$	
5-Chloro-7-iodo-8-hydroxyquinoline	2·7	7·9	3·88 (CHCl$_3$)	0·0585 (CHCl$_3$)	25°C, $\mu = 0\cdot1$	
5-Nitroso-8-hydroxyquinoline	2·56	7·59			15°C, $\mu = 0\cdot1$	I 23
1-Hydroxyacridine	5·31	9·84				B 70
Oximes:						
Dimethylglyoxime		10·6		5·4 × 10^{-3} (H$_2$O)	25°C, $\mu = 0\cdot05$	S 14
				4·5 × 10^{-4} (CHCl$_3$)		
				5·5 × 10^{-3} (H$_2$O)	18°C	P 21
				6 × 10^{-5} (CCl$_4$)		B 4
				3·6 × 10^{-4} (CHCl$_3$)		
			0·95 (isoamyl alcohol)	4·5 × 10^{-2} (isoamyl alcohol)		
			1·08 (butyl alcohol)	5·6 × 10^{-2} (butyl alcohol)		
α-Benzildioxime			2·0 (CHCl$_3$)			P 24

DISSOCIATION CONSTANTS K_{H_2A}, K_{HA}, PARTITION COEFFICIENTS p_{HA}, AND SOLUBILITY DATA OF ORGANIC REAGENTS THAT FORM EXTRACTABLE CHELATES (*continued*)

Organic reagent	pK_{H_2A}	pK_{HA}	$\log p_{HA}$ (solvent)	Solubility (Mol.) (solvent)	Remarks	Ref.
α-Benzildioxime (cont.)						
Salicylaldoxime		7·4	10·5 (CHCl$_3$)† 2·1 (CHCl$_3$)		30°C, $\mu = 0·1$	S 33
Nitrosophenols:						
1-Nitroso-2-naphthol		7·63	2·97 (CHCl$_3$) 2·55 (methylisobutyl-ketone)	1·35 (CHCl$_3$) 0·416 (methylisobutyl-ketone)	25°C, $\mu = 0·1$ 25°C, $\mu = 0·1$	D 33
2-Nitroso-1-naphthol		7·24	2·11 (CHCl$_3$) 2·23 (methylisobutyl-ketone)	1·06 × 10^{-3} (H$_2$O) 0·096 (CHCl$_3$) 0·13 (methylisobutyl-ketone)	25°C, $\mu = 0·1$ 25°C, $\mu = 0·1$ 25°C, $\mu = 0·1$	
				8·4 × 10^{-4} (H$_2$O)	25°C, $\mu = 0·1$	
Nitrosoarylhydroxylamines:						
N-Nitroso-N-phenylhydroxyl-amine (cupferron)		5·24 4·28 4·16			0°C, $\mu = 0$ 25°C 25°C, $\mu = 0·1$ 25°C, $\mu = 0·1$	H 12 P 61 D 26, D 38
			2·18 (CHCl$_3$) 1·93 (methylisobutyl-ketone) 1·80 (diethyl ether) 2·23 (butyl acetate) 3·34 (CCl$_4$) 2·15 (CHCl$_3$)		13°C 13–15°C 15°C 20°C 25°C	H 5 K 24 E 10, E 11 S 92
N-Nitroso-N-naphthylhydro-xylamine (neocupferron)		4·11	2·45 (ethyl acetate)			
Hydroxamic acids:			3·91		25°C	E 10
Benzhydroxamic acid		8·9			20°C, $\mu = 0·5$	W 30

DISSOCIATION CONSTANTS K_{H_2A}, K_{HA}, PARTITION COEFFICIENTS p_{HA}, AND SOLUBILITY DATA OF ORGANIC REAGENTS THAT FORM EXTRACTABLE CHELATES (continued)

Organic reagent	pK_{H_2A}	pK_{HA}	$\log p_{HA}$ (solvent)	Solubility (Mol.) solvent	Remarks	Ref.
Benzhydroxamic acid (cont.)		8·7		0·739 (CHCl₃)	20°C, μ = 1·0	D 37
N-Benzoyl-N-phenylhydroxyl-		8·15	2·33 (CHCl₃)	1·95 × 10⁻³ (H₂O)	25°C, μ = 0·1	C 56, A 30
amine				2·6 × 10⁻³ (H₂O)	25°C, μ = 0·1	
		7·97	2·33 (CHCl₃)	1·9 × 10⁻³ (H₂O)	20°C, μ = 1·0	L 24
			1·66 (C₆H₆)	2·6 × 10⁻² (CCl₄)	20°C, μ = 1·0	Z 7
				6·1 × 10⁻² (CH₃·C₆H₅)		
				0·15 (C₆H₆)		
				0·48 (ethyl acetate)		
				0·58 (CHCl₃)		
Dithizone and its derivatives:						
Diphenylthiocarbazone (dithizone)			8·7–8·8 (CCl₄)†			B 1, B 92
			9·5 (CHCl₃)†			B 92
		4·82	4·04 (CCl₄)	2 × 10⁻⁷ (H₂O)	μ = 0·1, 25°C	S 13
		4·46	8·80 (CCl₄)†	2·5 × 10⁻⁷ (H₂O)	μ = 0·14, 20°C	D 25
		4·55	9·09 (C₆H₆)†			I 10
			7·44 (C₆H₁₂)†			I 14
			10·58 (CHCl₃)†			
			8·92 (CCl₄)†	2·5 × 10⁻³ (CCl₄)	acet. buffer	K 60
			9·02 (CCl₄)†		0·1 M KCN	
			10·62 (CHCl₃)†	6·8 × 10⁻² (CHCl₃)	acet. buffer	
			10·64 (CHCl₃)†		0·1 M KCN	
			11·0 (isoamyl alcohol)†	9·5 × 10⁻² (isoamyl alcohol)		T 45, T 46,
				3·1 × 10⁻³ (CCl₄)	20°C	B 111
				1·65 × 10⁻² (C₆H₆)	20°C	B 111
				9·2 × 10⁻² (CHCl₃)	20°C	

DISSOCIATION CONSTANTS K_{H_2A}, K_{HA}, PARTITION COEFFICIENTS p_{HA}, AND SOLUBILITY DATA OF ORGANIC REAGENTS THAT FORM EXTRACTABLE CHELATES (continued)

Organic reagent	pK_{H_2A}	pK_{HA}	$\log p_{HA}$ (solvent)	Solubility (Mol.) solvent	Remarks	Ref.
P,p-Dimethyldithizone			10·6 (CCl$_4$)†	6·3 × 10^{-3} (CCl$_4$)		B 112
P,p-Dichlorodithizone			8·04 (CCl$_4$)†	1·3 × 10^{-3} (CCl$_4$)		
P,p-Dibromodithizone			8·27 (CCl$_4$)†	1·5 × 10^{-3} (CCl$_4$)		B 112
P,p-Diiododithizone			8·9 (CCl$_4$)†	1·5 × 10^{-3} (CCl$_4$)		
Di-(α-naphthyl)thiocarbazone			11·0 (CCl$_4$)†			G 47, G 49
Di-(β-naphthyl)thiocarbazone			12·7 (CCl$_4$)†			
Dithiocarbamates:						
Diethyldithiocarbamate		3·35	2·38 (CCl$_4$)† 3·37 (CHCl$_3$)†		0°C 20°C 20°C	B 76 B 77
Dithiols:						
Toluene-3,4-dithiol		5·4				G 13
Miscellaneous reagents:						
Salicylic acid		2·82	0·5 (CHCl$_3$) 2·51 (methylisobutyl-ketone) 1·81 (furfurol)	1·115 (furfurol) 0·17 (CHCl$_3$)	25°C, μ = 0·1 25°C, μ = 0·1	H 30, H 31
2-Hydroxy-1,4-naphtho-quinone		2·37	2·01 (C$_6$H$_6$) 2·25 (CHCl$_3$)	1·6 × 10^{-2} (H$_2$O)	25°C, μ = 0·1	C 37
Diphenylcarbazone		8·5	0·88 (CCl$_4$) 1·59 (CH$_3$·C$_6$H$_5$)	2·75 × 10^{-3} (CCl$_4$) 1·0 × 10^{-2} (CH$_3$·C$_6$H$_5$) 3·8 × 10^{-4} (H$_2$O)	21–23°C, μ = 0·1	W 7 Z 19 B 15
2-Mercaptobenzthiazole		7·8	2·2 (CHCl$_3$)		30°C, μ = 0·1	S 33

† Values of $pK_{HA} + \log p_{HA}$.

REFERENCES†

A 1. ABBOT D. C., POLHILL R. D. A.: *Analyst* **79**, 547 (1954).
A 2. ABBOT D. C., JOHNSON E. I.: *Analyst* **82**, 206 (1957).
A 3. ABRAHAMCZIK E.: *Mikrochem.* **25**, 228 (1938).
A 4. ABRAHAMCZIK E.: *Mikrochem. Mikrochim. Acta* **33**, 209 (1947).
A 5. ABRAHAMCZIK E.: *Angew. Chem.* **61**, 96 (1946).
A 6. ABRAHAMCZIK E.: *Microchem. Mikrochim. Acta* **36/37**, 104 (1951).
A 7. ABSON D., LIPSCOMB A. G.: *Analyst* **82**, 152 (1957).
A 8. ADAM J. A., BOOTH E., STRICKLAND J. D. H.: *Analyt. Chim. Acta* **6**, 462 (1952).
A 9. AGRINSKAYA N. A., PETRASHEN V. I.: *Zhur. analit. Khim.* **16**, 701 (1961).
A 10. ALCOCK K., BEDFORD F. C., HARDWICK W. H., MCKAY H. A. C.: *J. Inorg. Nuclear Chem.* **4**, 100 (1957).
A 11. ALEXANDER J. W.: *Summaries Doct. Diss. Univ. Wisconsin* **6**, 205 (1942).
A 12. ALEXANDER O. R., GODAR E. M., LINDE N. J.: *Ind. Eng. Chem., Analyt.* **18**, 206 (1946).
A 13. ALIMARIN I. P., GIBALO I. M.: *Vestnik Moskov. Univ., Ser. Mat., Mekh., Astr., Fiz., Khim.* **11**, No. 2, 185 (1956).
A 14. ALIMARIN I. P., GIBALO I. M.: *Vestnik Moskov. Univ., Ser. Fiz.-Mat. i Estestv. Nauk* **11**, No. 5, 55 (1956).
A 15. ALIMARIN I. P., GIBALO I. M.: *Doklady Akad. Nauk SSSR* **109**, 1137 (1956).
A 16. ALIMARIN I. P., GIBALO I. M.: *Zhur. analit. Khim.* **11**, 389 (1956).
A 17. ALIMARIN I. P., ZOLOTOV YU. A.: *Zhur. analit. Khim.* **12**, 176 (1957).
A 18. ALIMARIN I. P., POLYANSKIJ V. N.: *Sbornik Trudov. Moskov. Vetsernego Metalurg. Instituta*, No. 2, 235 (1957).
A 19. ALIMARIN I. P., PRZHEVALSKIJ E. S., PUZDRENKOVA I. V., GOLOVINA A. P.: *Trudy Kom. analit. Khim. Akad. Nauk SSSR* **8**, 152 (1958).
A 20. ALIMARIN I. P., GOLOVINA A. P., PUZDRENKOVA I. V.: *Vestnik Moskov. Univ., Ser. Mat., Mech., Astr., Fiz., Khim.* **14**, No. 2, 185 (1959).
A 21. ALIMARIN I. P., ZOLOTOV YU. A., PALSHIN E. S.: *Doklady Akad. Nauk SSSR* **124**, 328 (1959).
A 22. ALIMARIN I. P., CZE-YUNG-SCHAING: *Zavodskaya Lab.* **25**, 1435 (1959). *Talanta* **8**, 317 (1961).
A 23. ALIMARIN I. P., CZE-YUNG-SCHAING: *Vestnik Moskov. Univ., Ser. Khim.* **15**, No. 2, 53 (1960).
A 24. ALIMARIN I. P., ZOLOTOV YU. A., PALSHIN E. S.: *Radiokhimiya* **2**, 637 (1960).
A 25. ALIMARIN I. P., PETRUKHIN O. M., CZE-YUNG-SCHAING: *Doklady Akad. Nauk SSSR* **136**, 1073 (1961).
A 26. ALIMARIN I. P., BORZENKOVA N. P., ZAKARINA N. A.: *Zavodskaya Lab.* **27**, 958 (1961).
A 27. ALIMARIN I. P., BILIMOVISH G. N.: *Coll. Czech. Chem. Comm.* **26**, 255 (1961).
A 28. ALIMARIN I. P., PETRUKHIN O. M.: *Zhur. neorg. Khim.* **7**, 1191 (1962).
A 29. ALIMARIN I. P., BILIMOVISH G. N., CYU-SIAN-KHAN: *Zhur. neorg. Khim.* **7**, 2725 (1962).
A 30. ALIMARIN I. P., SUDAKOV F. P., GOLOVKIN B. G.: *Uspekhi Khim.* **31**, 989 (1962).
A 31. ALIMARIN I. P., ZOLOTOV YU. A.: *Talanta* **9**, 891 (1962).
A 32. ALIMARIN I. P., PETRUKHIN O. M., ZOLOTOV YU. A.: *Zhur. analit. Khim.* **17**, 554 (1962).
A 33. ALIMARIN I. P., BILIMOVISH G. N., YAN YUI-SEN: *Radiokhimiya* **4**, 510 (1962).
A 34. ALLEN S. H., HAMILTON M. B.: *Analyt. Chim. Acta* **7**, 483 (1952).

† The full titles of the principal journal abbreviations used are given on pages 228–230.

A 35. ALMOND H.: *Analyt. Chem.* **25**, 166 (1953).
A 36. AMANO H.: *Sci. Reports Res. Inst. Tôhoku Univ.* **A12**, 24 (1960).
A 37. ANDRUS S.: *Analyst* **80**, 514 (1955).
A 38. ARTHINGTON W., HULME A. C.: *Analyst* **76**, 211 (1951).
A 39. ASHBROOK A. W.: *Chemist–Analyst* **48**, 5 (1959).
A 40. ASHBROOK A. W., RITCEY G. M.: *Canad. J. Chem.* **39**, 1109 (1961).
A 41. ASHBROOK A. W., CONN K.: *Chemist–Analyst* **50**, 47 (1961).
A 42. ASHIZAWA T.: *Japan Analyst (Bunseki Kagaku)* **10**, 443 (1961).
A 43. ASSAF A. G., HOLLIBAUGH W. C.: *Ind. Eng. Chem., Analyt.* **12**, 695 (1940).
A 44. ASTACHOV K. V., MICHALEVA S. V., TESLIN V. I.: *Radiokhimiya* **4**, 540 (1962).
A 45. ATHAVALE V. T., RAMACHANDRAN T. P., TILLU M. M., VAIDYA G. M.: *Analyt. Chim. Acta* **22**, 56 (1960).
A 46. ATHAVALE V. T., PADMANABHA-IYER C. S., TILLU M. M., VAIDYA G. M.: *Analyt. Chim. Acta* **24**, 263 (1961).
A 47. ATHAVALE V. T., BHASIN R. L., JANGIDA B. L.: *Analyst* **87**, 217 (1962).
A 48. AUGER V., LAFONTAINE L., CASPAR C.: *Compt. rend.* **180**, 376 (1925).
A 49. AWAYA H., MIYOSHI S., MOTOJIMA K.: *Japan Analyst (Bunseki Kagaku)* **6**, 503 (1957).
A 50. AWAYA H.: *Japan Analyst (Bunseki Kagaku)* **9**, 305 (1960).
A 51. AYRES G. H., TUFFLY B. L.: *Analyt. Chem.* **24**, 949 (1952).

B 1. BABKO A. K., PILIPENKO A. T.: *Zhur. analit. Khim.* **1**, 275 (1946).
B 2. BABKO A. K., PILIPENKO A. T.: *Zhur. analit. Khim.* **2**, 33 (1947).
B 3. BABKO A. K.: *Zavodskaya Lab.* **16**, 527 (1950).
B 4. BABKO A. K., MICHELSON P. B.: *Ukrain. khim. Zhur.* **21**, 391 (1955).
B 5. BABKO A. K., MICHALTZITSIN G. T.: *Ukrain. khim. Zhur.* **22**, 676 (1956).
B 6. BABKO A. K., ZHAROVSKIJ F. G.: *Zavodskaya Lab.* **25**, 45 (1959).
B 7. BABKO A. K., *Zavodskaya Lab.* **25**, 515 (1959).
B 8. BABKO A. K., ZHAROVSKIJ F. G.: *Zavodskaya Lab.* **28**, 1287 (1962).
B 9. BACH J. M.: *Anales asoc. quím. argentina* **28**, 108 (1940), cf. *Chem. Abs.* **35**, 706 (1941).
B 10. BAGGETT W. L., HUYCK H. P.: *Analyt. Chem.* **31**, 1320 (1959).
B 11. BAGGOTT E. R., WILLCOCKS R. G. W.: *Analyst* **80**, 53 (1954).
B 12. BAGNALL K. W., ROBERTSON D. S.: *J.* 509 (1957).
B 13. BAGREEV V. V., ZOLOTOV YU. A.: *Zhur. analit. Khim.* **17**, 852 (1962).
B 14. BAGSHAWE B., TRUMAN R. J.: *Analyst* **72**, 189 (1947).
B 15. BALT, S., VAN DAHLEN E.: *Analyt. Chim. Acta* **27**, 188 (1962).
B 16. BAMBACH K.: *Ind. Eng. Chem., Analyt.* **11**, 400 (1939).
B 17. BAMBACH K.: *Ind. Eng. Chem., Analyt.* **12**, 63 (1940).
B 18. BAMBACH K., BURKEY R. E.: *Ind. Eng. Chem., Analyt.* **14**, 904 (1942).
B 19. BANERJEA D.: *Z. analyt. Chem.* **159**, 123 (1957).
B 20. BANKOVSKIJ YU. A.: *Izvest. Akad. Nauk Latv. SSR*, No. 12, 127 (1952).
B 21. BANKOVSKIJ YU. A., SCHVARC E. M., IYEVINSH A. F.: *Izvest. Akad. Nauk Latv. SSR*, No. 3, 121 (1958).
B 22. BANKOVSKIJ YU. A., IYEVINSH A. F.: *Zhur. analit. Khim.* **13**, 507 (1958).
B 23. BANKOVSKIJ YU. A., IYEVINSH A. F.: *Zhur. analit. Khim.* **13**, 643 (1958).
B 24. BANKOVSKIJ YU. A., BAUMAN V. K., IYEVINSH A. F.: *Biokhimiya* **23**, 845 (1958).
B 25. BANKOVSKIJ YU. A., IYEVINSH A. F., LUKSHA A. F.: *Izvest. Akad. Nauk Latv. SSR*, No. 4, 61 (1959).
B 26. BANKOVSKIJ YU. A., LOBANOVA E. F.: *Izvest. Akad. Nauk Latv. SSR*, No. 6, 103 (1959).
B 27. BANKOVSKIJ YU. A., IYEVINSH A. F., LUKSHA A. F.: *Zhur. analit. Khim.* **14**, 222 (1959).
B 28. BANKOVSKIJ YU. A., SCHVARC E. M., IYEVINSH A. F.: *Zhur. analit. Khim.* **14**, 313 (1959).

B 29. BANKOVSKIJ YU. A., LOBANOVA E. F.: *Zhur. analit. Khim.* **14**, 523 (1959).
B 30. BANKOVSKIJ YU. A., IYEVINSH A. F., LUKSHA E. A.: *Zhur. analit. Khim.* **14**, 714 (1959).
B 31. BANKOVSKIJ YU. A., IYEVINSH A. F., LIEPINA Z. E.: *Zhur. analit. Khim.* **15**, 4 (1960).
B 32. BANKOVSKIJ YU. A., LOBANOVA E. F.: *Izvest. Akad. Nauk Latv. SSR*, No. 1, 97 (1960).
B 33. BANKOVSKIJ YU. A., LOBANOVA E. F.: *Izvest. Akad. Nauk Latv. SSR*, No. 3, 113 (1960).
B 34. BANKOVSKIJ YU. A., MISULOVINA Z., IYEVINSH A. F., BUKA M.: *Izvest. Akad. Nauk Latv. SSR*, No. 11, 103 (1960).
B 35. BANKOVSKIJ YU. A., IYEVINSH A. F., LUKSHA O. E., BOCHKANS P. YA.: *Zhur. analit. Khim.* **16**, 150 (1961).
B 36. BANKOVSKIJ YU. A., TSIRULE YA. A., IYEVINSH A. F.: *Zhur. analit. Khim.* **16**, 562 (1961).
B 37. BANKOVSKIJ YU. A., MEZHARAUPS G. P., IYEVINSH A. F.: *Zhur. analit. Khim.* **17**, 721 (1962).
B 38. BANKS T. E., TUPPER R. L. F., WORMALL A.: *Biochem. J.* **47**, 466 (1950).
B 39. BANKS, T. E., TUPPER R. L. F., WATTS R. W. A., WORMALL A.: *Nature* **173**, 348 (1954).
B 40. BANKS C. V., SMITH R. V.: *Analyt. Chim. Acta* **21**, 308 (1959).
B 41. BARCZA L.: *Acta Chim. Acad. Sci. Hung.* **28**, 143 (1961).
B 42. BARNES H.: *Analyst* **71**, 578 (1946).
B 43. BARNES H.: *Analyst* **72**, 469 (1947).
B 44. BARNES H.: *Analyst* **76**, 220 (1951).
B 45. BARON H.: *Z. analyt. Chem.* **140**, 173 (1953).
B 46. BASKOVA Z. A.: *Zhur. analit. Khim.* **14**, 75 (1959).
B 47. BAUDISCH O., FÜRST R.: *Ber.* **50**, 324 (1917).
B 48. BECK G.: *Mikrochem. Mikrochim. Acta* **34**, 282 (1949).
B 49. BECKWITH R. S.: *Chem. and Ind.* 663 (1954).
B 50. BELEKAR G. K., ATHAVALE V. T.: *Analyst* **82**, 630 (1957).
B 51. BENDIX G. H., GRABENSTETTER D.: *Ind. Eng. Chem., Analyt.* **15**, 649 (1943).
B 52. BERG E. W., DAY M. C.: *Analyt. Chim. Acta* **18**, 578 (1958).
B 53. BERGER W., ELVERS H.: *Z. analyt. Chem.* **171**, 185 (1959).
B 54. BERGER W., ELVERS H.: *Z. analyt. Chem.* **171**, 256 (1959).
B 55. BERTHELOT M., JUNGFLEISCH J.: *Ann. Chim. Phys.* **26**, 396 (1872).
B 56. BERTRAND D.: *Bull. Soc. chim. France* **9**, 121 (1942).
B 57. BETTS R. H., LEIGH R. M.: *Canad. J. Res.* **B28**, 514 (1950).
B 58. BHADURI A. S.: *Z. analyt. Chem.* **151**, 109 (1956).
B 59. BHADURI A. S., RÂY P.: *Z. analyt. Chem.* **154**, 103 (1957).
B 60. BIEFELD L. P., PATRICK T. M.: *Ind. Eng. Chem., Analyt.* **14**, 275 (1942).
B 61. BJERRUM J.: *Dissertation*, Copenhagen (1941).
B 62. BJERRUM J., SCHWARZENBACH G., SILLÉN L. G.: Stability constants, *Chem. Soc. Spec. Publ.* No. 6, Part I, 1957; No. 7, Part II, 1958.
B 63. BLAIR A. J., PANTONY D. A.: *Analyt. Chim. Acta* **14**, 545 (1956).
B 64. BLAIR A. J., PANTONY D. A.: *Analyt. Chim. Acta* **16**, 121 (1957).
B 65. BLANK A. B., BULGAKOVA A. M.: *Zhur. analit. Khim.* **15**, 605 (1960).
B 66. BLANK A. B., BULGAKOVA A. M., SIZONENKO N. T.: *Zhur. analit. Khim.* **16**, 715 (1961).
B 67. BLOCH J. M., LAZARE J.: *Bull. Soc. chim. France* 1148 (1960).
B 68. BLUNDY, P. D., SIMPSON M. P.: *Analyst* **83**, 558 (1958).
B 69. BOCK R., HACKSTEIN K.-G.: *Z. analyt. Chem.* **138**, 337 (1953).
B 70. BOCQUET G., PÂRIS R. A.: *Analyt. Chim. Acta* **14**, 1 (1956).
B 71. BODE H., HENRICH G.: *Z. analyt. Chem.* **135**, 98 (1952).
B 72. BODE H.: *Z. analyt. Chem.* **142**, 414 (1954).
B 73. BODE H.: *Z. analyt. Chem.* **143**, 182 (1954).
B 74. BODE H.: *Z. analyt. Chem.* **144**, 90 (1955).

B 75. BODE H.: *Z. analyt. Chem.* **144,** 165 (1955).
B 76. BODE H., TUSCHE K.-J.: *Z. analyt. Chem.* **157,** 414 (1957).
B 77. BODE H., NEUMANN F.: *Z. analyt. Chem.* **172,** 1 (1960).
B 78. BOLLETER W. T.: *Analyt. Chem.* **31,** 201 (1959).
B 79. BOLOMEY R. A., WISH L.: *J. Amer. Chem. Soc.* **72,** 4483 (1950).
B 80. BORREL M., PÂRIS R. A.: *Analyt. Chim. Acta* **6,** 389 (1952).
B 81. BOUSSIÈRES G., FERRADINI C.: *Analyt. Chim. Acta* **4,** 610 (1950).
B 82. BOUSSIÈRES G., VERNOIS J.: *Compt. rend.* **244,** 2508 (1957).
B 83. BOUNSALL E. J., McBRYDE W. A. E.: *Canad. J. Chem.* **38,** 1488 (1960).
B 84. BOYLAND E.: *Analyst* **71,** 230 (1946).
B 85. BRANDŠTETR J., VŘEŠŤÁL J.: *Coll. Czech. Chem. Comm.* **26,** 392 (1961).
B 86. BREANT M.: *Bull. Soc. chim. France* **948** (1956).
B 87. BRICKER L. G., PROCTOR K. L.: *Ind. Eng. Chem., Analyt.* **17,** 511 (1945).
B 88. BRICKER L. G., WEINBERG S., PROCTOR K. L.: *Ind. Eng. Chem., Analyt.* **17,** 661 (1945).
B 89. BROWN E. A.: *Ind. Eng. Chem., Analyt.* **18,** 493 (1946).
B 90. BROWN W. B., STEINBACH J. F., WAGNER W. F.: *J. Inorg. Nuclear Chem.* **13,** 119 (1960).
B 91. BRYANT B. E., FERNELIUS W. C., DOUGLAS B. E.: *J. Amer. Chem. Soc.* **75,** 3784 (1953).
B 92. BUCH K., KOROLEFF F.: *Finska Kemistamfundets Medd.* **54,** 98 (1945), cf. *Chem. Abs.* **44,** 8750 (1950).
B 93. BUCHANAN J. D.: *J. Inorg. Nuclear Chem.* **7,** 140 (1958).
B 94. BULGAKOVA A. M., VOLKOVA A. M.: *Zhur. analit. Khim.* **15,** 591 (1960).
B 95. BULLWINKEL E. P., NOBLE P.: *J. Amer. Chem. Soc.* 2955 (1958).
B 96. BUSEV A. I.: *Zhur. analit. Khim.* **4,** 49 (1949).
B 97. BUSEV A. I., IVANYUTIN M. I.: *Vestnik Moskov. Univ., Ser. Mat., Mekh., Astr., Fiz., Khim.* **12,** No. 5, 157 (1957).
B 98. BUSEV A. I., IVANYUTIN M. I.: *Vestnik Moskov. Univ., Ser. Mat., Mekh., Astr., Fiz., Khim.* **13,** No. 2, 177 (1958).
B 99. BUSEV A. I., KISELEVA L. V.: *Vestnik Moskov. Univ., Ser. Mat., Mekh. Astr., Fiz., Khim.* **13,** No. 4, 179 (1958).
B 100. BUSEV A. I., IVANYUTIN M. I.: *Zhur. analit. Khim.* **13,** 18 (1958).
B 101. BUSEV A. I., IVANYUTIN M. I., FEIGINA E. M.: *Zavodskaya Lab.* **24,** 265 (1958).
B 102. BUSEV A. I., IVANYUTIN M. I.: *Trudy Kom. analit. Khim.* **11,** 172 (1960).
B 103. BUSEV A. I., BYR'KO V. M., GRANDBERG I. I.: *Vestnik Moskov. Univ., Ser. Khim.* **15,** No. 2, 76 (1960).
B 104. BUSEV A. I., IVANOV V. M.: *Vestnik Moskov. Univ., Ser. Khim.* **15,** No. 3, 52 (1960).
B 105. BUSEV A. I., ZHOLONDKOVSKAYA T. N., KUZNETSOVA Z. M.: *Zhur. analit. Khim.* **15,** 49 (1960).
B 106. BUSEV A. I., CZHAN FAN: *Zhur. analit. Khim.* **15,** 455 (1960).
B 107. BUSEV A. I., BORZENKOVA H. P.: *Zavodskaya Lab.* **27,** 13 (1961).
B 108. BUSEV A. I., BAZHANOVA L. A.: *Zhur. analit. Khim.* **16,** 399 (1961).
B 109. BUSEV A. I., CZHAN FAN: *Zhur. analit. Khim.* **16,** 578 (1961).
B 110. BUSEV A. I., CZHAN FAN: *Zhur. neorg. Khim.* **6,** 1308 (1961).
B 111. BUSEV A. I., BAZHANOVA L. A.: *Zhur. neorg. Khim.* **6,** 2210 (1961).
B 112. BUSEV A. I., BAZHANOVA L. A.: *Zhur. neorg. Khim.* **6,** 2805 (1961).
B 113. BUSEV A. I., BAZHANOVA L. A.: *Vestnik Moskov. Univ., Ser. Khim.* **16,** No. 6, 47 (1961).
B 114. BUSS H., KOHLCHÜTTER H. W., WALTER L.: *Z. analyt. Chem.* **191,** 273 (1962).

C 1. CALLAHAN C. M., FERNELIUS W. C., BLOCK B. P.: *Analyt. Chim. Acta* **16,** 101 (1957).
C 2. CALVIN M., WILSON K. W.: *J. Amer. Chem. Soc.* **67,** 2003 (1945).
C 3. CARLTON J. K., BRADBURY W. C.: *Analyt. Chem.* **26,** 1226 (1954).

C 4. CARLTON J. K., BRADBURY W. C., KRUH R.: *Analyt. Chim. Acta* **12,** 101 (1955).
C 5. CARTLEDGE G. H.: *J. Amer. Chem. Soc.* **73,** 4416 (1951).
C 6. CHENG K. L., BRAY R. H.: *Analyt. Chem.* **25,** 655 (1953).
C 7. CHENG K. L.: *Analyt. Chem.* **26,** 1894 (1954).
C 8. CHENG K. L., BRAY R. H., MELSTED S. W.: *Analyt. Chem.* **27,** 24 (1955).
C 9. CHENG K. L., BRAY R. H.: *Analyt. Chem.* **27,** 782 (1955).
C 10. CHENG K. L.: *Analyt. Chem.* **30,** 1027 (1958).
C 11. CHENG K. L.: *Analyt. Chem.* **30,** 1941 (1958).
C 12. CHENG K. L.: *Analyt. Chem.* **33,** 783 (1961).
C 13. CHENG K. L.: *Talanta* **9,** 739 (1962).
C 14. CHOLAK J., HUBBARD D. M., MCNARY R. R., STORY R. V.: *Ind. Eng. Chem., Analyt.* **9,** 488 (1937).
C 15. CHOLAK J., HUBBARD D. M., BURKEY R. E.: *Ind. Eng. Chem., Analyt.* **15,** 754 (1943).
C 16. CHOLAK J., HUBBARD D. M.: *Ind. Eng. Chem., Analyt.* **16,** 333 (1944).
C 17. CHOLAK J., HUBBARD D. M., BURKEY R. E.: *Analyt. Chem.* **20,** 671 (1948).
C 18. CHOWDHURY A. N., DAS SARMA B.: *Analyt. Chem.* **32,** 820 (1960).
C 19. CHRISTOPHERSON H., SANDELL E. B.: *Analyt. Chim. Acta* **10,** 1 (1954).
C 20. CHURCH F. W.: *J. Ind. Hyg.* **29,** 34 (1947).
C 21. CHWASTOWSKA J.: *Chem. Analit. (Warsaw)* **7,** 859 (1962).
C 22. CLAASSEN A., BASTINGS L.: *Rec. Trav. chim.* **73,** 783 (1954).
C 23. CLAASSEN A., BASTINGS L., VISSER J.: *Analyt. Chim. Acta* **10,** 373 (1954).
C 24. CLAASSEN A., DAAMEN A.: *Analyt. Chim. Acta* **12,** 547 (1955).
C 25. CLAASSEN A., BASTINGS L.: *Z. analyt. Chem.* **153,** 30 (1956).
C 26. CLARK L. J., AXLEY J. H.: *Analyt. Chem.* **27,** 2000 (1955).
C 27. CLARK R. E. D.: *Analyst* **82,** 177 (1957).
C 28. CLARK R. E. D.: *Analyst* **82,** 182 (1957).
C 29. CLARK L. J.: *Analyt. Chem.* **30,** 1153 (1958).
C 30. CLAYTON R. F., HARDWICK W. H., MORETON-SMITH M., TODD R.: *Analyst* **83,** 13 (1958).
C 31. CLIFFORD P. A.: *J. Assoc. Offic. Agric. Chemists* **26,** 26 (1943).
C 32. CLIFFORD W. E., BULLWINKEL E. P., MCCLAINE L. A., NOBLE P.: *J. Amer. Chem. Soc.* **80,** 2959 (1958).
C 33. CLINCH J., GUY M. J.: *Analyst* **83,** 429 (1958).
C 34. CLUETT M. L., YOE J. M.: *Analyt. Chem.* **29,** 1265 (1957).
C 35. CLULEY H. J.: *Analyst* **79,** 561 (1954).
C 36. COGAN E.: *Analyt. Chem.* **32,** 973 (1960).
C 37. COLE F. K., BROWN L. H.: *Ind. Eng. Chem.,* **51,** 58 (1959).
C 38. COLLAT J. W., ROGERS L. B.: *Analyt. Chem.* **27,** 961 (1955).
C 39. COLLINS T. A., KANZELMEYER J. H.: *Analyt. Chem.* **33,** 245 (1961).
C 40. COMPAAN H.: *Nature* **180,** 980 (1957).
C 41. COMYNS A. E., GATEHOUSE B. M., WAIT E.: *J.* 4655 (1958).
C 42. CONNICK R. E., MCVEY W. H.: *J. Amer. Chem. Soc.* **71,** 3182 (1949).
C 43. CONNICK R. E., REAS W. H.: *J. Amer. Chem. Soc.* **73,** 1171 (1951).
C 44. COOK E. H., TAFT R. W.: *J. Amer. Chem. Soc.* **74,** 6103 (1952).
C 45. COOPER S. S., KOFRON V. K.: *Analyt. Chem.* **21,** 1135 (1949).
C 46. COOPER S. S., SULLIVAN M. L.: *Analyt. Chem.* **23,** 613 (1951).
C 47. COOPER S. S., HIBBITS J. O.: *J. Amer. Chem. Soc.* **75,** 5084 (1953).
C 48. CORSINI A., MAI-LING YIH I., FERNANDO Q., FREISER H.: *Analyt. Chem.* **34,** 1090 (1962).
C 49. COWLING H., MILLER E. J.: *Ind. Eng. Chem., Analyt.* **13,** 145 (1941).
C 50. CRAIG L. C.: *Analyt. Chem.* **24,** 66 (1952).
C 51. CRONHEIM G.: *Ind. Eng. Chem., Analyt.* **14,** 445 (1942).
C 52. CRONHEIM G., WINK W.: *Ind. Eng. Chem., Analyt.* **14,** 447 (1942).
C 53. CUNINGHAME J. G., MILES G. L.: *J. Inorg. Nuclear Chem.* **3,** 54 (1956).
C 54. CUNINGHAME J. G., MILES G. L.: *J. Appl. Chem. (London)* **7,** 72 (1957).

C 55.   CYRANKOWSKA M.: *Chem. Analit.* (*Warsaw*), **6**, 649 (1961).
C 56.   CZE YUNG-SCHAING: *Dissertation Moscow Univ.* (1960).

D 1.   DAWSON E. C.: *Analyst* **73**, 618 (1948).
D 2.   DAY R. A., STOUGHTON R. W.: *J. Amer. Chem. Soc.* **72**, 5662 (1950).
D 3.   DAY R. A., POWERS R. M.: *J. Amer. Chem. Soc.* **76**, 3895 (1954).
D 4.   DE A. K., KHOPKAR S. M.: *Chem. and Ind.* **854** (1959).
D 5.   DE A. K.: *Separation of Heavy Metals*, Pergamon Press, Oxford 1961.
D 6.   DE A. K., KHOPKAR S. M.: *J. Sci. Ind. Res., India* **21A**, 131 (1962).
D 7.   DE A. K., MAJUMDAR S. K.: *Analyt. Chim. Acta* **27**, 153 (1962).
D 8.   DE A. K., RAHAMAN M. S.: *Analyt. Chim. Acta* **27**, 591 (1962).
D 9.   DE BRUIN H. J., TEMPLE R. B.: *Austral. J. Chem.* **15**, 153 (1962).
D 10.   DE BRUIN H. J., KAIRAITIS D., SZEGO L.: *Austral. J. Chem.* **15**, 218 (1962).
D 11.   DE VOE J. R., MEINKE W. W.: *Analyt. Chem.* **31**, 1428 (1959).
D 12.   DINSTL G., HECHT F.: *Mikrochim. Acta* **321** (1962).
D 13.   DISTANCOV B. G., KRESAL'NAYA L. Z., STEPANOVA N. S., KIPRIANOVA S. S.: *Zhur. neorg. Khim.* **7**, 1464 (1962).
D 14.   DONO T., NAKAGAWA G., HAYASHI M.: *J. Chem. Soc. Japan* (*Nippon Kagaku Zasshi*), Pure Chem. Sect. **81**, 1703 (1960).
D 15.   DONO T., NAKAGAWA G., WADA H.: *J. Chem. Soc. Japan* (*Nippon Kagaku Zasshi*), Pure Chem. Sect. **82**, 590 (1961).
D 16.   DREULLE N.: *Chim. analyt.* **43**, 165 (1961).
D 17.   DUFFIELD W. D.: *Analyst* **84**, 455 (1959).
D 18.   DUNCAN J. F., THOMAS F. G.: *J. Inorg. Nuclear Chem.* **4**, 376 (1957).
D 19.   DUNCAN J. F., THOMAS F. G.: *J.* 2814 (1960).
D 20.   DUNLEAVY R. A., WIBERLEY S. E., HARLEY J. H.: *Analyt. Chem.* **22**, 170 (1950).
D 21.   DUTTA R. L.: *J. Ind. Chem. Soc.* **36**, 339 (1959).
D 22.   DUTTA R. L.: *J. Ind. Chem. Soc.* **37**, 167 (1960).
D 23.   DUX J. P., FEAIRHELLER W. R.: *Analyt. Chem.* **33**, 445 (1961).
D 24.   DYER F. F., SCHWEITZER G. K.: *Analyt. Chim. Acta* **23**, 1 (1960).
D 25.   DYRSSEN D., HÖK B.: *Svensk kem. Tidskr.* **64**, 80 (1952).
D 26.   DYRSSEN D.: *Svensk kem. Tidskr.* **64**, 213 (1952).
D 27.   DYRSSEN D.: *Svensk kem. Tidskr.* **65**, 43 (1953).
D 28.   DYRSSEN D., DAHLBERG V.: *Acta Chem. Scand.* **7**, 1186 (1953).
D 29.   DYRSSEN D., SILLÉN L. G.: *Acta Chem. Scand.* **7**, 663 (1953).
D 30.   DYRSSEN D.: *Acta Chem. Scand.* **8**, 1394 (1954).
D 31.   DYRSSEN D.: *Svensk kem. Tidskr.* **66**, 234 (1954).
D 32.   DYRSSEN D.: *Svensk kem. Tidskr.* **67**, 311 (1955).
D 33.   DYRSSEN D., JOHANSSON E.: *Acta Chem. Scand.* **9**, 763 (1955).
D 34.   DYRSSEN D.: *Acta Chem. Scand.* **9**, 1567 (1955).
D 35.   DYRSSEN D., DYRSSEN M., JOHANSSON E.: *Acta Chem. Scand.* **10**, 106 (1956).
D 36.   DYRSSEN D., DYRSSEN M., JOHANSSON E.: *Acta Chem. Scand.* **10**, 341 (1956).
D 37.   DYRSSEN D.: *Acta Chem. Scand.* **10**, 353 (1956).
D 38.   DYRSSEN D.: *Svensk kem. Tidskr.* **68**, 212 (1956).
D 39.   DYRSSEN D.: *Rec. Trav. chim.* **75**, 753 (1956).
D 40.   DYRSSEN D.: *J. Inorg. Nuclear Chem.* **8**, 291 (1958).
D 41.   DYRSSEN D., HEFFEZ M., SEKINE T.: *J. Inorg. Nuclear Chem.* **16**, 367 (1961).
D 42.   DYRSSEN D.: *Acta Chem. Scand.* **15**, 1614 (1961).
D 43.   DYRSSEN D.: Extraction of Metal Ions with β-isopropyltropolone, *Trans. Roy. Inst. Technol.* No. 188, Stockholm 1962.
D 44.   DYRSSEN M.: *Rec. Trav. chim.* **75**, 748 (1956).
D 45.   DZIOMKO V. M.: *Doklady Akad. Nauk SSSR* **134**, 1091 (1960).

E 1.   EBERLE A. R., LERNER M. W.: *Analyt. Chem.* **34**, 627 (1962).
E 2.   ECKERT H. W.: *Ind. Eng. Chem., Analyt.* **15**, 406 (1943).

E 3. ECKERT G.: *Z. analyt. Chem.* **148,** 14 (1955/56).
E 4. ECKERT G.: *Z. analyt. Chem.* **153,** 261 (1956).
E 5. ECKERT G.: *Z. analyt. Chem.* **155,** 23 (1957).
E 6. EIDINOFF M. L.: *J. Amer. Chem. Soc.* **67,** 2072 (1945).
E 7. ELINSON S. V., POBEDINA L. I., MIRZOYAN N. A.: *Zhur. analit. Khim.* **15,** 334 (1960).
E 8. ELLIOT C. R., PRESTON P. F., THOMPSON J. H.: *Analyst* **84,** 237 (1959).
E 9. ELLIS G. H., THOMPSON J. F.: *Ind. Eng. Chem., Analyt.* **17,** 254 (1945).
E 10. ELVING P. J., OLSON E. C.: *J. Amer. Chem. Soc.* **78,** 4206 (1956).
E 11. ELVING P. J., OLSON E. C.: *J. Amer. Chem. Soc.* **79,** 2697 (1957).
E 12. ERÄMETSÄ O., HÄMÄLÄ S.: *Suomen Kem.* **31B,** 204 (1958).
E 13. ERDEY L., RÁDY G., FLEPS V.: *Analyt. Chem.* **135,** 1 (1952).
E 14. ERDEY L., RÁDY G.: *Acta. Chim. Acad. Sci. Hung.* **5,** 133 (1954).
E 15. ESHELMAN H. C., DEAN J. A., MENIS O., RAINS T. S.: *Analyt. Chem.* **31,** 183 (1959).
E 16. ESHELMAN H. C., DEAN J. A.: *Analyt. Chem.* **33,** 1339 (1961).
E 17. EVE D. J., STRASHEIM A.: *J. S. African Chem. Inst.* **9,** 5 (1956).

F 1. FILIPPOVA N. A., LURJE YU. YU.: *Zavodskaya Lab.* **16,** 912 (1950).
F 2. FISCHER H.: *Wiss. Veröff. Siemens–Werken* **4,** 158 (1925).
F 3. FISCHER H.: *Angew. Chem.* **42,** 1025 (1929).
F 4. FISCHER H.: *Mikrochem.* **8,** 319 (1930).
F 5. FISCHER H.: *Wiss. Veröff. Siemens–Werken* **12,** 44 (1933).
F 6. FISCHER H.: *Angew. Chem.* **46,** 442 (1933).
F 7. FISCHER H.: *Angew. Chem.* **46,** 517 (1933).
F 8. FISCHER H., LEOPOLDI G.: *Angew. Chem.* **47,** 90 (1934).
F 9. FISCHER H.: *Angew. Chem.* **47,** 685 (1934).
F 10. FISCHER H., LEOPOLDI G., VON USLAR H.: *Z. analyt. Chem.* **101,** 1 (1935).
F 11. FISCHER H., LEOPOLDI G.: *Z. analyt. Chem.* **103,** 241 (1935).
F 12. FISCHER H.: *Angew. Chem.* **50,** 919 (1937).
F 13. FISCHER H., LEOPOLDI G.: *Mikrochim. Acta* **1,** 30 (1937).
F 14. FISCHER H.: *Angew. Chem.* **50,** 919 (1937).
F 15. FISCHER H., LEOPOLDI G.: *Angew. Chem.* **119,** 161 (1940).
F 16. FISCHER H.: *Mikrochem.* **30,** 38 (1942).
F 17. FISCHER H., PASSER M., LEOPOLDI G.: *Mikrochem.* **30,** 307 (1942).
F 18. FLASCHKA H.: *Mikrochim. Acta* 784 (1956).
F 19. FOREMAN J. K., RILEY C. J., SMITH T. D.: *Analyst* **82,** 89 (1957).
F 20. FORSTER W. A.: *Analyst* **78,** 613 (1953).
F 21. FOX J. J.: *J.* **97,** 1119 (1910).
F 22. FRANCIS A. C., PILGRIM A. J.: *Analyst* **82,** 289 (1957).
F 23. FREISER H., MORRISON G. H.: *Ann. Rev. Nuclear Sci.* **9,** 221 (1959).
F 24. FREISER H.: *Chemist–Analyst* **50,** 62 (1961).
F 25. FREISER H.: *Chemist–Analyst* **50,** 94 (1961).
F 26. FRIEDENBERG H.: *Analyt. Chem.* **27,** 305 (1955).
F 27. FRITZ J. S., RICHARD M. J., BYSTROFF A. S.: *Analyt. Chem.* **29,** 577 (1957).
F 28. FRITZ J. S., BRADFORD E. C.: *Analyt. Chem.* **30,** 1021 (1958).
F 29. FRITZ J. S., RICHARD M. J., LANE W. J.: *Analyt. Chem.* **30,** 1776 (1958).
F 30. FUJINAGA T., ISIBASI M., YAMASITA K.: *Japan Analyst (Bunseki Kagaku)* **11,** 1122 (1962).
F 31. FUJINAGA T., MORII F., KANCHIKU Y.: *J. Chem. Soc. Japan (Nippon Kagaku Zasshi),* Pure Chem. Sect. **83,** 1033 (1962).
F 32. FUKAI R., MEINKE W. W.: *Progress Report* No. 7, Dept. Chem. Univ. Michigan, 63 (1958).
F 33. FURMAN N. H., MASON W. B., PECOLA J. S.: *Analyt. Chem.* **21,** 1325 (1949).

G 1. GAGE J. C.: *Analyst* **80,** 789 (1955).
G 2. GAGE J. C.: *Analyst* **82,** 453 (1957).

G 3.   GAHLER A. R., MITCHELL A. M., MELLON M. G.: *Analyt. Chem.* **23**, 500 (1951).
G 4.   GALLEGO R., DEIJS W. B., FELDMEIJER J. H.: *Rec. Trav. chim.* **71**, 987 (1952).
G 5.   GARDNER K.: *Analyst* **76**, 485 (1951).
G 6.   GEIGER R. W., SANDELL E. B.: *Analyt. Chim. Acta* **8**, 197 (1953).
G 7.   GEILMAN W., BODE H.: *Z. analyt. Chem.* **128**, 495 (1948).
G 8.   GEILMAN W., BODE H.: *Z. analyt. Chem.* **133**, 177 (1951).
G 9.   GEILMAN W., NEEB R.: *Z. analyt. Chem.* **151**, 401 (1956).
G 10. GEILMAN W., NEEB R.: *Z. analyt. Chem.* **152**, 96 (1956).
G 11. GENTRY C. H. R., SHERRINGTON L. G.: *Analyst* **71**, 432 (1946).
G 12. GENTRY C. H. R., SHERRINGTON L. G.: *Analyst* **75**, 17 (1950).
G 13. GILBERT T. W., SANDELL E. B.: *J. Amer. Chem. Soc.* **82**, 1087 (1960).
G 14. GILLIS J., HOSTE J., VAN MOFFAERT Y.: *Chim. analyt.* (*Paris*) **36**, 43 (1954).
G 15. GOLDSTEIN G., MANNING D. L., MENIS O.: *Analyt. Chem.* **30**, 539 (1958).
G 16. GOLDSTEIN G., MANNING D. L., MENIS O.: *Analyt. Chem.* **31**, 192 (1959).
G 17. GOLDSTEIN G., MANNING D. L., MENIS O.: *Talanta* **2**, 52 (1959).
G 18. GOLDSTEIN G., MENIS O., MANNING D. L.: *Analyt. Chem.* **32**, 400 (1960).
G 19. GOLDSTEIN G., MANNING D. L., MENIS O., DEAN J. A.: *Talanta* **7**, 307 (1961).
G 20. GOLKOWSKA A.: *Chem. Analit.* (*Warsaw*) **5**, 389 (1960).
G 21. GOLOVINA A. P., ALIMARIN I. P.: *Vestnik Moskov. Univ., Ser. Mat., Mekh., Astr., Fiz., Khim.* **12**, No. 3, 211 (1957).
G 22. GOLOVINA A. P., ALIMARIN I. P., KUZNETSOV D. I.: *Vestnik Moskov. Univ., Ser. Mat., Mekh., Astr., Fiz., Khim.* **12**, No. 5, 187 (1957).
G 23. GOLUBTSOVA R. B.: *Zhur. analit. Khim.* **14**, 493 (1959).
G 24. GOON E., PETLEY J. E., McMULLEN W. H., WIBERLEY S. E.: *Analyt. Chem.* **25**, 608 (1953).
G 25. GORBACH G., POHL F.: *Mikrochem.* **38**, 258 (1951).
G 26. GORDIEYEFF V. A.: *Analyt. Chem.* **22**, 1166 (1950).
G 27. GOTÔ H., KAKITA Y.: *Sci. Reports Res. Inst. Tôhoku Univ.* **A8**, 243 (1956).
G 28. GOTÔ H., HIROKAWA K.: *Sci. Reports Res. Inst. Tôhoku Univ.* **A10**, 10 (1958).
G 29. GOTÔ H., SUDÔ E.: *Sci. Reports Res. Inst. Tôhoku Univ.* **A11**, 355 (1959).
G 30. GOTÔ H., SUDÔ E.: *Japan Analyst* (*Bunseki Kagaku*) **10**, 171 (1961).
G 31. GOTÔ H., SUDÔ E.: *Japan Analyst* (*Bunseki Kagaku*) **10**, 175 (1961).
G 32. GOTÔ H., SUDÔ E.: *Japan Analyst* (*Bunseki Kagaku*) **10**, 456 (1961).
G 33. GOTÔ H., SUDÔ E.: *Japan Analyst* (*Bunseki Kagaku*) **10**, 463 (1961).
G 34. GOTÔ H., SUDÔ E.: *Japan Analyst* (*Bunseki Kagaku*) **10**, 1213 (1961).
G 35. GOTÔ K., OCHI H., OKURA T.: *Bull. Chem. Soc. Japan* **31**, 783 (1958).
G 36. GOTÔ K.: *Chem. and Ind.* 329 (1957).
G 37. GÖTTE H.: *Angew. Chem.* **60**, 19 (1948).
G 38. GRAY D. J. S.: *Analyst* **77**, 436 (1952).
G 39. GRAY T. D.: *Ind. Eng. Chem., Analyt.* **14**, 110 (1942).
G 40. GREENBERG P.: *Analyt. Chem.* **29**, 896 (1957).
G 41. GRIFFING M. E., ROZEK A., SNYDER L. J., HENDERSON S. R.: *Analyt. Chem.* **29**, 190 (1957).
G 42. GRINBERG A. A., SIMONOVA L. K.: *Zhur. prikl. Khim.* **26**, 880 (1953).
G 43. GRISEVICH A. N., KLADNITSKAYA K. B.: *Zavodskaya Lab.* **27**, 1343 (1961).
G 44. GROSSMANN P.: *Z. phys. Chem.* **109**, 305 (1924).
G 45. GRUBITSCH M., SINIGOJ J.: *Z. analyt. Chem.* **114**, 30 (1938).
G 46. GRUBITSCH H., HEGGEBÖ T.: *Monatsh.* **93**, 274 (1962).
G 47. GRZHEGORZHEVSKIJ A. S.: *Zhur. analit. Khim.* **11**, 689 (1956).
G 48. GRZHEGORZHEVSKIJ A. S.: *Nauch. Doklady Vyshey Skholy, Khim. i Khim. Tekhnol.* 479 (1958).
G 49. GRZHEGORZHEVSKIJ A. S.: *Trudy Kom. analit. Khim.* **11**, 165 (1960).
G 50. GUETTEL CH. L.: *Ind. Eng. Chem., Analyt.* **11**, 639 (1939).
G 51. GUTER G. A., HAMMOND G. S.: *J. Amer. Chem. Soc.* **78**, 5166 (1956).

H 1. HAAR R., UMLAND F.: *Z. analyt. Chem.* **191**, 81 (1962).
H 2. HÄBERLI E.: *Z. analyt. Chem.* **160**, 15 (1958).
H 3. HADDOCK L. A.: *Analyst* **59**, 163 (1934).
H 4. HAGEMANN F.: *J. Amer. Chem. Soc.* **72**, 768 (1950).
H 5. HAGIWARA Z.: *Technol. Reports Tôhoku Univ.* **18**, 16 (1935), cf. *Chem. Abs.* **48**, 8118 (1954).
H 6. HAGIWARA Z.: *Technol. Reports Tôhoku Univ.* **18**, 32 (1953), cf. *Chem. Abs.* **48**, 8118 (1954).
H 7. HAGIWARA Z.: *Technol. Reports Tôhoku Univ.* **19**, 73 (1954), cf. *Chem. Abs.* **49**, 10123 (1955).
H 8. HAGIWARA K., SUZUKI N., MURAKI I.: *Japan Analyst (Bunseki Kagaku)* **10**, 607 (1961).
H 9. HAKKILA E. A., WATERBURY G. R.: *Analyt. Chem.* **32**, 1340 (1960).
H 10. HALL A. J., YOUNG R. S.: *Analyst* **71**, 479 (1946).
H 11. HALL D.: *J. Amer. Chem. Soc.* **44**, 1462 (1922).
H 12. HANTZSCH A.: *Ber.* **35**, 265 (1902).
H 13. HARA T., SANDELL E. B.: *Analyt. Chim. Acta* **23**, 65 (1961).
H 14. HARDWICK W. H., MORETON-SMITH M.: *Analyst* **83**, 9 (1958).
H 15. HARDY C. J., SCARGILL D.: *J. Inorg. Nuclear Chem.* **9**, 322 (1959).
H 16. HART H. V.: *Analyst* **76**, 693 (1951).
H 17. HARVEY B. G., HEAL H. G., MADDOCK A. G., ROWLEY E. L.: *J.* 1010 (1947).
H 18. HASHITANI H., MOTOJIMA K.: *Japan Analyst (Bunseki Kagaku)* **7**, 478 (1958).
H 19. HASHITANI H., YAMAMOTO K.: *J. Chem. Soc. Japan (Nippon Kagaku Zasshi)*, Pure Chem. Sect. **80**, 727 (1959).
H 20. HASTINGS J., McCLARITY T. A., BRODERICH E. J.: *Analyt. Chem.* **26**, 379 (1954).
H 21. HENDRIXSON W. S.: *Z. anorg. Chem.* **13**, 73 (1897).
H 22. HERCULES D. M.: *Talanta* **8**, 485 (1961).
H 23. HEVESY G., HOBBIE R.: *Z. analyt Chem.* **88**, 1 (1932).
H 24. HEVESY G., LEVI H.: *Kgl. danske Videnskab. Selskab, Mat.-fys. Medd.*, **14**, No. 5 (1936).
H 25. HIBBARD P. L.: *Ind. Eng. Chem., Analyt.* **9**, 127 (1937).
H 26. HIBBARD P. L.: *Ind. Eng. Chem., Analyt.* **10**, 615 (1938).
H 27. HOBARD E. W., HURLEY E. P.: *Analyt. Chim. Acta* **27**, 144 (1962).
H 28. HOENES H. J., STONE K. G.: *Talanta* **4**, 250 (1960).
H 29. HOLLINGSHEAD R. G. W.: *Oxine and its Derivatives*, Parts I, II, III, IV, London 1954–1956.
H 30. HÖK B.: *Svensk Kem. Tidskr.* **65**, 106 (1953).
H 31. HÖK B.: *Svensk Kem. Tidskr.* **65**, 182 (1953).
H 32. HÖK-BERNSTRÖM B.: *Acta Chem. Scand.* **10**, 163 (1956).
H 33. HÖK-BERNSTRÖM B.: *Acta Chem. Scand.* **10**, 174 (1956).
H 34. HORDYNSKA S., LEGATOVA B., BERNSTEIN I.: *Chem Analit.* (*Warsaw*) **7**, 567 (1962).
H 35. HUBBARD D. M.: *Ind. Eng. Chem., Analyt.* **9**, 493 (1937).
H 36. HUBBARD D. M.: *Ind. Eng. Chem., Analyt.* **11**, 343 (1939).
H 37. HUBBARD D. M.: *Ind. Eng. Chem., Analyt.* **12**, 768 (1940).
H 38. HUBBARD D. M., SCOTT E. W.: *J. Amer. Chem. Soc.* **65**, 2390 (1943).
H 39. HUBBARD D. M.: *Analyt. Chem.* **20**, 363 (1948).
H 40. HUBBARD D. M.: *Analyt. Chem.* **28**, 1802 (1956).
H 41. HUFFMAN E. H., BEAUFAIT L. J.: *J. Amer. Chem. Soc.* **71**, 3179 (1949).
H 42. HUFFMAN E. H., IDDINGS G. M., OSBORNE R. N., SHALIMOFF G. V.: *J. Amer. Chem. Soc.* **77**, 881 (1955).
H 43. HYNEK R. J., WRANGEL L. J.: *Analyt. Chem.* **28**, 1520 (1956).

I 1. IKEDA S., NAGAL H.: *Japan Analyst (Bunseki Kagaku)* **7**, 76 (1958).
I 2. IKRAMOV L. T.: *Zhur. analit. Khim.* **16**, 368 (1961).
I 3. INARIDA M.: *J. Chem. Soc. Japan (Nippon Kagaku Zasshi)*, Pure Chem. Sect. **79**, 968 (1958).

I 4.   IRVING H., ANDREW G., RISDON E. J.: *Nature* **161**, 805 (1948).
I 5.   IRVING H., WILLIAMS R. J. P.: *Nature* **162**, 746 (1948).
I 6.   IRVING H., RISDON E. J., ANDREW G.: *J.* 537 (1949).
I 7.   IRVING H., ANDREW G., RISDON E. J.: *J.* 541 (1949).
I 8.   IRVING H., BUTLER E. J., RING M. F.: *J.* 1489 (1949).
I 9.   IRVING H., WILLIAMS R. J. P.: *J.* 1841 (1949).
I 10. IRVING H., COOKE S. J. H., WOODGER S. C., WILLIAMS R. J. P.: *J.* 1847 (1949).
I 11. IRVING H., EWART J. A. D., WILSON J. T.: *J.* 2672 (1949).
I 12. IRVING H. M.: *Quart. Rev.* **5**, 200 (1951).
I 13. IRVING H., BELL C. F., WILLIAMS R. J. P.: *J.* 356 (1952).
I 14. IRVING H., BELL C. F.: *J.* 1216 (1952).
I 15. IRVING H. M., WILLIAMS R. J. P.: *Analyst* **77**, 813 (1952).
I 16. IRVING H., WILLIAMS R. J. P.: *J.* 3192 (1952).
I 17. IRVING H., BELL C. F.: *J.* 3538 (1953).
I 18. IRVING H., BUTLER E. J.: *Analyst* **78**, 571 (1953).
I 19. IRVING H., WILLIAMS R. J. P., FERRETT D. J., WILLIAMS A. E.: *J.* 3494 (1954).
I 20. IRVING H., ROSSOTTI F. J. C., WILLIAMS R. J. P.: *J.* 1906 (1955).
I 21. IRVING H., ROSSOTTI F. J. C.: *J.* 1938 (1955).
I 22. IRVING H., ROSSOTTI H. S.: *Analyst* **80**, 245 (1955).
I 23. IRVING H., HOLLINGSHEAD R. G. W., HARRIS G.: *Analyst* **80**, 260 (1955).
I 24. IRVING H., ROSSOTTI H.: *Acta Chem. Scand.* **10**, 72 (1956).
I 25. IRVING H., VAN R. SMIT J., SALMON L.: *Analyst* **82**, 549 (1957).
I 26. IRVING H., EDGINGTON D. N.: *Proc. Chem. Soc.* 360 (1959).
I 27. IRVING H., RAMAKRISHNA R. S.: *Analyst* **85**, 860 (1960).
I 28. IRVING H., EDGINGTON D. N.: *J. Inorg. Nuclear Chem.* **15**, 158 (1960).
I 29. IRVING H., EDGINGTON D. N.: *J. Inorg. Nuclear Chem.* **20**, 314 (1961).
I 30. IRVING H., EDGINGTON D. N.: *J. Inorg. Nuclear Chem.* **20**, 321 (1961).
I 31. IRVING H., EDGINGTON D. N.: *J. Inorg. Nuclear Chem.* **21**, 169 (1961).
I 32. IRVING H., EDGINGTON D. N.: *Chem. and Ind.* 77 (1961).
I 33. IRVING H., WILLIAMS R. J. P.: *Liquid–Liquid Extraction* in *Treatise on Analytical Chemistry*, Part I, Vol. 3, Edited by I. Kolthoff and P. Elving, Interscience, New York, 1961.
I 34. ISHIBASHI M., SHIGEMATSU T., NISHIKAWA Y.: *J. Chem. Soc. Japan* (*Nippon Kagaku Zasshi*), Pure Chem. Sect. **77**, 1474 (1956), cf. *Chem. Abs.* **52**, 2655 (1958).
I 35. ISHIBASHI M., SHIGEMATSU T., NISHIKAWA Y.: *J. Chem. Soc. Japan* (*Nippon Kagaku Zasshi*), Pure Chem. Sect. **77**, 1479 (1956), cf. *Chem. Abs.* **52**, 2656 (1958).
I 36. ISHIBASHI M., SHIGEMATSU T., NISHIKAWA Y.: *J. Chem. Soc. Japan* (*Nippon Kagaku Zasshi*), Pure Chem. Sect. **78**, 1139 (1957), cf. *Chem. Abs.* **52**, 11656 (1958).
I 37. ISHIBASHI M., SHIGEMATSU T., NISHIKAWA Y.: *J. Chem. Soc. Japan* (*Nippon Kagaku Zasshi*), Pure Chem. Sect. **78**, 1143 (1957), cf. *Chem. Abs.* **52**, 11656 (1958).
I 38. ISHIBASHI M., YAMAMOTO Y., YAMADA H.: *Bull. Chem. Soc. Japan* **32**, 1064 (1959).
I 39. ISHIBASHI M.: *Japan Analyst* (*Bunseki Kagaku*) **11**, 426 (1962).
I 40. ISHIHARA Y., SHIBATA K., KISHI H., HORI T.: *Japan Analyst* (*Bunseki Kagaku*) **11**, 91 (1962).
I 41. ISHIHARA Y., KISHI H., KOMURO H.: *Japan Analyst* (*Bunseki Kagaku*) **11**, 932 (1962).
I 42. ISHII D., TAKEUCHI T.: *Japan Analyst* (*Bunseki Kagaku*) **11**, 52 (1962).
I 43. ISHIMORI T.: *Bull. Chem. Soc. Japan* **28**, 203 (1955).
I 44. ISHIMORI T., HATAE I.: *J. Chem. Soc. Japan* (*Nippon Kagaku Zasshi*), Pure Chem. Sect. **77**, 122 (1956), cf. *Chem. Abs.* **51**, 15045 (1957).
I 45. ISHIMORI T., TATEDA A.: *J. Chem. Soc. Japan* (*Nippon Kagaku Zasshi*), Pure Chem. Sect. **78**, 78 (1957), cf. *Chem. Abs.* **52**, 7895 (1958).
I 46. ISONO K.: *Japan Analyst* (*Bunseki Kagaku*) **6**, 557 (1957).
I 47. IWANTSCHEFF G.: *Angew. Chem.* **62**, 361 (1950).
I 48. IWANTSCHEFF G.: *Das Dithizone und seine Anwendung in der Mikro und Spurenanalyse*, Weinheim 1958.

I 49. IZATT R. M., FERNELIUS W. C., BLOCK B. P.: *J. Phys. Chem.* **59**, 235 (1955).
I 50. IRVING H., COX J. J.: *Analyst* **83**, 526 (1958).

J 1. JANKOWSKI S. J., FREISER H.: *Analyt. Chem.* **33**, 776 (1961).
J 2. JAMES J. C., SPEAKMAN J. C.: *Trans. Faraday Soc.* **48**, 474 (1952).
J 3. JASIM F., MAGEE R. J., WILSON C. L.: *Rec. Trav. chim.* **79**, 541 (1960).
J 4. JASKOLSKA H., MINCZEWSKI J.: *Chem. Analit. (Warsaw)* **6**, 149 (1961).
J 5. JEAN M.: *Analyt. Chem. Acta* **11**, 79 (1954).
J 6. JEFFERY P. G.: *Analyst* **81**, 104 (1956).
J 7. JEFFERY P. G.: *Analyst* **82**, 558 (1957).
J 8. JEFIMOV I. P., PESHKOVA V. M.: *Vestnik Moskov. Univ., Ser. Khim.* **17**, No. 3, 62 (1962).
J 9. JENKINS E. N.: *Analyst* **79**, 209 (1954).
J 10. JEWSBURY A.: *Analyst* **78**, 363 (1953).
J 11. JOB P.: *Ann. Chim. (France)* **9**, 113 (1928).
J 12. JOHNSON J. E., LAVINE M. C., ROSENBERG A. J.: *Analyt. Chem.* **30**, 2055 (1958).
J 13. JONES G. B.: *Analyt. Chim. Acta* **17**, 254 (1957).
J 14. JONES G. B.: *Analyt. Chim. Acta* **7**, 578 (1952).
J 15. JONES G. B., WATKINSON J. H.: *Analyt. Chem.* **31**, 1344 (1959).
J 16. JONES P. D., NEWMAN E. J.: *Analyst* **87**, 66 (1962).
J 17. JUNG W., CARDINI C. E., FUKMAN M.: *Anales Soc. Cient. Argentina* **31**, 122 (1943), cf. *Chem. Abs.* **38**, 1181 (1944).

K 1. KÄGI J. H. R., VALLEE B. L.: *Analyt. Chem.* **30**, 1951 (1958).
K 2. KAKITA Y., YOKOYAMA Y.: *Sci. Reports Res. Inst., Tôhoku Univ.* **A8**, 332 (1956).
K 3. KAKITA Y., GOTO H.: *Sci. Reports Res. Inst., Tôhoku Univ.* **A12**, 334 (1960).
K 4. KALINKIN I. P., SEMIKOZOV G. S.: *Zavodskaya Lab.* **27**, 17 (1961).
K 5. KAMBARA T., HASHITANI H.: *Analyt. Chem.* **31**, 567 (1959).
K 6. KANAZAWA J., SATO R.: *Japan Analyst (Bunseki Kagaku)* **8**, 440 (1959).
K 7. KANNO T.: *Japan Analyst (Bunseki Kagaku)* **8**, 714 (1959).
K 8. KASSNER J. L., OZIER M. A.: *Analyt. Chem.* **23**, 1453 (1951).
K 9. KASSNER J. L., GARCIA-PORRATA A., GROVE E. L.: *Analyt. Chem.* **27**, 492 (1955).
K 10. KASSNER J. L., TING S. F., GROVE E. L.: *Talanta* **7**, 269 (1961).
K 11. KATO T., TAKEI S.: *Japan Analyst (Bunseki Kagaku)* **2**, 208 (1953), cf. *Chem. Abs.* **47**, 12117 (1953).
K 12. KATO T., TAKEI S.: *Technol. Reports Tôhoku Univ.* **17**, 170 (1953), cf. *Chem. Abs.* **47**, 10395 (1953).
K 13. KATO T., TAKEI S., OKAGAMI A.: *Japan Analyst (Bunseki Kagaku)* **5**, 689 (1956).
K 14. KAWAHATA M., MOCHIZUKI H., MISAKI T.: *Japan Analyst (Bunseki Kagaku)* **9**, 1023 (1960).
K 15. KAWAHATA M., MOCHIZUKI H., MISAKI T.: *Japan Analyst (Bunseki Kagaku)* **11**, 448 (1962).
K 16. KAWAHATA M., MOCHIZUKI M., MISAKI T.: *Japan Analyst (Bunseki Kagaku)* **11**, 1017 (1962).
K 17. KAWAHATA M., MOCHIZUKI M., MISAKI T.: *Japan Analyst (Bunseki Kagaku)* **11**, 1020 (1962).
K 18. KAWASE A.: *Japan Analyst (Bunseki Kagaku)* **11**, 621 (1962).
K 19. KAWASE A.: *Japan Analyst (Bunseki Kagaku)* **11**, 628 (1962).
K 20. KAWASE A.: *Japan Analyst (Bunseki Kagaku)* **11**, 844 (1962).
K 21. KAWASE A.: *Japan Analyst (Bunseki Kagaku)* **11**, 1162 (1962).
K 22. KEENAN T. K., SUTTLE J. F.: *J. Amer. Chem. Soc.* **76**, 2184 (1954).
K 23. KEMP D. M., SMALES A. A.: *Analyt. Chim. Acta* **23**, 397 (1960).
K 24. KEMP D. M.: *Analyt. Chim. Acta* **27**, 480 (1962).
K 25. KEMULA W., BRACHACZEK W., HULANICKI A.: *Chem. Analit. (Warsaw)* **5**, 215 (1960).

K 26. KENNY A. W., MATON W. R. E., SPRAGG W. T.: *Nature* **165**, 483 (1950).
K 27. KENYON O. A., BEWICK H. A.: *Analyt. Chem.* **24**, 1826 (1952).
K 28. KETT M.: *Hutnické Listy* **13**, 250 (1958).
K 29. KHOPKAR S. M., DE A. K.: *Chem. and Ind.* 291 (1959).
K 30. KHOPKAR S. M., DE A. K.: *Z. analyt. Chem.* **171**, 241 (1959).
K 31. KHOPKAR S. M., DE A. K.: *Analyt. Chim. Acta* **22**, 223 (1960).
K 32. KHOPKAR S. M., DE A. K.: *Analyst* **85**, 376 (1960).
K 33. KHOPKAR S. M., DE A. K.: *Analyt. Chem.* **32**, 478 (1960).
K 34. KIBA T., MIZUKAMI S.: *Bull. Chem. Soc. Japan* **31**, 1007 (1958).
K 35. KIBA T., KANETANI M.: *Bull. Chem. Soc. Japan* **31**, 1013 (1958).
K 36. KIBA T., OHASHI S., MAEDA T.: *Bull. Chem. Soc. Japan* **33**, 818 (1960).
K 37. KIDA K., ABE M., NISHIGAKI S., KOBAYASHI K.: *Japan Analyst (Bunseki Kagaku)* **9**, 1031 (1960).
K 38. KIMURA K., MURAKAMI Y.: *Mikrochem.* **36/37** (1951).
K 39. KIMURA K., ISHIMORI T.: *Proc. Sec. Int. Conf. Peaceful Uses of Atomic Energy*, **28**, 151 (1958).
K 40. KING E. L., REAS W. H.: *J. Amer. Chem. Soc.* **73**, 1804 (1951).
K 41. KINNUNEN J., WENNERSTRAND B.: *Chemist–Analyst* **43**, 65 (1954).
K 42. KIRSTEN W. J.: *Mikrochim. Acta* **43**, 1086 (1955).
K 43. KITAGAWA H., SHIBATA N.: *Japan Analyst (Bunseki Kagaku)* **7**, 284 (1958).
K 44. KLADNITSKAYA K. B., GRISEVICH A. N.: *Ukrain. khim. Zhur.* **27**, 803 (1961).
K 45. KLEIN A. K., VORHES F. A.: *J. Assoc. Offic. Agric. Chem.* **22**, 121 (1939).
K 46. KLEIN A. K., WICHMANN H. J.: *J. Assoc. Offic. Agric. Chem.* **28**, 257 (1954).
K 47. KLEINER K. E., MARKOVA L. B.: *Zhur. analit. Khim.* **7**, 279 (1953).
K 48. KLYGIN A. E., KOLYADA N. S.: *Zhur. neorg. Khim.* **6**, 216 (1961).
K 49. KOCH O. G., DEDIC G. A.: *Chemist–Analyst* **46**, 88 (1957).
K 50. KOCHER J.: *Chim. analyt. (Paris)* **44**, 161 (1962).
K 51. KOLAŘÍK Z., PÁNKOVÁ H.: *Coll. Czech. Chem. Comm.* **27**, 166 (1962).
K 52. KOLTHOFF I. M.: *Chem. Weekblad.* **24**, 606 (1927).
K 53. KOLTHOFF I. M., SANDELL E. B.: *J. Amer. Chem. Soc.* **63**, 1906 (1941).
K 54. KOLTHOFF I. M., JACOBSEN E.: *J. Amer. Chem. Soc.* **79**, 3677 (1957).
K 55. KOMATSU S., KAMIYAMA S.: *J. Chem. Soc. Japan (Nippon Kagaku Zasshi)*, Pure Chem. Sect. **81**, 1094 (1960).
K 56. KOMATSU S., KAMIYAMA S.: *J. Chem. Soc. Japan (Nippon Kagaku Zasshi)*, Pure Chem. Sect. **82**, 1172 (1961).
K 57. KORENMAN I. M., SHEYANOVA F. R.: *Zhur. neorg. Khim.* **1**, 852 (1956).
K 58. KORENMAN I. M., SHEYANOVA F. R.: *Zhur. analit. Khim.* **12**, 285 (1957).
K 59. KORENMAN I. M., SHEYANOVA F. R.: *Izvest. Vysshikh Uchebn. Zavedenij, Khim. i Khim. Tekhnol.* **2**, 151 (1959).
K 60. KOROLEFF F.: *Merentutkimuslaitoksen Julkaisu Havsforskinginstitutes Skrift*, No. 145, 7 (1950), Helsinki.
K 61. KORTÜM G., FINCKH B.: *Angew. Chem.* **57**, 73 (1944).
K 62. KOSTA L., DULAR M.: *Talanta* **8**, 265 (1961).
K 63. KOTLYAR E. E., NAZARCHUK T. N.: *Zhur. analit. Khim.* **16**, 688 (1961).
K 64. KOVÁCS E., GUYER H.: *Chimia (Switz.)* **13**, 164 (1952).
K 65. KOVÁCS E., GUYER H.: *Z. analyt. Chem.* **186**, 267 (1962).
K 66. KOVÁCS E., GUYER H.: *Z. analyt. Chem.* **187**, 188 (1962).
K 67. KOZELKA F. L., KLUCHENSKY E. F.: *Ind. Eng. Chem., Analyt.* **13**, 492 (1941).
K 68. KOZELKA F. L.: *Analyt. Chem.* **19**, 494 (1947).
K 69. KRATZ P. D., LEWIS J. I., FELDMAN A.: *Analyt. Chem.* **24**, 524 (1952).
K 70. KREJMER S. E., BUTYLKIN L. P.: *Zavodskaya Lab.* **24**, 131 (1958).
K 71. KREJMER S. E., STOGOVA A. V., LOMEKHOV A. S.: *Zavodskaya Lab.* **26**, 1104 (1960).
K 72. KREJMER S. E., STOGOVA A. V., LOMEKHOV A. S.: *Zavodskaya Lab.* **27**, 386 (1961).
K 73. KREJMER S. E., LOMEKHOV A. S., STOGOVA A. V.: *Zhur. analit. Khim.* **17**, 674 (1962).
K 74. KRESS K. E.: *Analyt. Chem.* **30**, 432 (1958).
K 75. KRISHEN A., FREISER H.: *Analyt. Chem.* **29**, 288 (1957).

K 76. KRISHEN A., FREISER H.: *Analyt. Chem.* **31**, 923 (1959).
K 77. KRÖHNKE F.: *Ber.* **B60**, 527 (1927).
K 78. KUEHN P. R., HOWARD O. H., WEBER C. W.: *Analyt. Chem.* **33**, 740 (1961).
K 79. KURODA K.: *Bull. Chem. Soc. Japan* **17**, 419 (1942).
K 80. KUTZELNIGG A.: *Z. anorg. Chem.* **256**, 46 (1948).
K 81. KUZNETSOV V. I., KARANOVICH G. G., DRAPKINA D. A.: *Zavodskaya Lab.* **16**, 784 (1950).
K 82. KUZNETSOV V. I.: *Zhur. analit. Khim.* **6**, 139 (1951).
K 83. KUZNETSOV V. I.: *Zhur. analit. Khim.* **7**, 226 (1952).
K 84. KUZNETSOV V. I.: *Uspekhi Khim.* **23**, 654 (1954).
K 85. KUZNETSOV V. I., BANKOVSKIJ YU. A., IYEVINSH A. F.: *Zhur. analit. Khim.* **13**, 267 (1958).
K 86. KUZNETSOV V. I., FAN-MIN-E: *Zhur. neorg. Khim.* **7**, 422 (1962).
K 87. KUZNETSOV V. I., FAN-MIN-E: *Zhur. neorg. Khim.* **7**, 425 (1962).

L 1. LACOSTE R. J., EARING M. H., WIBERLEY S. E.: *Analyt. Chem.* **23**, 871 (1951).
L 2. LACROIX S.: *Analyt. Chim. Acta* **1**, 260 (1947).
L 3. LACROIX S.: *Analyt. Chim. Acta* **2**, 167 (1948).
L 4. LADENBAUER I. M., SLAMA O.: *Mikrochim. Acta* 1219 (1956).
L 5. LAMPREY H.: *Ann. New York Acad. Sci.* **88**, 519 (1960).
L 6. LAPIN L. N., REIS N. V.: *Zhur. analit. Khim.* **13**, 426 (1958).
L 7. LARSEN E. M., TERRY, G.: *J. Amer. Chem. Soc.* **75**, 1560 (1953).
L 8. LAWSON K. L., KAHN M.: *J. Inorg. Nuclear Chem.* **5**, 87 (1957).
L 9. LAZAREV A. I., LAZAREVA V. I.: *Zavodskaya Lab.* **25**, 783 (1959).
L 10. LAUG E. P.: *Analyt. Chem.* **21**, 188 (1949).
L 11. LEDEN I.: Dissertation, Lund 1943.
L 12. LEFORT M.: *Bull. Soc. chim. France* 616 (1962).
L 13. LIESER K. H., SCHROEDER H.: *Z. analyt. Chem.* **174**, 174 (1960).
L 14. LINNELL R. H., RAAB F. H.: *Analyt. Chem.* **33**, 154 (1961).
L 15. LOCKWOOD H. C.: *Analyt. Chim. Acta* **10**, 97 (1954).
L 16. LOCKWOOD H. C.: *Analyst* **79**, 143 (1954).
L 17. LOUNAMAA K.: *Z. analyt. Chem.* **150**, 7 (1956).
L 18. LUKE C. L.: *Analyt. Chem.* **24**, 1122 (1952).
L 19. LUKE C. L., CAMPBELL M. E.: *Analyt. Chem.* **25**, 1588 (1953).
L 20. LUKE C. L., CAMPBELL M. E.: *Analyt. Chem.* **26**, 1778 (1954).
L 21. LUKE C. L.: *Analyt. Chem.* **28**, 1276 (1956).
L 22. LUKE C. L., CAMPBELL M. E.: *Analyt. Chem.* **28**, 1340 (1956).
L 23. LUKE C. L.: *Analyt. Chem.* **28**, 1443 (1956).
L 24. LUTWICK G. D., RYAN D. E.: *Canad. J. Chem.* **32**, 949 (1954).

M 1. MABUCHI H.: *Bull. Chem. Soc. Japan* **29**, 842 (1956).
M 2. McCORD W. M., ZEMP J. W.: *Analyt. Chem.* **27**, 1171 (1955).
M 3. McDOWELL B. L., MEYER A. S., FEATHERS R. E., WHITE J. C.: *Analyt. Chem.* **31**, 931 (1959).
M 4. McINTYRE R. T., BERG E. W., CAMPBELL D. N.: *Analyt. Chem.* **28**, 1316 (1956).
M 5. McKAVENEY J. P., FREISER H.: *Analyt. Chem.* **29**, 290 (1957).
M 6. McKAVENEY J. P., FREISER H.: *Analyt. Chem.* **30**, 526 (1958).
M 7. McKAVENEY J. P., FREISER H.: *Analyt. Chem.* **30**, 1965 (1958).
M 8. MADDOCK A. G., MILES G. L.: *J. S* 248 (1949).
M 9. MADDOCK A. G., MILES G. L.: *J. S* 253 (1949).
M 10. MADERA J.: *Analyt. Chem.* **27**, 2003 (1955).
M 11. MAECK W. J., BOOMAN G. L., ELLIOTT M. C., REIN J. E.: *Analyt. Chem.* **32**, 605 (1960).
M 12. MAECK W. J., KUSSY M. E., REIN J. E.: *Analyt. Chem.* **33**, 235 (1961).
M 13. MAECK W. J., KUSSY M. E., REIN J. E.: *Analyt. Chem.* **33**, 237 (1961).

M 14. MAEKAWA S., YONEYAMA Y., FUJIMORI E.: *Japan Analyst (Bunseki Kagaku)* **9**, 244 (1960).
M 15. MAGNUSSON L. B., ANDERSON M. L.: *J. Amer. Chem. Soc.* **76**, 6207 (1954).
M 16. MAJER V.: *Základy jaderné chemie, Nakl. AV ČSSR*, Praha 1961.
M 17. MAJUMDAR A. K.: *J. Indian Chem. Soc.* **21**, 240 (1944).
M 18. MAJUMDAR A. K., DE A. K.: *Z. analyt. Chem.* **177**, 97 (1960).
M 19. MAJUMDAR A. K., DE A. K.: *Analyt. Chem.* **32**, 1337 (1960).
M 20. MALISSA H., MILLER F. F.: *Mikrochem.* **40**, 63 (1952).
M 21. MALISSA H., GOMIŠČEK S.: *Z. analyt. Chem.* **169**, 402 (1959).
M 22. MALISSA H.: *Analyt. Chim. Acta* **27**, 402 (1962).
M 23. MALOWAN S. L.: *Z. anorg. Chem.* **108**, 73 (1919).
M 24. MALOWAN S. L.: *Z. analyt. Chem.* **79**, 201 (1930).
M 25. MANNING P. G., MONK C. B.: *Trans. Faraday Soc.* **58**, 938 (1962).
M 26. MARCHENKO P. V.: *Zavodskaya Lab.* **26**, 532 (1960).
M 27. MARCHENKO P. V., VDOVENKO M. E., NABIVANEC B. I., OBOLONCHIK N. V., SPIBAKOVSKAYA N. E.: *Zavodskaya Lab.* **27**, 638 (1961).
M 28. MARGERUM D. W., SPRAIN W., BANKS C. V.: *Analyt. Chem.* **25**, 249 (1953).
M 29. MARGERUM D. W., SANTACANA F.: *Analyt. Chem.* **32**, 1157 (1960).
M 30. MARSH S. F., MAEK W. J., BOOMAN G. L., REIN J. E.: *Analyt. Chem.* **33**, 870 (1961).
M 31. MARTELL A. E., CALVIN M.: *Chemistry of the Metal Chelate Compounds*, Prentice Hall, New York 1952.
M 32. MARTIN A. E.: *Analyt. Chem.* **25**, 1260 (1953).
M 33. MARTIN A. E.: *Analyt. Chem.* **25**, 1853 (1953).
M 34. MARTIN F. S., HOLT R. J. W.: *Quart. Rev.* **13**, 327 (1959).
M 35. MASHIMA M.: *J. Chem. Soc. Japan (Nippon Kagaku Zasshi)*, Pure Chem. Sect. **80**, 1260 (1959).
M 36. MASHIMA M.: *J. Chem. Soc. Japan (Nippon Kagaku Zasshi)*, Pure Chem. Sect. **80**, 1263 (1959).
M 37. MASHIMA M.: *Japan Analyst (Bunseki Kagaku)* **9**, 269 (1960).
M 38. MASHIMA M.: *Japan Analyst (Bunseki Kagaku)* **9**, 272 (1960).
M 39. MAY I., HOFFMAN J. I.: *J. Washington Acad. Sci.* **38**, 329 (1948).
M 40. MAYER F. X., SCHWEDA P.: *Mikrochim. Acta* 485 (1956).
M 41. MAYNES A. D., McBRYDE W. A. E.: *Analyt. Chem.* **29**, 1259 (1957).
M 42. MEDLIN W. L.: *Analyt. Chem.* **32**, 632 (1960).
M 43. MEINKE W. W., ANDERSON R. E.: *Analyt. Chem.* **24**, 708 (1952).
M 44. MEL'CHAKOVA N. V., MEZENTSOVA N. N., PEN-AN, PESHKOVA V. M., YUR'EV YU. K.: *Vestnik Moskov. Univ., Ser. Khim.* **17**, No. 1, 63 (1962).
M 45. MEL'CHAKOVA N. V., PESHKOVA V. M.: *Vestnik Moskov. Univ., Ser. Khim.* **17**, No. 6, 61 (1962).
M 46. MELLOR D. P., MALEY L.: *Nature* **161**, 436 (1948).
M 47. MELOAN C. E., HOLKEBOER P., BRANDT W. W.: *Analyt. Chem.* **32**, 791 (1960).
M 48. MENIS O., RAINS T. C.: *Analyt. Chem.* **27**, 1932 (1955).
M 49. MENIS O., RAINS T. C., DEAN J. A.: *Analyt. Chem.* **31**, 187 (1959).
M 50. MERRILL J. R., HONDA M., ARNOLD J. R.: *Analyt. Chem.* **32**, 1420 (1960).
M 51. MERRITT L. L., WALKER J. K.: *Ind. Eng. Chem., Analyt.* **16**, 387 (1944).
M 52. MERVEL R. V.: *Zhur. analit. Khim.* **2**, 103 (1947).
M 53. MEUNIER P.: *Compt. rend.* **199**, 1250 (1934).
M 54. MEYER K. H., HOPFF H.: *Ber.* **54**, 579 (1921).
M 55. MEYER S., KOCH O. G.: *Mikrochim. Acta* 744 (1958).
M 56. MILLER A. D., LIBINA P. I.: *Zhur. analit. Khim.* **13**, 664 (1958).
M 57. MILLER A. D., ARANOVITZ M. I.: *Zavodskaya Lab.* **26**, 426 (1960).
M 58. MILLER C. C., CHALMERS R. A.: *Analyst* **78**, 686 (1953).
M 59. MILLER F. F., GEDDA K., MALISSA H.: *Mikrochem.* **40**, 373 (1953).
M 60. MILLER F. J., THOMASON P. F.: *Analyt. Chem.* **33**, 404 (1961).
M 61. MILLER V. L., SWANBERG F.: *Analyt. Chem.* **29**, 391 (1957).
M 62. MILLER W. L., WACHTER L. E.: *Analyt. Chem.* **22**, 1312 (1950).

M 63. MILNER G. W. C.: *Analyst* **76**, 488 (1951).
M 64. MILNER G. W. C., TOWNEND J.: *Analyt. Chim. Acta* **5**, 584 (1951).
M 65. MILNER G. W. C., EDWARDS J. W.: *Analyt. Chim. Acta* **18**, 513 (1958).
M 66. MILTON R. F., HOSKINS J. L.: *Analyst* **72**, 6 (1947).
M 67. MINCZEWSKI J., MALESZWESKA H.: *Chem. Analit.* (*Warsaw*) **3**, 655 (1958).
M 68. MINCZEWSKI J., STOLARCZYK U., MARCZENKO Z.: *Chem. Analit.* (*Warsaw*) **6**, 51 (1961).
M 69. MINCZEWSKI J., MALESZEWSKA H., STECIAK T.: *Chem. Analit.* (*Warsaw*) **7**, 791 (1962).
M 70. MISUMI S., NAGANO N.: *Analyt. Chem.* **34**, 1723 (1962).
M 71. MIYAMOTO M.: *Japan Analyst* (*Bunseki Kagaku*) **9**, 869 (1960).
M 72. MIYAMOTO M.: *Japan Analyst* (*Bunseki Kagaku*) **9**, 925 (1960).
M 73. MIYAMOTO M.: *Japan Analyst* (*Bunseki Kagaku*) **10**, 317 (1961).
M 74. MOELLER T.: *Ind. Eng. Chem., Analyt.* **15**, 270 (1943).
M 75. MOELLER T.: *Ind. Eng. Chem., Analyt.* **15**, 346 (1943).
M 76. MOELLER T., COHEN A. J.: *Analyt. Chem.* **22**, 686 (1950).
M 77. MOELLER T., JACKSON D. E.: *Analyt. Chem.* **22**, 1393 (1950).
M 78. MOELLER T., COHEN A. J.: *Analyt. Chim. Acta* **4**, 316 (1950).
M 79. MOELLER T., COHEN A. J.: *J. Amer. Chem. Soc.* **72**, 3546 (1950).
M 80. MOELLER T., PUNDSACK F. L.: *J. Amer. Chem. Soc.* **75**, 2258 (1953).
M 81. MOELLER T., RAMANIAH M. V.: *J. Amer. Chem. Soc.* **75**, 3946 (1953).
M 82. MOELLER T., PUNDSACK F. L., COHEN A. J.: *J. Amer. Chem. Soc.* **76**, 2615 (1954).
M 83. MOISEV I. V., BORODINA N. N., TSVETKOVA V. T.: *Zhur. neorg. Khim.* **6**, 543 (1961).
M 84. MONNIER D., HAERDI W.: *Analyt. Chim. Acta* **20**, 444 (1959).
M 85. MONNIER D., HAERDI W., VOGEL J.: *Helv. Chim. Acta* **44**, 897 (1961).
M 86. MOORE F. L.: *Analyt. Chem.* **28**, 997 (1956).
M 87. MOORE F. L.: *Analyt. Chem.* **29**, 941 (1957).
M 88. MOORE F. L., HUDGENS J. E.: *Analyt. Chem.* **29**, 1767 (1957).
M 89. MOORE F. L.: *Analyt. Chem.* **30**, 1020 (1958).
M 90. MOORE F. L.: *Analyt. Chem.* **30**, 1368 (1958).
M 91. MOORE F. L., FAIRMAN W. D., GANCHOFF J. G., SURAK J. G.: *Analyt. Chem.* **31**, 1148 (1959).
M 92. MORII F.: *J. Chem. Soc. Japan* (*Nippon Kagaku Zasshi*), Pure Chem. Sect. **82**, 1507 (1961).
M 93. MORII F.: *J. Chem. Soc. Japan* (*Nippon Kagaku Zasshi*), Pure Chem. Sect. **82**, 1510 (1961).
M 94. MORIMOTO Y., ASHIZAWA T.: *Japan Analyst* (*Bunseki Kagaku*) **10**, 1383 (1961).
M 95. MORIMOTO Y., ASHIZAWA T., ARAYA S.: *Japan Analyst* (*Bunseki Kagaku*) **10**, 1387 (1961).
M 96. MORIMOTO Y., ASHIZAWA T., TAKANI S.: *Japan Analyst* (*Bunseki Kagaku*) **11**, 56 (1962).
M 97. MORIMOTO Y., ASHIZAWA T., MIYAHARA K.: *Japan Analyst* (*Bunseki Kagaku*) **11**, 61 (1962).
M 98. MORRISON G. H.: *Analyt. Chem.* **22**, 1388 (1950).
M 99. MORRISON G. H., FREISER H.: *Solvent Extraction in Analytical Chemistry*, J. Wiley, New York 1957.
M 100. MORRISON G. H., FREISER H.: *Analyt. Chem.* **30**, 632 (1958).
M 101. MORRISON G. H., FREISER H.: *Analyt. Chem.* **32**, R 37 (1960).
M 102. MORRISON G. H., FREISER H.: *Analyt. Chem.* **34**, R 64 (1962).
M 103. MORRISON S. L., PAIGE H. L.: *Ind. Eng. Chem., Analyt.* **18**, 211 (1946).
M 104. MOTOJIMA K.: *Bull. Chem. Soc. Japan* **29**, 71 (1956).
M 105. MOTOJIMA K.: *Bull. Chem. Soc. Japan* **29**, 75 (1956).
M 106. MOTOJIMA K.: *Bull. Chem. Soc. Japan* **29**, 455 (1956).
M 107. MOTOJIMA K., HASHITANI H.: *Bull. Chem. Soc. Japan* **29**, 458 (1956).
M 108. MOTOJIMA K., HASHITANI H.: *Japan Analyst* (*Bunseki Kagaku*) **6**, 642 (1957).
M 109. MOTOJIMA K., HASHITANI H.: *Japan Analyst* (*Bunseki Kagaku*) **7**, 28 (1958).
M 110. MOTOJIMA K.: *Japan Analyst* (*Bunseki Kagaku*) **8**, 66 (1959).

M 111. MOTOJIMA K., HASHITANI H.: *Japan Analyst* (*Bunseki Kagaku*) **8**, 526 (1959).
M 113. MOTOJIMA K., HASHITANI H.: *Japan Analyst* (*Bunseki Kagaku*) **9**, 151 (1960).
M 114. MOTOJIMA K., HASHITANI H., KATSUAYAMA K.: *Japan Analyst* (*Bunseki Kagaku*) **9**, 517 (1960).
M 115. MOTOJIMA K., HASHITANI H., KATSUAYAMA K.: *Japan Analyst* (*Bunseki Kagaku*) **9**, 628 (1960).
M 116. MOTOJIMA K., HASHITANI H., YOSHIDA H.: *Japan Analyst* (*Bunseki Kagaku*) **10**, 79 (1961).
M 117. MOTOJIMA K., HASHITANI H.: *Analyt. Chem.* **33**, 48 (1961).
M 118. MOTOJIMA K., HASHITANI H.: *Analyt. Chem.* **33**, 239 (1961).
M 119. MOTOJIMA K., HASHITANI H., IMANASHI T.: *Analyt. Chem.* **34**, 571 (1962).
M 120. MOTOJIMA K., HASHITANI H., YOSHIDA H.: *Japan Analyst* (*Bunseki Kagaku*) **11**, 659 (1962).
M 121. MOTOJIMA K., YOSHIDA H., IMANASHI T.: *Japan Analyst* (*Bunseki Kagaku*) **11**, 1028 (1962).
M 122. MOUČKA V., STARÝ J.: *Coll. Czech. Chem. Comm.* **26**, 763 (1961).
M 123. MRKVA M., JANÁČKOVÁ J.: *Chem. průmysl* **11**, 139 (1961).
M 124. MUCHINA Z. S., TIKHONOVA A. A., ZHEMCZHUZHNAYA I. A.: *Trudy Kom. analit. Khim.* **12**, 298 (1960).
M 125. MÜLLER H.: *Z. analyt. Chem.* **113**, 161 (1938).
M 126. MULLIN J. B., RILEY J. P.: *Nature* **174**, 42 (1954).
M 127. MUKOYAMA T., ICHINOSE N.: *Japan Analyst* (*Bunseki Kagaku*) **10**, 107 (1961).
M 128. MYASSOEDOV B., MUXARD R.: *Bull. Soc. chim. France* 237 (1962).
M 129. MYASSOEDOV B., MUXARD R.: *Zhur. analit. Khim.* **17**, 340 (1962).

N 1. NADALIN R. J., BROZDA W. B.: *Analyt. Chem.* **32**, 1141 (1960).
N 2. NAITO H., SUGAWARA K.: *Bull. Chem. Soc. Japan* **30**, 799 (1957).
N 3. NAKAGAWA G., WADA H.: *J. Chem. Soc. Japan* (*Nippon Kagaku Zasshi*), Pure Chem. Sect. **83**, 1098 (1962).
N 4. NANCE K. W.: *Analyt. Chem.* **23**, 1034 (1951).
N 5. NÄSÄNEN R., LUMME P., MUKULA A.: *Acta Chem. Scand.* **5**, 1199 (1951).
N 6. NAZARENKO V. A., FLYATNIAKOVA G. V., LEBEDEVA N. V.: *Zavodskaya Lab.* **23**, 891 (1957).
N 7. NAZARENKO V. A., SHITAREVA G. G.: *Zavodskaya Lab.* **24**, 932 (1958).
N 8. NAZARENKO V. A., BIRYUK E. A.: *Zavodskaya Lab.* **25**, 28 (1959).
N 9. NERNST W.: *Z. phys. Chem.* **8**, 110 (1891).
N 10. NICHOL W. E.: *Canad. J. Chem.* **31**, 145 (1953).
N 11. NIELSCH W.: *Z. analyt. Chem.* **140**, 267 (1953).
N 12. NIELSCH W.: *Z. analyt. Chem.* **142**, 30 (1954).
N 13. NIELSCH W.: *Z. analyt. Chem.* **143**, 272 (1954).
N 14. NIELSCH W.: *Z. analyt. Chem.* **150**, 114 (1956).
N 15. NIELSCH W., GIEFER L.: *Mikrochim. Acta* 522 (1956).
N 16. NIELSCH W.: *Mikrochim. Acta* 725 (1959).
N 17. NIESE S., BEER M., NAUMANN D., KÖPSEL R.: *Extraktive Aufarbeitung bestrahlter Kernbremstoffe*, Academie Verlag, Berlin 1960.
N 18. NISHIKAWA Y.: *J. Chem. Soc. Japan* (*Nippon Kagaku Zasshi*), Pure Chem. Sect. **79**, 236 (1958), cf. *Chem. Abs.* **52**, 13531 (1958).
N 19. NISHIKAWA Y.: *J. Chem. Soc. Japan* (*Nippon Kagaku Zasshi*), Pure Chem. Sect. **79**, 351 (1958), cf. *Chem. Abs.* **52**, 13564 (1958).
N 20. NISHIMURA M., SANDELL E. B.: *Analyt. Chim. Acta* **26**, 242 (1962).
N 21. NOLL C. A., BETZ L. D.: *Analyt. Chem.* **24**, 1894 (1952).
N 22. NORWITZ G., COHEN J., EVERETT M. E.: *Analyt. Chem.* **32**, 1132 (1960).

O 1. OELSCHLÄGER W.: *Z. analyt. Chem.* **146**, 339 (1955).
O 2. OELSCHLÄGER W.: *Z. analyt. Chem.* **146**, 346 (1955).

O 3.   OELSCHLÄGER W.: *Z. analyt. Chem.* **188**, 190 (1960).
O 4.   OGAWA K.: *J. Chem. Soc. Japan (Nippon Kagaku Zasshi)*, Pure Chem. Sect. **78**, 438 (1957), cf. *Chem. Abs.* **52**, 10801 (1958).
O 5.   OGAWA K.: *J. Chem. Soc. Japan (Nippon Kagaku Zasshi)*, Pure Chem. Sect. **78**, 441 (1957), cf. *Chem. Abs.* **52**, 10801 (1958).
O 6.   OI N.: *J. Chem. Soc. Japan (Nippon Kagaku Zasshi)*, Pure Chem. Sect. **80**, 1151 (1959).
O 7.   OKURA T., GOTO K., YOTOYANAGI T.: *Analyt. Chem.* **34**, 581 (1962).
O 8.   ONISHI H.: *Bull. Chem. Soc. Japan* **30**, 567 (1957).
O 9.   ONISHI H., ISHIWATARI N.: *Talanta* **8**, 753 (1961).
O 10.   OOSTING M.: *Analyt. Chim. Acta* **21**, 301 (1959).
O 11.   OOSTING M.: *Analyt. Chim. Acta* **21**, 397 (1959).
O 12.   OOSTING M.: *Analyt. Chim. Acta* **21**, 505 (1959).
O 13.   OOSTING M.: *Rec. Trav. chim.* **79**, 627 (1960).
O 14.   OTA K., MORI S.: *Japan Analyst (Bunseki Kagaku)* **5**, 442 (1956).
O 15.   OVENSTON T. C. J., PARKER C. A., HATCHARD C. G.: *Analyt. Chim. Acta* **6**, 7 (1952).

P 1.   PANOVA M. G., LEVIN V. I., BREZHNEVA N. E.: *Radiokhimiya* **2**, 197 (1960).
P 2.   PANOVA M. G., BREZHNEVA N. E., LEVIN V. I.: *Radiokhimiya* **2**, 208 (1960).
P 3.   PAULAIS R.: *Compt. rend.* **206**, 783 (1938).
P 4.   PAVLOVA N. V., VASILEVA N. G., KASHLINSKAYA S. E.: *Zavodskaya Lab.* **27**, 965 (1961).
P 5.   PEACH S. M.: *Analyst* **81**, 371 (1956).
P 6.   PELKINS P. S., PUPKO L. S., DUBENKO R. G.: *Zhur. obschei Khim.* **27**, 1849 (1957).
P 7.   PEN-AN, PESHKOVA V. M.: *Vestnik Moskov. Univ., Ser. Khim.* **17**, No. 3, 60 (1962).
P 8.   PENDER H. W.: *Analyt. Chem.* **30**, 1915 (1958).
P 9.   PEPPARD D. F., STUDIER M. H., GERGEL M. V., MASON G. W., SULLIVAN J. C., MECH J. F.: *J. Amer. Chem. Soc.* **73**, 2529 (1951).
P 10.   PERKINS R. W., KAHLWARF D. R.: *Analyt. Chem.* **28**, 1989 (1956).
P 11.   PERKINS M., REYNOLDS G. F.: *Analyt. Chim. Acta* **18**, 625 (1958).
P 12.   PERRY M. H., SERFASS E. J.: *Analyt. Chem.* **22**, 565 (1950).
P 13.   PESHKOVA V. M., GONTSAROVA G. A., GRIBOVA E. A., PUZDRENKOVA I. V.: *Zhur. analit. Khim.* **8**, 114 (1953).
P 14.   PESHKOVA V. M., SHLENSKAYA V. I., RASHEVSKAYA A. I.: *Vestnik Moskov. Univ., Ser. Fiz.-Mat. i Estestv. Nauk* **9**, No. 5, 83 (1954).
P 15.   PESHKOVA V. M.: *Zhur. analit. Khim.* **10**, 86 (1955).
P 16.   PESHKOVA V. M., ZAGOREVSKIJ V. A., BOCHKOVA V. M., KUZNETSOV D. I.: *Vestnik Moskov. Univ., Ser. Mat., Mekh., Astr., Fiz., Khim.* **12**, No. 1, 117 (1957).
P 17.   PESHKOVA V. M., ZOZULYA A. P.: *Nauch. Doklady Vyshey Skholy, Khim. i Khim. Tekhnol.* **1**, 470 (1958).
P 18.   PESHKOVA V. M., BOCHKOVA V. M.: *Trudy Kom. analit. Khim.* **8**, 125 (1958).
P 19.   PESHKOVA V. M., ZOZULYA A. P.: *Zhur. analit. Khim.* **14**, 411 (1959).
P 20.   PESHKOVA V. M., BOCHKOVA V. M., LAZAREVA L. I.: *Zhur. analit. Khim.* **15**, 610 (1960).
P 21.   PESHKOVA V. M., ZOZULYA A. P.: *Trudy Kom. analit. Khim.* **11**, 69 (1960).
P 22.   PESHKOVA V. M., SHLENSKAYA V. I., SOKOLOV S. S.: *Trudy Kom. analit. Khim.* **11**, 328 (1960).
P 23.   PESHKOVA V. M., TSON-UN-AM: *Vestnik Moskov. Univ., Ser. Khim.* **15**, No. 4, 59 (1960).
P 24.   PESHKOVA V. M., BOCHKOVA V. M., ASTACHOVA E. K.: *Zhur. analit. Khim.* **16**, 596 (1961).
P 25.   PESHKOVA V. M., MEL'ĆHAKOVA N. V., ZHEMCHUZHIN S. G.: *Zhur. neorg. Khim.* **6**, 1233 (1961).
P 26.   PESHKOVA V. M., PEN-AN: *Zhur. neorg. Khim.* **6**, 2082 (1961).
P 27.   PESHKOVA V. M., PEN-AN: *Zhur. neorg. Khim.* **7**, 1484 (1962).

P 28. PESHKOVA V. M., PEN-AN: *Zhur. neorg. Khim.* **7**, 2110 (1962).
P 29. PESHKOVA V. M., IGNATIEVA N. G.: *Zhur. analit. Khim.* **17**, 1086 (1962).
P 30. PETERSON S.: *J. Inorg. Nuclear Chem.* **14**, 126 (1960).
P 31. PETZOLD A., LANGE I.: *Z. analyt. Chem.* **146**, 1 (1955).
P 32. PFEIFER V., HECHT F.: *Z. analyt. Chem.* **177**, 175 (1960).
P 33. PFEIFER V., HECHT F.: *Mikrochim. Acta* 378 (1960).
P 34. PHILLIPS J. P., MERRITT L. L.: *J. Amer. Chem. Soc.* **70**, 410 (1948).
P 35. PHILLIPS J. P., FERNANDO Q.: *J. Amer. Chem. Soc.* **75**, 3768 (1953).
P 36. PIERCE T. B., PECK P. F.: *Analyt. Chim. Acta* **27**, 392 (1962).
P 37. PILIPENKO A. T.: *Zhur. analit. Khim.* **5**, 14 (1950).
P 38. PILIPENKO A. T.: *Zhur. analit. Khim.* **8**, 286 (1953).
P 39. PILIPENKO A. T.: *Zhur. analit. Khim.* **10**, 299 (1955).
P 40. PILIPENKO A. T.: *Uspekhi Khim.* **25**, 1402 (1956).
P 41. PIPER C. S., BECKWITH R. S.: *J. Soc. Chem. Ind.* **67**, 374 (1948).
P 42. PODTZAYNOVA V. H.: *Trudy Kom. analit. Khim.* **11**, 146 (1960).
P 43. POHL F. A.: *Z. analyt. Chem.* **139**, 241 (1953).
P 44. POHL F. A., DEMMEL H.: *Analyt. Chim. Acta* **10**, 554 (1954).
P 45. POHL H.: *Analyt. Chim. Acta* **12**, 54 (1955).
P 46. POKRAS L., BERNAYS P. M.: *J. Amer. Chem. Soc.* **73**, 7 (1951).
P 47. POKRAS L., BERNAYS P. M.: *Analyt. Chem.* **23**, 757 (1951).
P 48. POPOVA O. I., KORNILOVA V. I.: *Zhur. analit. Khim.* **16**, 651 (1961).
P 49. POSKANZER A. M., FOREMAN B. M.: *J. Inorg. Nuclear Chem.* **16**, 323 (1961).
P 50. POWELL R. A., KINSER C. A.: *Analyt. Chem.* **30**, 1139 (1958).
P 51. PREOBRAZHENSKIJ B. K., KATYLKIN G. S.: *Radiokhimiya* **4**, 536 (1962).
P 52. PŘIBIL R., KENÍK J., KOBROVÁ M.: *Chem. Listy* **46**, 603 (1952).
P 53. PŘIBIL R., KOBROVÁ M., JENÍK J.: *Chem. Listy* **47**, 842 (1953).
P 54. PŘIBIL R., JELÍNEK M.: *Chem. Listy* **47**, 1326 (1953).
P 55. PRIYADARSHINI U., TANDON S. G.: *Chem. and Ind.* 931 (1960).
P 56. PRIYADARSHINI U., TANDON S. G.: *Analyst* **86**, 544 (1961).
P 57. PRIYADATSHINI U., TANDON S. G.: *Analyt. Chem.* **33**, 435 (1961).
P 58. PROVAZNÍK J., KNÍŽEK M.: *Chem. Listy* **55**, 79 (1961).
P 59. PRZHEVALSKIJ E. S., NIKOLAEVA E. R., KLIMOVA N. S.: *Vestnik Moskov. Univ., Ser. Mat., Mekh., Astr., Fiz., Khim.* **13**, No. 3, 217 (1958).
P 60. PSHENITSYN N. K., IVONINA O. M.: *Zavodskaya Lab.* **24**, 1185 (1962).
P 61. PYATNITSKIJ I. V.: *Zhur. analit. Khim.* **1**, 135 (1946).

R 1. RAINES M. M., LARIONOVA YU. A.: *Zavodskaya Lab.* **14**, 1000 (1948).
R 2. RAINS T. C., HOUSE H. P., MENIS O.: *Analyt. Chim. Acta* **22**, 315 (1960).
R 3. RAINS T. C., FERGUSON M., HOUSE H. P.: *Analyt. Chem.* **33**, 1645 (1961).
R 4. RÄKER K. O.: *Z. analyt. Chem.* **173**, 57 (1960).
R 5. RALPH W. D., SWEET T. R., MENCIS I.: *Analyt. Chem.* **34**, 92 (1962).
R 6. REES W. T.: *Analyst* **87**, 202 (1962).
R 7. REID J. C., CALVIN M.: *J. Amer. Chem. Soc.* **72**, 2948 (1950).
R 8. REITH J. F., GERRITSMA K. W.: *Rec. Trav. chim.* **64**, 41 (1945).
R 9. REYNOLDS G. F., SHALGOSKY H. I.: *Analyt. Chim. Acta* **18**, 607 (1958).
R 10. RIEDEL K.: *Z. analyt. Chem.* **159**, 25 (1957).
R 11. RIENÄCKER G., SCHIFF W.: *Z. analyt. Chem.* **94**, 409 (1933).
R 12. RIGAMONTI R., MAZZA M. T. C.: *Ricerca sci.* **30**, 855 (1960), cf. *Chem. Abs.* **54**, 23620 (1960).
R 13. RILEY J. P.: *Analyt. Chim. Acta* **19**, 413 (1958).
R 14. RILEY J. P.: *Analyt. Chim. Acta* **21**, 317 (1959).
R 15. RILEY J. P., WILLIAMS H. P.: *Mikrochim. Acta* 825 (1959).
R 16. RINGBOM A., STILL E.: *Finska Kemistsamfundets Medd.* **69**, 17 (1960).
R 17. ROONEY R. C.: *Analyst* **83**, 546 (1958).
R 18. ROSOTTE R.: *Chim. analyt. (Paris)* **38**, 250 (1956).
R 19. ROSS L. E., KESSER G., KUCERA E. T.: *Analyt. Chem.* **32**, 1367 (1960).

R 20. ROSSOTTI F. J. C.: *Rec. Trav. chim.* **75**, 743 (1956).
R 21. ROSSOTTI F. J. C., ROSSOTTI H.: *Acta Chem. Scand.* **10**, 779 (1956).
R 22. RUDENKO N. P.: *Zhur. neorg. Khim.* **1**, 1091 (1956).
R 23. RUDENKO N. P.: *Zhur. neorg. Khim.* **1**, 1680 (1956).
R 24. RUDENKO N. P., STARÝ J.: *Trudy Kom. analit. Khim.* **9**, 28 (1958).
R 25. RUDENKO N. P., STARÝ J.: *Radiokhimiya* **1**, 52 (1959).
R 26. RUDENKO N. P., STARÝ J.: *Radiokhimiya* **1**, 700 (1959).
R 27. RUDENKO N. P.: *Zhur. neorg. Khim.* **4**, 220 (1959).
R 28. RUDENKO N. P.: unpublished work.
R 29. RUF E.: *Z. analyt. Chem.* **162**, 9 (1958).
R 30. RULFS CH. L., DE A. K., LAKRITZ J., ELVING P. J.: *Analyt. Chem.* **27**, 1802 (1955).
R 31. RŮŽIČKA J., STARÝ J.: *Talanta* **8**, 228 (1961).
R 32. RŮŽIČKA J., STARÝ J.: *Talanta* **8**, 535 (1961).
R 33. RŮŽIČKA J., STARÝ J.: *Talanta* **9**, 617 (1962).
R 34. RŮŽIČKA J.: *Chem. Listy* **56**, 783 (1962).
R 35. RŮŽIČKA J., STARÝ J.: *Talanta* **10**, 287 (1963).
R 36. RŮŽIČKA J., STARÝ J., ZEMAN A.: *Talanta* **10**, (1963).
R 37. RŮŽIČKA J., STARÝ J.: *Chem. Listy* **57**, 1025 (1963).
R 38. RYAN D. E., LUTWICK G. D.: *Canad. J. Chem.* **31**, 9 (1953).
R 39. RYAN D. E.: *Analyst* **85**, 569 (1960).
R 40. RYAN D. E.: *Canad. J. Chem.* **39**, 2389 (1961).
R 41. RYDBERG J.: *Svensk kem. Tidskr.* **62**, 179 (1950).
R 42. RYDBERG J.: *Acta Chem. Scand.* **4**, 1503 (1950).
R 43. RYDBERG J.: *Arkiv Kemi* **5**, 413 (1953).
R 44. RYDBERG J.: *Arkiv Kemi* **5**, 517 (1953).
R 45. RYDBERG J.: *Svensk. kem. Tidskr.* **65**, 37 (1953).
R 46. RYDBERG J.: *Arkiv Kemi* **8**, 101 (1955).
R 47. RYDBERG J.: *Arkiv Kemi* **8**, 113 (1955).
R 48. RYDBERG J.: *Rec. Trav. chim.* **75**, 737 (1956).
R 49. RYDBERG J., RYDBERG B.: *Arkiv Kemi* **9**, 81 (1956).
R 50. RYDBERG J.: *Arkiv Kemi* **9**, 95 (1956).
R 51. RYDBERG J.: *Arkiv Kemi* **9**, 109 (1956).
R 52. RYDBERG J., SULLIVAN J. C.: *Acta Chem. Scand.* **13**, 2057 (1959).
R 53. RYDBERG J.: *Acta Chem. Scand.* **15**, 1723 (1961).

S 1. SAITO K., IKEDA S., SAITO M.: *Bull. Chem. Soc. Japan* **33**, 884 (1960).
S 2. SAITO K., ISHII D., TAKEUCHI T.: *Japan Analyst (Bunseki Kagaku)* **9**, 299 (1960).
S 3. SAITO K., TAKEUCHI T.: *Japan Analyst (Bunseki Kagaku)* **10**, 152 (1961).
S 4. SALVINIEN I., GARRIGUES C.: *Compt. rend.* **242**, 504 (1956).
S 5. SALTZMAN B. E.: *Analyt. Chem.* **25**, 493 (1953).
S 6. SANDELL E. B.: *Ind. Eng. Chem., Analyt.* **8**, 336 (1936).
S 7. SANDELL E. B.: *Ind. Eng. Chem., Analyt.* **9**, 464 (1937).
S 8. SANDELL E. B., PERLICH R. W.: *Ind. Eng. Chem., Analyt.* **11**, 309 (1939).
S 9. SANDELL E. B.: *Ind. Eng. Chem., Analyt.* **11**, 364 (1939).
S 10. SANDELL E. B.: *Ind. Eng. Chem., Analyt.* **13**, 844 (1941).
S 11. SANDELL E. B.: *Analyt. Chem.* **19**, 63 (1947).
S 12. SANDELL E. B., CUMMINGS P. F.: *Analyt. Chem.* **21**, 1356 (1949).
S 13. SANDELL E. B.: *J. Amer. Chem. Soc.* **72**, 4660 (1950).
S 14. SANDELL E. B.: *Colorimetric Determination of Traces of Metals,* Interscience, New York 1950 (Second edition), 1959 (Third edition).
S 15. SANO H.: *Analyt. Chim. Acta* **27**, 398 (1962).
S 16. SAWADA T., KATO S.: *Japan Analyst (Bunseki Kagaku)* **11**, 544 (1962).
S 17. SCHARRER K.: *Z. analyt. Chem.* **128**, 435 (1948).
S 18. SCHERFF H. L., HERRMANN G.: *J. Inorg. Nuclear Chem.* **11**, 247 (1959).
S 19. SCHNEIDER R. A.: *Analyt. Chem.* **32**, 522 (1962).
S 20. SCHÖFFMANN E., MALISSA H.: *Mikrochim. Acta* 319 (1961).

S 21. SCHULEK E., LASZLOVSZKY J.: *Mikrochim. Acta* 41 (1961).
S 22. SCHÜLLER H.: *Mikrochim. Acta* 107 (1959).
S 23. SCHULTZ B. G., LARSEN E. M.: *J. Amer. Chem. Soc.* **72**, 3610 (1950).
S 24. SCHULTZ J., GOLDBERG M. A.: *Ind. Eng. Chem., Analyt.* **15**, 155 (1943).
S 25. SCHWARZENBACH G., LUTZ K.: *Helv. Chim. Acta* **23**, 1147 (1940).
S 26. SCHWARZENBACH G., ACKERMANN H., RUCKSTUHL P.: *Helv. Chim. Acta* **32**, 1175 (1949).
S 27. SCHWEITZER G. K., BISHOP W. N.: *J. Amer. Chem. Soc.* **76**, 4321 (1954).
S 28. SCHWEITZER G. K., SCOTT H. E.: *J. Amer. Chem. Soc.* **77**, 2753 (1955).
S 29. SCHWEITZER G. K., DYER F. F.: *Analyt. Chim. Acta* **22**, 172 (1960).
S 30. SCHWEITZER G. K., BRAMLITT E. T.: *Analyt. Chim. Acta* **23**, 419 (1960).
S 31. SCHWEITZER G. K., COE G. R.: *Analyt. Chim. Acta* **24**, 311 (1961).
S 32. SCHWEITZER G. K., MOTTERN J. L.: *Analyt. Chim. Acta* **26**, 120 (1962).
S 33. SCHWEITZER G. K., RANDOLPH D. R.: *Analyt. Chim. Acta* **26**, 567 (1962).
S 34. SCHWEITZER G. K., RIMSTIDT J. R.: *Analyt. Chim. Acta* **27**, 389 (1962).
S 35. SEABORG G. T., KATZ J. J.: *The Actinide Elements*, McGraw-Hill, New York 1954.
S 36. ŠEBESTIAN I., ŽINTANSKÝ B.: *Chem. Listy* **56**, 948 (1962).
S 37. ŠEDIVEC V., VAŠÁK V.: *Coll. Czech. Chem. Comm.* **15**, 260 (1950).
S 38. ŠEDIVEC V., VAŠÁK V.: *Chem. Listy* **44**, 103 (1950).
S 39. ŠEDIVEC V., VAŠÁK V.: *Chem. Listy* **45**, 435 (1951).
S 40. ŠEDIVEC V., VAŠÁK V.: *Chem. Listy* **46**, 607 (1952).
S 41. SEKERSKIJ S., KOTLINSKAYA B.: *At. Energ.* (*USSR*) **7**, 160 (1959).
S 42. SEKIDO E.: *J. Chem. Soc. Japan* (*Nippon Kagaku Zasshi*), Pure Chem. Sect. **80**, 1011 (1959).
S 43. SEN B.: *Analyt. Chem.* **31**, 881 (1959).
S 44. SEN B.: *Analyt. Chim. Acta* **21**, 35 (1959).
S 45. SEN B.: *Analyt. Chim. Acta* **22**, 55 (1960).
S 46. SENO H., KAKITA Y.: *J. Chem. Soc. Japan* (*Nippon Kagaku Zasshi*), Pure Chem. Sect. **82**, 452 (1961).
S 47. SENO H., KAKITA Y.: *J. Chem. Soc. Japan* (*Nippon Kagaku Zasshi*), Pure Chem. Sect. **82**, 1365 (1961).
S 48. SERFASS E. J., LEVINE W. S.: *Chemist–Analyst* **36**, 55 (1947).
S 49. SERFASS E. J., LEVINE W. S., SMITH G. F., DUKE F.: *Plating* **35**, 458 (1948), cf. *Chem. Abs.* **42**, 5798 (1948).
S 50. SERVIGNE M.: *J. Chim. phys.* **31**, 47 (1934).
S 51. SHEPERD E., MEINKE W. W.: *U.S. Atomic Energy Comm. Report* AECU-3879.
S 52. SHERWOOD R. M., CHAPMAN F. W.: *Analyt. Chem.* **27**, 88 (1955).
S 53. SHEYANOVA F. R., AIRAPETYAN A. G., RYABOVA S. A., RYABOV V. M.: *Trudy Khim. i Khim. Tekhnol.* **2**, 410 (1959), cf. *Chem. Abs.* **55**, 11184 (1961).
S 54. SHEYANOVA F. R., KOZHOKINA G. YA.: *Trudy Khim. i Khim. Tekhnol.* **3**, 70 (1960), cf. *Chem. Abs.* **56**, 4115 (1962).
S 55. SHIBATA S.: *Analyt. Chim. Acta* **22**, 479 (1960).
S 56. SHIBATA S.: *Analyt. Chim. Acta* **23**, 367 (1960).
S 57. SHIBATA S.: *Analyt. Chim. Acta* **23**, 434 (1960).
S 58. SHIBATA S.: *Analyt. Chim. Acta* **25**, 348 (1961).
S 59. SHIBATA S., NIIMI Y., MATSUMAE T.: *Nagoya Kogyo Gijutsu Shikensho Hokoku* **11**, 275 (1962), cf. *Chem. Abs.* **57**, 4024 (1962).
S 60. SHIBATA S., ISHIGURO Y.: *Nagoya Kogyo Gijutsu Shikensho Hokoku* **11**, 318 (1962), cf. *Chem. Abs.* **57**, 6590 (1962).
S 61. SHIGEMATSU T.: *Japan Analyst* (*Bunseki Kagaku*) **7**, 787 (1958).
S 62. SHIGEMATSU T., TABUSHI M.: *J. Chem. Soc. Japan* (*Nippon Kagaku Zasshi*), Pure Chem. Sect. **80**, 159 (1959).
S 63. SHIGEMATSU T., TABUSHI M.: *J. Chem. Soc. Japan* (*Nippon Kagaku Zasshi*), Pure Chem. Sect. **80**, 162 (1959).
S 64. SHIGEMATSU T., TABUSHI M.: *J. Chem. Soc. Japan* (*Nippon Kagaku Zasshi*), Pure Chem. Sect. **81**, 262 (1960).

S 65. SHIGEMATSU T., TABUSHI M.: *J. Chem. Soc. Japan (Nippon Kagaku Zasshi)*, Pure Chem. Sect. **81**, 265 (1960).
S 66. SHIGEMATSU T., TABUSHI M.: *Bull. Inst. Chem. Res., Kyoto Univ.* **39**, 35 (1961).
S 67. SHIGEMATSU T., TABUSHI M., ISOJIMA F.: *Japan Analyst (Bunseki Kagaku)* **11**, 752 (1962).
S 68. SHIGEMATSU T., TABUSHI M.: *J. Chem. Soc. Japan (Nippon Kagaku Zasshi)*, Pure Chem. Sect. **83**, 814 (1962).
S 69. SHIMOJIMA H.: *J. Chem. Soc. Japan (Nippon Kagaku Zasshi)*, Pure Chem. Sect. **82**, 1186 (1961).
S 70. SHIRLEY R. L., BENNE E. J., MILLER E. J.: *Analyt. Chem.* **21**, 300 (1949).
S 71. SHORT H. G.: *Analyst* **75**, 420 (1950).
S 72. SHORT H. G.: *Analyst* **76**, 710 (1951).
S 73. SIDERIS C. P.: *Ind. Eng. Chem., Analyt.* **12**, 232 (1940).
S 74. SILL C. W., PETERSON H. E.: *Analyt. Chem.* **21**, 1268 (1949).
S 75. SILVERMAN L.: *Analyt. Chem.* **20**, 906 (1948).
S 76. SILVERMAN L., MOUDY L., HAWLEY D. W.: *Analyt. Chem.* **25**, 1369 (1953).
S 77. SILVERMAN L., SEITZ R. L.: *Analyt. Chim. Acta* **20**, 340 (1959).
S 78. SIMONSEN S. H., BURNETT H. M.: *Analyt. Chem.* **27**, 1336 (1955).
S 79. SINYAKOVA S. I., TSVETKOVA L. A.: *Trudy Kom. analit. Khim.* **12**, 191 (1960).
S 80. SKYTTE J. B.: *Acta Chem. Scand.* **13**, 1347 (1959).
S 81. SKYTTE J. B.: *Acta Chem. Scand.* **13**, 1890 (1959).
S 82. SLEE L. J., PHILLIPS G., JENKINS E. N.: *Analyst* **84**, 596 (1959).
S 83. SMITH G. W., MOORE F. L.: *Analyt. Chem.* **29**, 448 (1957).
S 84. SNYDER L. J.: *Analyt. Chem.* **19**, 684 (1947).
S 85. SNYDER L. J., BARNES W. R., TOKOS J. V.: *Analyt. Chem.* **20**, 772 (1948).
S 86. SPECKER H., KUCHTNER M., HARTKAMP H.: *Z. analyt. Chem.* **142**, 166 (1954).
S 87. SPECKER H., HARTKAMP H., KUCHTNER M.: *Z. analyt. Chem.* **143**, 425 (1954).
S 88. SPITSYN V. I., GOLUTVINA M. M.: *At. Energ. (USSR)* **8**, 117 (1960).
S 89. SPITSYN V. I., KUZINA A. F., ZAMOSHNIKOVA N. N., TAGIL, T. S.: *Doklady Akad. Nauk SSSR* **144**, 1066 (1962).
S 90. SPITZY H.: *Mikrochim. Acta* 789 (1960).
S 91. SPRAIN W., BANKS C. V.: *Analyt. Chim. Acta* **6**, 363 (1952).
S 92. STANDER C. M.: *Analyt. Chem.* **32**, 1296 (1960).
S 93. STANTON R. E., McDONALD A. J., CARMICHAEL I.: *Analyst* **87**, 134 (1962).
S 94. STARIK I. E.: *Problemy Sov. Geologii* **3**, 70 (1933).
S 95. STARÝ J., RUDENKO N. P.: *Nauch. Doklady Vyshey Skholy, Khim. i Khim. Tekhnol.* **1**, 624 (1958).
S 96. STARÝ J., RUDENKO N. P.: *Zhur. neorg. Khim.* **4**, 2405 (1959).
S 97. STARÝ J.: *Zhur. neorg. Khim.* **4**, 2412 (1959).
S 98. STARÝ J.: *Chem. Listy* **53**, 556 (1959).
S 99. STARÝ J.: *Coll. Czech. Chem. Comm.* **25**, 86 (1960).
S 100. STARÝ J.: *Coll. Czech. Chem. Comm.* **25**, 890 (1960).
S 101. STARÝ J.: *Coll. Czech. Chem. Comm.* **25**, 2630 (1960).
S 102. STARÝ J., PRÁŠILOVÁ J.: *J. Inorg. Nuclear Chem.* **17**, 361 (1961).
S 103. STARÝ J., RŮŽIČKA J.: *Talanta* **8**, 296 (1961).
S 104. STARÝ J., RŮŽIČKA J.: *Talanta* **8**, 775 (1961).
S 105. STARÝ J., BALEK V.: *Coll. Czech. Chem. Comm.* **27**, 809 (1962).
S 106. STARÝ J.: *Analyt. Chim. Acta* **28**, 132 (1963).
S 107. STARÝ J., HLADKÝ E.: *Analyt. Chim. Acta* **28**, 227 (1963).
S 108. STARÝ J., RŮŽIČKA J., ZEMAN A.: *Analyt. Chim. Acta* **29**, 103 (1963).
S 109. STARÝ J., SMIŽANSKÁ J.: *Analyt. Chim. Acta* **29**, 546 (1963).
S 110. STARÝ J., RŮŽIČKA J., SALAMON M.: *Talanta* **9**, 617 (1963).
S 111. STATEN F. W., HUFFMAN E. W. D.: *Analyt. Chem.* **31**, 2003 (1959).
S 112. STEIGER B.: *Mikrochem.* **16**, 193 (1934–1935).
S 113. STEINBACH J. F., FREISER H.: *Analyt. Chem.* **25**, 881 (1953).
S 114. STEINBACH J. F., FREISER H.: *Analyt. Chem.* **26**, 375 (1954).
S 115. STENE S.: *Tidsskr. Kjemi Bergvesen Met.* **19**, 6 (1939), cf. *Chem. Abs.* **33**, 5101 (1939).

S 116. STEPANOVA N. A., YAKUNINA G. A.: *Zhur. analit. Khim.* **17**, 858 (1962).
S 117. STEWARD J. A., BARTLET J. C.: *Analyt. Chem.* **30**, 404 (1958).
S 118. STOLYAROV K. P.: *Zhur. analit. Khim.* **16**, 452 (1961).
S 119. STONE I., ETTINGER R., GANTZ C.: *Analyt. Chem.* **25**, 893 (1953).
S 120. STONE K. G., FRIEDMAN L.: *J. Amer. Chem. Soc.* **69**, 209 (1947).
S 121. STONER R. E., DASLER W.: *Analyt. Chem.* **32**, 1207 (1960).
S 122. STONHILL L. G.: *Chemist–Analyst* **47**, 68 (1958).
S 123. STOUT P. R., LEVY J., WILLIAMS L. C.: *Coll. Czech. Chem. Comm.* **10**, 129 (1938).
S 124. STRAFFORD N., WYATT P. F., KERSHAW F. G.: *Analyst* **70**, 232 (1945).
S 125. STRAFFORD N., WYATT P. F.: *Analyst* **72**, 54 (1947).
S 126. STRAFFORD N., WYATT P. F., KERSHAW F. G.: *Analyst* **78**, 624 (1953).
S 127. STRELNIKOVA N. P., PAVLOVA V. N.: *Zavodskaya Lab.* **26**, 63 (1960).
S 128. STRELNIKOVA N. P., LYSCOVA G. G., DOLGORUKOVA G. S.: *Zavodskaya Lab.* **28**, 1319 (1962).
S 129. STRODE A. CH., KINDERMAN E. M.: *Phys. Rev.* **93**, 1029 (1954).
S 130. STROMBERG A. G.: *Zhur. fiz. Khim.* **23**, 962 (1949).
S 131. ŠŮCHA L.: *Chem. Listy* **54**, 1019 (1960).
S 132. SUDARIKOV B. N., ZAITSEV V. A., PUCHKOV Y. G.: *Nauch. Doklady Vyshey Skholy, Khim. i Khim. Tekhnol.* **1**, 80 (1959).
S 133. SUDO E.: *J. Chem. Soc. Japan* (*Nippon Kagaku Zasshi*), Pure Chem. Sect. **72**, 718 (1951), cf. *Chem. Abs.* **46**, 6031 (1952).
S 134. SUDO E.: *J. Chem. Soc. Japan* (*Nippon Kagaku Zasshi*), Pure Chem. Sect. **72**, 817 (1951), cf. *Chem. Abs.* **46**, 6034 (1952).
S 135. SUDO E.: *Sci. Reports Res. Inst. Tôhoku Univ.* A **4**, 268 (1952).
S 136. SUDO E.: *Sci. Reports Res. Inst. Tôhoku Univ.* A **4**, 347 (1952).
S 137. SUGAWARA K., TANAKA M., NAITO H.: *Bull. Chem. Soc. Japan* **26**, 417 (1953).
S 138. SUGAWARA K., TANAKA M., KANAMORI S.: *Bull. Chem. Soc. Japan* **29**, 670 (1956).
S 139. SULLIVAN J. C., HINDMAN J. C.: *J. Amer. Chem. Soc.* **76**, 5931 (1954).
S 140. SUNDERMAN D. N., ACKERMANN I. B., MEINKE W. W.: *Analyt. Chem.* **31**, 40 (1959).
S 141. SUPRUNOVICH I. B.: *Zhur. obschei Khim.* **8**, 839 (1938).
S 142. SUTER H., HADORN H.: *Z. analyt. Chem.* **160**, 335 (1958).
S 143. SUZUKI N., YOSHIDA H.: *J. Chem. Soc. Japan* (*Nippon Kagaku Zasshi*), Pure Chem. Sect. **80**, 1005 (1959).
S 144. SUZUKI N., YOSHIDA H.: *J. Chem. Soc. Japan* (*Nippon Kagaku Zasshi*), Pure Chem. Sect. **80**, 1008 (1959).
S 145. SUZUKI N.: *Japan Analyst* (*Bunseki Kagaku*) **8**, 283 (1959).
S 146. SUZUKI N.: *Japan Analyst* (*Bunseki Kagaku*) **8**, 349 (1959).
S 147. SUZUKI N.: *Japan Analyst* (*Bunseki Kagaku*) **8**, 395 (1959).
S 148. SUZUKI N.: *Japan Analyst* (*Bunseki Kagaku*) **8**, 432 (1959).
S 149. SUZUKI N., KATO T.: *Sci. Reports Res. Inst. Tôhoku Univ.* A **43**, 152 (1959).
S 150. SUZUKI N.: *Sci. Reports Res. Inst. Tôhoku Univ.* A **43**, 161 (1959).
S 151. SUZUKI N., OKI S.: *Bull. Chem. Soc. Japan* **35**, 233 (1962).
S 152. SUZUKI N., OKI S.: *Bull. Chem. Soc. Japan* **35**, 237 (1962).
S 153. SUZUKI N., OMORI T.: *Bull. Chem. Soc. Japan* **35**, 595 (1962).

T 1. TABUSHI M.: *Bull. Inst. Chem. Res., Kyoto Univ.* **36**, 156 (1958).
T 2. TABUSHI M.: *Bull. Inst. Chem. Res., Kyoto Univ.* **37**, 226 (1959).
T 3. TABUSHI M.: *Bull. Inst. Chem. Res., Kyoto Univ.* **37**, 232 (1959).
T 4. TABUSHI M.: *Bull. Inst. Chem. Res., Kyoto Univ.* **37**, 237 (1959).
T 5. TABUSHI M.: *Bull. Inst. Chem. Res., Kyoto Univ.* **37**, 245 (1959).
T 6. TAKEI S., SHIBUYA K.: *Japan Analyst* (*Bunseki Kagaku*) **5**, 695 (1956).
T 7. TAKEI S.: *Japan Analyst* (*Bunseki Kagaku*) **6**, 630 (1957).
T 8. TAKEI S., KATO T.: *Technol. Reports Tôhoku Univ.* **24**, 67 (1959).
T 9. TAKEI S., KATO T.: *Technol. Reports Tôhoku Univ.* **24**, 75 (1959).
T 10. TAKEI S., KATO T.: *Technol. Reports Tôhoku Univ.* **24**, 85 (1959).
T 11. TAKEI S.: *Japan Analyst* (*Bunseki Kagaku*) **9**, 288 (1960).

T 12. TAKEI S.: *Japan Analyst (Bunseki Kagaku)* **9**, 294 (1960).
T 13. TAKEI S.: *Japan Analyst (Bunseki Kagaku)* **9**, 402 (1960).
T 14. TAKEI S.: *Japan Analyst (Bunseki Kagaku)* **9**, 409 (1960).
T 15. TAKEI S., KATO T.: *Technol. Reports Tôhoku Univ.* **25**, 127 (1961).
T 16. TAKEI S., KATO T.: *Technol. Reports Tôhoku Univ.* **25**, 143 (1961).
T 17. TALVITIE N. A.: *Analyt. Chem.* **25**, 604 (1953).
T 18. TANAKA M.: *Mikrochim. Acta* 701 (1954).
T 19. TANDON J. P., MEHROTRA R. C.: *Z. analyt. Chem.* **176**, 87 (1960).
T 20. TANDON S. G., BHATTACHARYYA S. C.: *Analyt. Chem.* **33**, 1267 (1961).
T 21. TAUBE M.: *Radiokhimiya* **4**, 260 (1960).
T 22. TAYLOR C. G.: *Analyst* **81**, 369 (1956).
T 23. TEICHER H., GORDON L.: *Analyt. Chem.* **25**, 1182 (1953).
T 24. TEREPETYEV A. P., RUKHAZE E. G.: *Zhur. analit. Khim.* **6**, 303 (1951).
T 25. TEREPETYEV A. P., RUKHADZE E. G., FADEEVA Z. A.: *Zhur. analit. Khim.* **7**, 120 (1952).
T 26. TERTOOLEN J. F. W., DETMAR D. A., BUIJZE C.: *Z. analyt. Chem.* **167**, 401 (1959).
T 27. TESTA C.: *Analyt. Chim. Acta* **25**, 525 (1961).
T 28. THALER H., MÜHLBERGER F. H.: *Z. analyt. Chem.* **144**, 241 (1955).
T 29. THOMPSON J. H., PETTERS B. W.: *Analyst* **84**, 180 (1959).
T 30. THOMPSON J. H., RAVENSCROFT M. J.: *Analyst* **85**, 735 (1960).
T 31. TITLEY A. W.: *Analyst* **87**, 349 (1962).
T 32. TOMPSETT S. L.: *Analyst* **81**, 330 (1956).
T 33. TORIBARA T. Y., CHEN P. S.: *Analyt. Chem.* **24**, 539 (1952).
T 34. TORIBARA T. Y., SHERMAN R. E.: *Analyt. Chem.* **25**, 1594 (1953).
T 35. TORII T.: *J. Chem. Soc. Japan (Nippon Kagaku Zasshi)*, Pure Chem. Sect. **76**, 328 (1955), cf. *Chem. Abs.* **50**, 4717 (1956).
T 36. TORII T.: *J. Chem. Soc. Japan (Nippon Kagaku Zasshi)*, Pure Chem. Sect. **76**, 333 (1955), cf. *Chem. Abs.* **50**, 4717 (1956).
T 37. TRÉMILLON B.: *Bull. Soc. chim. France* 1156 (1954).
T 38. TRÉMILLON B.: *Bull. Soc. chim. France* 1160 (1954).
T 39. TRIBALAT S.: *Compt. rend.* **224**, 469 (1947).
T 40. TROITSKIJ K. V.: *Primenenie Mechenych Atomov Analiticheskoj Khimii*, Akad. Nauk SSSR, Moscow, p. 148, 1955.
T 41. TRUSELL F., DIEHL H.: *Analyt. Chem.* **31**, 1978 (1959).
T 42. TSCHERNIKOV YU. A., DOBKINA B. M.: *Zavodskaya Lab.* **15**, 906 (1949).
T 43. TSCHERNIKOV YU. A., DOBKINA B. M.: *Zavodskaya Lab.* **15**, 1143 (1949).
T 44. TSCHERNIKOV YU. A., DOBKINA B. M.: *Zavodskaya Lab.* **25**, 131 (1959).
T 45. TSCHERNITSKAYA R. E.: *Zhur. obschei Khim.* **22**, 403 (1952).
T 46. TSCHERNITSKAYA R. E.: *Zhur. obschei Khim.* **22**, 408 (1952).
T 47. TSYVINA B. S., KON'KOVA O. V.: *Zavodskaya Lab.* **25**, 403 (1959).

U 1. UMLAND F., HOFFMANN W.: *Angew. Chem.* **68**, 704 (1956).
U 2. UMLAND F., HOFFMANN W.: *Angew. Chem.* **69**, 396 (1957).
U 3. UMLAND F., HOFFMANN W.: *Analyt. Chim. Acta* **17**, 234 (1957).
U 4. UMLAND F., PUCHELT H.: *Analyt. Chim. Acta* **16**, 334 (1957).
U 5. UMLAND F., MECKENSTOCK K.-U.: *Angew. Chem.* **71**, 373 (1959).
U 6. UMLAND F., MECKENSTOCK K.-U.: *Z. analyt. Chem.* **165**, 161 (1959).
U 7. UMLAND F., HOFFMANN W.: *Z. analyt. Chem.* **168**, 268 (1959).
U 8. UMLAND F., HOFFMANN W., MECKENSTOCK K.-U.: *Z. analyt. Chem.* **173**, 211 (1960).
U 9. UMLAND F., MECKENSTOCK K.-U.: *Z. analyt. Chem.* **177**, 244 (1960).
U 10. UMLAND F., PODDAR B. K., MECKENSTOCK K.-U.: *Z. analyt. Chem.* **185**, 362 (1962).
U 11. USATENKO YU. I., TULYUPA F. M.: *Zavodskaya Lab.* **26**, 783 (1960).
U 12. UZUMASA Y., WASHIZUKA S.: *Bull. Chem. Soc. Japan* **29**, 403 (1956).

V 1. VAN ERKELENS P. C.: *Analyt. Chim. Acta* **24**, 526 (1961).
V 2. VAN ERKELENS P. C.: *Analyt. Chim. Acta* **25**, 129 (1961).
V 3. VANOSSI R.: *Anales Soc. Cient. Argentina* **131**, 137 (1941), cf. *Chem. Abs.* **35**, 5412 (1941).
V 4. VANOSSI R.: *Anales Soc. Cient. Argentina* **131**, 226 (1941), cf. *Chem. Abs.* **35**, 5412 (1941).
V 5. VANOSSI R.: *Anales Soc. Cient. Argentina* **135**, 97 (1945), cf. *Chem. Abs.* **39**, 4₹3 (1945).
V 6. VAN UITERT L. G., HAAS C. G., FERNELIUS W. C., DOUGLAS B. E.: *J. Amer. Chem. Soc.* **75**, 455 (1953).
V 7. VAN UITERT L. G., FERNELIUS W. C., DOUGLAS B. E.: *J. Amer. Chem. Soc.* **75**, 457 (1953).
V 8. VAN UITERT L. G., FERNELIUS W. C., DOUGLAS B. E.: *J. Amer. Chem. Soc.* **75**, 2736 (1953).
V 9. VAŠÁK V., ŠEDIVEC V.: *Chem. Listy* **45**, 10 (1951).
V 10. VASILEVSKAYA A. E., SHCHERBAKOV V. P., KLIMENCHUK V. I.: *Zavodskaya Lab.* **28**, 415 (1962).
V 11. VDOVENKO V. M.: *Zhur. analit. Khim.* **12**, 593 (1957).
V 12. VDOVENKO V. M.: *Zhur. neorg. Khim.* **3**, 145 (1958).
V 13. VEALE C. R., WOOD R. G.: *Analyst* **85**, 371 (1960).
V 14. VESTERBERG R., SJÖHOLM O.: *Mikrochem.* **38**, 81 (1951).
V 15. VLÁČIL F., ZÁTKA V.: *Chem. průmysl* **11**, 139 (1961).
V 16. VOLKOVA A. I., ZACHAROVA N. N.: *Ukrain. khim. Zhur.* **23**, 530 (1957).
V 17. VON E. DOERING W., KNOX L. H.: *J. Amer. Chem. Soc.* **73**, 828 (1951).
V 18. VOUK V. B., WEBER O. A.: *Analyst* **85**, 46 (1960).

W 1. WAGGENER W. C., STOUGHTON R. W.: *J. Phys. Chem.* **56**, 1 (1952).
W 2. WAKAMATSU S.: *Japan Analyst (Bunseki Kagaku)* **8**, 298 (1959).
W 3. WAKAMATSU S.: *Japan Analyst (Bunseki Kagaku)* **9**, 284 (1960).
W 4. WAKAMATSU S.: *Japan Analyst (Bunseki Kagaku)* **9**, 858 (1960).
W 5. WATKINSON J. H.: *Analyt. Chem.* **32**, 981 (1960).
W 6. WEBER O. A., VOUK V. B.: *Analyst* **85**, 40 (1960).
W 7. WELCHER F. J.: *Organic Analytical Reagents*, Parts I, II, III, IV; Van Nostrand, New York 1947.
W 8. WELLS J. E., PEMBERTON R.: *Analyst* **72**, 185 (1947).
W 9. WEST P. W.: *Analyt. Chem.* **24**, 76 (1952).
W 10. WEST P. W., MUHERJI A. K.: *Analyt. Chem.* **31**, 947 (1959).
W 11. WEST T. S.: *Metallurgia* **53**, 91 (1956).
W 12. WEST T. S.: *Metallurgia* **53**, 185 (1956).
W 13. WEST T. S.: *Metallurgia* **53**, 234 (1956).
W 14. WEST T. S.: *Metallurgia* **53**, 240 (1956).
W 15. WEST T. S.: *Metallurgia* **53**, 292 (1956).
W 16. WEST T. S.: *Metallurgia* **54**, 47 (1957).
W 17. WEST T. S.: *Metallurgia* **54**, 103 (1957).
W 18. WEST T. S.: *Ind. Chemist* **38**, 34 (1962).
W 19. WEST T. S.: *Ind. Chemist* **38**, 81 (1962).
W 20. WESTWOOD W., MAYER A.: *Analyst* **73**, 275 (1948).
W 21. WHITE W. E.: *Ind. Eng. Chem., Analyt.* **8**, 231 (1936).
W 22. WIBERLEY S. E., BASSETT L. G.: *Analyt. Chem.* **21**, 609 (1949).
W 23. WICHMANN H. J.: *Ind. Eng. Chem., Analyt.* **11**, 66 (1939).
W 24. WILLARD H. H., HORTON CH. A.: *Analyt. Chem.* **24**, 862 (1952).
W 25. WILLARD H. H., MARTIN E. L., FELTHAM R.: *Analyt. Chem.* **25**, 1863 (1953).
W 26. WILLIS J. B.: *Analyt. Chem.* **34**, 614 (1962).
W 27. WILKINS E. S., WILLOUGHBY C. E., KRAEMER E. O., SMITH F. L.: *Ind. Eng. Chem., Analyt.* **7**, 33 (1935).
W 28. WILKINSON G.: *J Amer. Chem. Soc.* **74**, 6146 (1952).

W 29. WINTER O. B., ROBINSON H. M., LAMB F. W., MILLER E. J.: *Ind. Eng. Chem.*, *Analyt.* **7**, 265 (1935).
W 30. WISE W. M., BRANDT W. W.: *J. Amer. Chem. Soc.* **77**, 1058 (1955).
W 31. WISE W. M., BRANDT W. W.: *Analyt. Chem.* **27**, 1392 (1955).
W 32. WISH L.: *Analyt. Chem.* **34**, 625 (1962).
W 33. WÖLBLING H., STEIGER B.: *Angew. Chem.* **46**, 279 (1933).
W 34. WOLD A., BAIRD J. H., HOUGH CH. R.: *Analyt. Chem.* **26**, 546 (1954).
W 35. WOOD D. F., CLARK R. T.: *Analyst* **83**, 509 (1958).
W 36. WOOD D. F., NICHOLS H. A.: *Analyst* **85**, 139 (1960).
W 37. WYATT P. F.: *Analyst* **78**, 656 (1953).
W 38. WYATT F. F.: *Analyst* **80**, 368 (1955).

Y 1. YAMAMURA S. S.: *Analyt. Chem.* **32**, 1896 (1960).
Y 2. YANAGIHARA T., MATANO N., KAWASE A.: *Japan Analyst (Bunseki Kagaku)* **8**, 10 (1959).
Y 3. YANAGIHARA T., MATANO N., KAWASE A.: *Japan Analyst (Bunseki Kagaku)* **8**, 14 (1959).
Y 4. YANAGIHARA T., MATANO N., KAWASE A.: *Japan Analyst (Bunseki Kagaku)* **11**, 108 (1962).
Y 5. YAO Y.: *Ind. Eng. Chem.*, *Analyt.* **17**, 114 (1945).
Y 6. YATSIMIRSKIJ K. B., VASILEV V. P.: *Konstanty Nestoikosti Kompleksnych Soedinenij*, Akad. Nauk SSSR, Moscow 1959.
Y 7. YOKOSUKA S.: *Japan Analyst (Bunseki Kagaku)* **4**, 99 (1955).
Y 9. YOKOSUKA S.: *Japan Analyst (Bunseki Kagaku)* **5**, 71 (1956).
Y 10. YOKOSUKA S.: *Japan Analyst (Bunseki Kagaku)* **6**, 431 (1957).
Y 11. YOSHIMORI T., HIRANO S.: *Japan Analyst (Bunseki Kagaku)* **3**, 470 (1954).
Y 12. YOUNG R. S., LEIBOWITZ A.: *Analyst* **71**, 477 (1946).
Y 13. YOUNG R. S., STRICKLAND E. H., LEIBOWITZ A.: *Analyst* **71**, 474 (1946).
Y 14. YOUNG R. S.: *Analyst* **76**, 49 (1951).

Z 1. ZEBROSKI E. L., ALTER H. W., HEUMANN F. K.: *J. Amer. Chem. Soc.* **73**, 5646 (1951).
Z 2. ZEMAN A., RŮŽIČKA J., STARÝ J.: *Talanta* **10**, 685 (1963).
Z 3. ZEMAN A., STARÝ J., RŮŽIČKA J.: *Talanta* **10**, 981 (1963).
Z 4. ZHAROVSKIJ F. G.: *Ukrain. khim. Zhur.* **17**, 209 (1951).
Z 5. ZHAROVSKIJ F. G., PILIPENKO A. T.: *Ukrain. khim. Zhur.* **25**, 230 (1959).
Z 6. ZHAROVSKIJ F. G.: *Ukrain. khim. Zhur.* **25**, 245 (1959).
Z 7. ZHAROVSKIJ F. G., SHNAK E. A.: *Ukrain. khim. Zhur.* **25**, 800 (1959).
Z 8. ZHAROVSKIJ F. G., RYZHENKO V. L.: *Ukrain. khim. Zhur.* **28**, 306 (1962).
Z 9. ZIBULSKY H., SLOWINSKI M. F., WHITE J. A.: *Analyt. Chem.* **31**, 280 (1959).
Z 10. ZIEGLER M., GLEMSER O., PETRI N.: *Z. analyt. Chem.* **153**, 415 (1956).
Z 11. ZIEGLER M., GLEMSER O., PETRI N.: *Z. analyt. Chem.* **154**, 170 (1957).
Z 12. ZIEGLER M., GLEMSER O., PETRI N.: *Angew. Chem.* **69**, 174 (1957).
Z 13. ZIEGLER M., GLEMSER O., PETRI N.: *Mikrochim. Acta* 215 (1957).
Z 14. ZIELEN A. I., CONNICK R. E.: *J. Amer. Chem. Soc.* **78**, 5785 (1956).
Z 15. ZOLOTOV YU. A., ALIMARIN I. P.: *Doklady Akad. Nauk SSSR* **136**, 603 (1961).
Z 16. ZOLOTOV YU. A.: *Acta Chim. Acad. Sci. Hung.* **32**, 327 (1962).
Z 17. ZOLOTOV YU. A., ALIMARIN I. P.: *Radiokhimiya* **4**, 272 (1962).
Z 18. ZOLOTOV YU. A.: *Zavodskaya Lab.* **28**, 1404 (1962).
Z 19. ZOZULYA A. P., MEZENTSEVA N. N., PESHKOVA V. M., YURIEV YU. K.: *Zhur. analit. Khim.* **14**, 17 (1959).
Z 20. ZOZULYA A. P., PESHKOVA V. M.: *Zhur. neorg. Khim.* **4**, 379 (1959).
Z 21. ZOZULYA A. P., PESHKOVA V. M.: *Uspekhi Khim.* **29**, 234 (1960).

PRINCIPAL ABBREVIATIONS USED IN THE REFERENCES

Reference	Full Title
Acta Chem. Scand.	Acta Chemica Scandinavica.
Acta Chim. Acad. Sci. Hung.	Acta Chimica Academiae Scientiarum Hungaricae.
Anales asoc. quím. argentina	Anales de la asociación química argentina.
Anales Soc. Cient. Argentina	Anales de la sociedad científica argentina.
Analyst	Analyst.
Analyt. Chem.	Analytical Chemistry.
Analyt. Chim. Acta	Analytica Chimica Acta.
Angew. Chem.	Angewandte Chemie.
Ann. Chim. Phys.	Annales de Chimie et de Physique.
Ann. Rev. Nuclear Sci.	Annual Review of Nuclear Science.
Arkiv Kemi	Arkiv för Kemi.
Atomic Energy (U.S.S.R.)	Atomnaya Energiya SSSR (English translation)
Austral. J. Chem.	Australian Journal of Chemistry.
Ber.	Berichte der deutschen chemischen Gesellschaft.
Biochem. J.	Biochemical Journal.
Biokhimiya	Biokhimiya.
Bull. Chem. Soc. Japan	Bulletin of the Chemical Society of Japan.
Bull. Inst. Chem. Res., Kyoto Univ.	Bulletin of the Institute for Chemical Research, Kyoto University.
Bull. Soc. chim. France	Bulletin de la Société chimique de France.
Canad. J. Chem.	Canadian Journal of Chemistry.
Canad. J. Res.	Canadian Journal of Research.
Chem. Abs.	Chemical Abstracts.
Chem. Analit.	Chemia Analityczna, Warsaw.
Chem. and Ind.	Chemistry and Industry.
Chem. Listy	Chemické Listy.
Chem. průmysl	Chemický průmysl.
Chem. Soc. Spec. Publ.	Chemical Society Special Publications.
Chem. Weekblad.	Chemisch Weekblad.
Chemist–Analyst	Chemist–Analyst.
Chim. analyt.	Chimie analytique.
Chimia (*Switz.*)	Chimia.
Coll. Czech. Chem. Comm.	Collection of Czechoslovak Chemical Communications.
Compt. rend.	Comptes rendus hebdomadaires des Séances de l'Académie des Sciences.
Doklady Akad. Nauk SSSR	Doklady Akademii Nauk SSSR.
Finska Kemistsamfundets Medd.	Finska Kemistsamfundets Meddelanden (Suomen Kemistiseuran Tiedonantoja).

Helv. Chim. Acta	Helvetia Chimica Acta.
Ind. Chemist	Industrial Chemist.
Ind. Eng. Chem., Analyt.	Industrial and Engineering Chemistry: Analytical Edition.
Izvest. Akad. Nauk Latv. SSR	Izvestiya Akademii Latviiskoi SSR.
Izvest. Vysshikh Uchebn. Zavedenij, Khim. i Khim. Tekhnol.	Izvestiya Vysshikh Uchebnych Zavednik, Khimiya i Khimicheskaya Teknologiya.
J.	Journal of the Chemical Society.
J. Amer. Chem. Soc.	Journal of the American Chemical Society.
J. App. Chem.	Journal of Applied Chemistry.
J. Assoc. Offic. Agric. Chem.	Journal of the Association of Official Agricultural Chemists.
J. Chem. Soc. Japan (Nippon Kagaku Zasshi)	Journal of the Chemical Society of Japan.
J. Chim. phys.	Journal de Chimie physique.
J. Ind. Chem. Soc.	Journal of the Indian Chemical Society.
J. Ind. Hyg.	Journal of Industrial Hygiene and Toxicology.
J. Inorg. Nuclear Chem.	Journal of Inorganic and Nuclear Chemistry.
J. S. African Chem. Inst.	Journal of the South African Chemical Institute.
J. Sci. Ind. Res., India	Journal of Scientific and Industrial Research, India.
J. Washington Acad. Sci.	Journal of the Washington Academy of Sciences.
Japan Analyst (Bunseki Kagaku)	Japan Analyst.
Kgl. danske Videnskab. Selskab, Mat.-fys. Skrifter	Kongelige danske Videnskabernes Selskab, Matematisk-fysiske Skrifter.
Metallurgia	Metallurgia. British Journal of Metals.
Mikrochem.	Mikrochemie.
Mikrochem. Mikrochim. Acta	Mikrochemie vereinigt mit Mikrochimica Acta.
Mikrochim. Acta	Mikrochimica Acta.
Monatsh.	Monatshefte für Chemie und verwandte Teile anderer Wissenschaften.
Nature	Nature.
Nauch. Doklady Vyshey Skholy Khim. i Khim. Tekhnol.	Nauchnye Doklady Vysshei Skholy, Khimiya Khimicheskaya Tekhnologiya.
Phys. Rev.	Physical Review.
Plating	Plating.
Problemy Sov. Geologii	Problemy Sovetskoi Geologii.
Proc. Chem. Soc.	Proceedings of the Chemical Society.
Quart. Rev.	Quarterly Reviews.
Radiokhimiya	Radiokhimiya.
Rec. Trav. chim.	Recueil des Travaux chimiques des Pays-Bas et de la Belgique.
Ricerca sci.	Ricerca scientifica.

Sbornik Trudov Moskov. Vetser- *nego Metalurg. Instituta*	Sbornik Trudov Moskovskogo Vetsernego Metalur- gicheskogo Instituta.
Sci. Reports Res. Inst. Tôhoku *Univ.*	Science Reports of the Research Institute, Tôhoku University.
Suomen Kem.	Suomen Kemistilehti.
Svensk kem. Tidskr.	Svensk kemisk Tidskrift.

Talanta	Talanta.
Technol. Reports Tôhoku Univ.	Technology Reports of Tôhoku University.
Tidsskr. Kjemi, Bergvesen Met.	Tidsskrift for Kjemi, Bergvesen og Metallurgi.
Trans. Faraday Soc.	Transactions of the Faraday Society.
Trans. Roy. Inst. Technol.	Transactions of the Royal Institute of Technology, Stockholm.
Trudy Khim. i Khim. Tekhnol.	Trudy po Khimii i Khimicheskoi Tekhnologii.
Trudy Kom. analit. Khim. (Akad. *Nauk SSSR)*	Trudy Koimssii po analiticheskoi Khimii, Akademia Nauk SSSR.

Ukrain. khim. Zhur.	Ukrainskii khimicheskii Zhurnal.
Uspekhi Khim.	Uspekhi Khimii.

Vestnik Moskov. Univ., Ser. Mat. *Mekh., Astr., Fiz., Khim.*	Vestnik Moskovskogo Universiteta, Seriya Mate- matiki, Mekhaniki, Astronomii, Fiziki i Khimii.
Vestnik Moskov. Univ., Ser. Khim.	Vestnik Moskovskogo Universiteta, Seriya Khimii.
Vestnik Moskov. Univ., Ser. Fiz.- *Mat. i Estestv. Nauk*	Vestnik Moskovskogo Universiteta, Seriya Fiziko- Matematicheskikh i Estestvennykh Nauk.

Wiss. Veröff. Siemens–Werken	Wissenschaftliche Veröffentlichungen aus den Sie- mens–Werken.

Z. analyt. Chem.	Zeitschrift für analytische Chemie.
Z. phys. Chem.	Zeitschrift für physikalische Chemie.
Zavodskaya Lab.	Zavodskaya Laboratoria.
Zhur. analit. Khim.	Zhurnal analiticheskoi Khimii.
Zhur. fiz. Khim.	Zhurnal fizicheskoi Khimii.
Zhur. neorg. Khim.	Zhurnal neorganicheskoi Chemie.
Zhur. obschei Khim.	Zhurnal obschei Khimii.

INDEX